PERSPECTIVES IN EVOLUTION

PERSPECTIVES IN EVOLUTION

by

Robert T. Francoeur

HELICON   Baltimore-Dublin

Helicon Press, Inc.
1120 N. Calvert Street
Baltimore, Maryland 21202

Library of Congress Catalog Card Number 65-24122

Nihil Obstat: Myles M. Bourke
                   Censor Deputatus

Imprimatur: ✠ John K. Mussio, J.C.D.
              Bishop of Steubenville
              September 2, 1965

The *Nihil Obstat* and *Imprimatur* are official declarations that a book or pamphlet is free of doctrinal or moral error. No implication is contained therein that those who have granted the *Nihil Obstat* and *Imprimatur* agree with the opinions expressed.

PRINTED IN THE UNITED STATES OF AMERICA

Preface

This book is a summary and synthesis of the state of our knowledge today on evolution in all its aspects, scientific, philosophic and theological.

In the past hundred years, the generalized concept of evolution has spread out from its narrow biological field to embrace *all* fields of human learning. This new dimension of thought was reluctantly received by the scientific world in the days of Darwin, but since then it has been adopted by scholars in every field: sociologists, educators, economists, historians, psychologists. Yet until very recently this historical perspective, so in keeping with the essential spirit of Christian revelation, has been totally rejected by Catholic philosophers and theologians. A few pioneers have courageously pointed out that the theologian or philosopher who wishes to *communicate* with modern man must either express his ideas in terms of an evolving world vision or suffer the rightly deserved fate of remaining unintelligible and irrelevant. Teilhard de Chardin, whose inspiration sparked this book, has proven to be the turning point in this irrational refusal to face and accept the world we live in, a universe in which everything is caught up in the dynamic and cosmic process of evolution.

The battle, however, continues even today. And so it is my purpose here first to present the reader, scholar or amateur, with a history of man's thought on evolution, his understanding of time, and then a summary of where science stands today on questions of the evolution of the universe, life and man. In

1

the second part I have applied this evolutionary perspective to certain theological and philosophical problems: the origin and nature of man, mankind's "original sin and fall," creation, death and its aftermath. In attempting this synthesis I have drawn heavily on the latest thought of some of today's most challenging and advanced thinkers, Catholic, non-Roman and non-Christian. Their fascinating and often brilliant insights may be new—even startling—to some of my readers (both laymen and specialists) mainly because they have been expressed only in scholarly journals abroad or in lectures and discussions. From this angle, *Perspectives in Evolution* is not original; it only presents the views of experts and professional theologians.

Yet there is, I hope, a certain quality of originality in the book. This lies in the attempt to gather the scattered details and insights worked out by the experts and the effort to piece these together into a harmonious and logical over-all picture of man and his place in the world which will make sense to any person living in this post-Darwinian world. It is my hope that this picture, even though it is not complete or fully detailed, will nevertheless prove interesting and enlightening to the teacher and specialist in science, philosophy and theology, as well as for the college and high school student, and the educated Christian puzzled by the impossibility of reconciling a scientific picture of an evolving universe with a philosophy and theology expressed in static, pre-Darwinian terms. I have tried to keep the text in a popular, untechnical and interesting format for the general reader; documentation and critical comments are reserved to the footnotes for the reader interested in sources and further reading.

ROBERT T. FRANCOEUR
Fairleigh Dickinson University
October 1, 1965

Acknowledgements

I am very grateful to the many friends who have lent their valuable aid and advice during the months in which this book came into being. Especially to Mlle. Jeanne Mortier of the *Teilhard de Chardin Fondation* and *Association* in Paris, who has supplied me with many of Teilhard's unpublished works; Mme. Dorothy Poulain, a faithful Paris correspondent and intermediary; Piet Schoonenberg, S.J., who has contributed so much to our ideas on original sin and the nature of man; Prof. Theodosius Dobzhansky of the Rockefeller Institute and Dr. Henry Elkin of the New School for Social Research, who shared their insights as biologist and psychiatrist into the reality of "original sin"; and to John Heidenry of Herder & Herder, Fred Weick of Harper & Row, Prof. Louis Marks of Pace College, New York City, Prof. Petro Bilaniuk of St. Michael's College, University of Toronto, Myroslav Tracz, Anna Kotlarchyk and Joan Dennihy.

I should also mention the patient audiences at the universities of North Dakota, Minnesota, Michigan, Toronto, Vermont, Delaware, Detroit, Dayton, Louisiana State and Oklahoma, who shared their reactions with me and gave more precision and polish to quite a few ideas presented in this book, for many of them developed out of the give-and-take question and answer sessions following these lectures. I would like especially to thank my editor, Joseph Caulfield, for his patient assistance.

Contents

PART I

The Circle and Arrow of Time

CHAPTER I

From the Dawn to the Dark Ages

> One must always be drunk. That says everything. There is no
> other point. In order not to feel the horrible burden of Time
> that bruises your shoulders and bends you to the ground, you
> must get drunk incessantly.[1]

Such was the reaction of the French poet, Baudelaire, as he
confronted that universal reality which no man can escape yet
which always eludes our grasp. Baudelaire's reaction was
neither unique nor unusual. In fact, it seems to find a sympa-
thetic chord in very many men no matter what their particular
position in history—whether educated or not, member of a
highly civilized and cultured society or of a stone-age aborigi-
nal tribe. The unknown past and the inscrutable future balance
precariously on the ever-elusive pinpoint of the present—is
there any wonder that even the most mature men find the

1. Baudelaire, *Oeuvres, I,* p. 468.
For much of the historical and literary references related to the cyclic and
linear concepts of time discussed in this chapter, we have drawn heavily
on Georges Poulet, *Studies in Human Time* (Johns Hopkins University,
1956); Oscar Cullmann, *Christ and Time: The Primitive Christian Conception of Time and History* (Westminster, 1950); William F. Lynch,
Christ and Apollo. The Dimensions of the Literary Imagination (Sheed &
Ward, 1960; Mentor Omega, 1963); Ernest C. Messenger, *Evolution and
Theology* (Burns & Oates, 1931); Philip Fothergill, *Historical Aspects of
Organic Evolution* (Hollis & Carter, 1952); Claude Tresmontant, *A Study
of Hebrew Thought* (Desclée, 1959); and several works by Mircea Eliade
which will be referred to specifically in the notes.

9

mystery of time both perplexing and disturbing? And while those of us who are just emerging from the black-and-white, careless wonderland of childhood or approaching the ebb of life may find time a truly horrible burden, every human being confronts the reality of time at least occasionally.

To escape the burden of time that bruises our shoulders and bends us to the ground is a difficult task for any man. With the King of Siam, we might muse:

> When I was a child, world was better place.
> What was so was so and what was not was not.
> Now I am a man, world has changed a lot.
> Some things nearly so, some things nearly not.
> 'Tis a puzzlement![2]

But most of us are not extremist enough to be lured by the schizophrenic retreat of childhood dreams or the constant inebriation urged by Baudelaire. We soon realize we must live in and accept this world where time flows on with undeviating and inexorable sureness, but we mortal men insist on some solution to its burden.

The easiest and oldest flight from time devised by man is simply to deny its reality and existence. In denying time we can eliminate its burden, for we also deny that things really change from one day to the next. It is actually the unpredictable changes in our lives, in the unknown future, that terrify us. This is what drives us to deny time. If we do not deny it, we must face the phenomena of change and movement. Around the world and through the ages, primitive people have been able to achieve this denial by developing a very complete mythology, replete with archetypal rites of imitation. Looking at the frightening and mysterious world in which they are engulfed, the primitives have seen only an unstable world of motion and change, an unpredictable and erratic cosmos. Such a world can be very terrifying to uncluttered minds and

---

2. Lyric from the Rodgers and Hammerstein musical, *The King and I*.

so, in a perennial pattern that can be traced in any number of primitive cultures, aborigines have centered their lives on the cycles of nature. The seasons, the moon, the sun, everything seems to move so naturally in cycles. Perhaps this is the illusion of time and change—if time is cyclic then there is never anything really new or unique. Everything is only a repetition, a recurrence of the eternal cycle: what we think is new, or a change, is only the repetition of an act of the gods in the beginning. Mircea Eliade has very aptly termed this escape from time "the myth of the eternal return," and demonstrated its universal appeal among primitive societies.[3]

A few examples might help to clarify this time-worn solution. Sacrifice to a deity is a phenomenon common to all mankind, but with the primitive societies it has a special meaning. There a sacrifice is not only the exact reproduction of the first sacrifice revealed by a god to man at the beginning of time, it also has a magical effect in that by ritual imitation it is removed from this profane and unreal world of time, change and illusion. The sacrifice, because it imitates an action of the gods, occurs at the same mythical instant as its model in the beginning. Another example can be found in the wide-spread "initiation ceremonies" of primitive cultures which, by a sacred and ritual imitation of birth, project the initiate back into the time of the gods and redeem him. Coronation ceremonies for new kings and chiefs can be shown to have the same meaning, for the concept of a ritual death and resurrection (new birth) is very evident in many of these ceremonies. As in the initiation ceremonies of primitive societies, this ritual death and resurrection usually contains definite references to the creation or birth of the world in the beginning, in

3. Mircea Eliade, *Cosmos and History: The Myth of the Eternal Return* (Pantheon, 1954; Harper Torchbook, 1959); *Images & Symbols, Studies in Religious Symbolism* (Sheed & Ward, 1961); *Myth and Reality* (Harper & Row, 1963). See also Stephen Toulmin and June Goodfield, *The Discovery of Time* (Harper & Row, 1965), pp. 23-32.

that mythical era of timelessness. The new king or chief not only "reincarnates" his predecessors or the tribal ancestral hero, his "new birth" is also a repetition of the creation of the world in the beginning. "The king is dead; long live the king!" Along these lines, the natives of the Fiji Islands are very definite in their belief that the cosmic creation is repeated every time they enthrone a new king. Some Fijian tribes speak of their coronation ceremony as the creation of the world, while other tribes give the ceremony a name that can be roughly translated as meaning "the fashioning of the land." The discovery of a new land is viewed by the primitive in somewhat the same context. When the Scandinavians, for instance, discovered a new island, they immediately took possession of it with a ceremony equivalent to a repetition of the original creation of the world in the beginning.[4]

In every birth water plays an essential role, be it the watery sac surrounding the newborn babe, or the watery milieu enclosed in eggs laid on dry land. This primordial element is often found in the complex picture of fertility and ritual imitation. When Dido consummates her love and marriage with Aeneas, it is in the midst of a violent rain storm. Among the peasants of China, young couples went out into their fields in the spring to make love, hoping by their ritual union to stir the "cosmic regeneration" and the "universal germination" of their own farm and the earth in general. For the primitive cultures, the marital union is a sacred ritual closely integrated with the whole rhythm of the universe. It is important because every sexual union repeats the original union of heaven and earth and, by entering the cycle of mythical time, strengthens the fruitfulness of the cosmic creation.[5]

This denial of time and change by a ritual imitation of the gods extends into every area of daily primitive life. When the

4. M. Eliade, *Cosmos and History*, pp. 35, 80-82.

5. M. Eliade, *Cosmos and History*, pp. 23-27. Also: *Images & Symbols*, pp. 151-60.

Navajo Indian decides to become a medicine man or when he wants to be cured of some sickness, he must go through a ceremony which teaches him the whole history of creation, the mythic accounts of the gods, his ancestors and mankind. The Navajo can learn the art of medicine or be cured only by studying the intricate sand paintings of a man who knows the story of the gods and creation. Through the medium of these paintings, he must project himself into the mythical time of the gods, repeating and recreating through them all the events that occurred at the beginning of the universe. Once again in this ritual we find the symbolism of water. Often after listening to the cosmogonic myths related by the medicine man and contemplating the sand paintings, the Indian would take a bath to indicate to all his rebirth and newly won power over the universe, for now he knew the story of the earth's origins.[6]

Besides the community advantages found in ritual imitations and cyclic time, there is a very personal psychological advantage to this escape from time for the individual. The sacred ritual claims to be an imitation of the action of the gods. Thus if a person were to invest all his actions with sacred rituals, he would only be imitating the gods. He would have no personal responsibility for his actions, he would do nothing new or unique. (We should mention here that there is a fundamental difference between the ritual imitation of primitive societies with its roots in magic and cyclic time and the imitation of Christ and the saints spoken of in the Christian tradition. This is rooted in a linear concept of time which is quite the opposite of the pagan ritual imitation. The two concepts are opposed and contradictory, as we will see later.[7])

Such a simple solution to the perplexing problem of time and change may be quite satisfactory for the unsophisticated and primitive man, but for the men of the Academies, the disciples of Socrates, Plato and Aristotle, they were a bit too

6. M. Eliade, *Cosmos and History,* pp. 83-84.
7. O. Cullmann, *op. cit.,* pp. 51-60.

naive to be attractive. Not that the philosophers were unsympathetic to the assumptions and principles behind the ritual imitation and cyclic view of time. It was just that as philosophers they were a bit more sophisticated in their flight from time and change.

The most influential philosophers believed that they could only understand something which was authentic and complete —in other words, the eternal and immutable. Things which are in the process of changing and becoming are not fully intelligible; they are inferior degrees of reality. In fact, the philosophers felt one could understand these changing things only in so far as they contained something of the permanent. For this world, permanence lies in recurrence, for only circular movement insures that things will endure. According to the Platonic definition, time is the moving image of unmoving eternity, which it imitates by revolving in a circle. Time itself is determined and measured by the unchanging cycles of the heavenly bodies. As a result, everything in our world that is involved in a process of becoming moves in a circle or in accord with an indefinite series of cycles during which the same reality is made, unmade and remade over and over again. Nothing is really lost, nothing really created, for the same sum of existence is preserved throughout. Out of all the movements and changes they observed in nature, those which showed a repetition of cycles attracted the Greeks most. In movement they could see only a degradation, a fall, a *katagenesis*. In the fourth book of his *Physics* (222b), the great master Aristotle noted that all change is by its very nature an undoing. Time is the cause of destruction and not of generation, for change itself is only an undoing. Only by chance accident is time the cause of existence and generation.[8]

8. C. Tresmontant, *Hebrew Thought,* p. 26. See also Toulmin and Goodfield, *op. cit.,* pp. 33-41. Our modern Western mentality is influenced by such evolutionary sciences as biology, astrophysics, and paleontology, with their linear conception of time. Because of this we might be inclined to see in

To this negative outlook we can add the fact that some of the later Greek philosophers, Pythagoreans, Stoics and Platonists down to the days of Plotinus, even claimed that within each cycle of time the same situations and beings are reproduced as appeared in previous turns of the cycle and will reappear in subsequent revolutions. No event, no person can be considered unique or as occurring but once. Cosmic duration is, then, a ceaseless repetition, an *anakuklosis* or eternal return.[9]

Both the simple mythological ritual and its more sophisticated sister, the archetypal philosophies, revolve around a cyclic conception of time which in effect denies reality to time, change and movement. Time is a circle, not a line progressing from past to present and into the future in an irreversible flow. In both cyclic solutions no person, event or change is unique, for everything is either magically transposed into the mythical timeless age in the beginning through a ritual imitation of the gods or absorbed in ceaseless cycles as fallen shadows of some primordial, immutable and eternal archetype.[10]

Even as the cyclic concept of time pervaded the primitive cultures and early philosophies, we can discern vague hints of another appraisal of the phenomenon of time, the linear conception. Instead of seeing time as a burden and threat, instead of striving to escape our temporal condition, man can view time as the duration required for a true growth, development

---

the Heraclitan process of everything being in flux, *panta rei,* our own modern interpretation of a process. But for the Greeks, the process of becoming meant just the opposite of what we mean. For them it meant that everything passes away, escapes and flees us. The Greek philosophers viewed time and becoming as carrying a negative sign; time and becoming march towards death, for there is more being in the immutable than in the moving.

9. Henri-Charles Puech, "La Gnose et le temps," *Eranos-Jahrbuch* (Zurich), 20 (1951), pp. 60-61.

10. M. Eliade, *Cosmos and History,* pp. 88-91.

and evolution. Instead of seeing time as the endless circle of repetitious and never-new events, a few thinkers in the early days of recorded history began to see time as a linear process.

In the autumn of the Chou dynasty, when the great empire of Wu Wang had dissolved into thousands of small states and before the Tartar threatened the northern border, a great sage lived in what is now the province of Shantung. He came from an old and distinguished family, but the times were hard and he spent his early years in poverty. After working for an education, he began to teach at the age of twenty-two. His name was K'ung Futzu, the "philosopher K'ung," better known to us as Confucius. Pupils flocked to him and for the next fifty years he was honored and esteemed, so much so that after his death he became for the people a god.

Besides editing and collecting the Chinese "Classics," he also wrote an important work entitled *Yi-Chang,* in which he tried to show how all complex things were actually derived from a simple and single source through a gradual process of unfolding and branching. To express his idea of a directional process or change, Confucius used the word *Yi.* Another school of Chinese thought, the Taoists, had somewhat the same idea of a linear time. Lao Tzu, the founder of this school, was an older contemporary of Confucius, but he spoke another dialect, one in which *Tao* expressed much the same idea of change and process as *Yi* did for the Confucians. A number of writers in both these schools seem to have recognized and perhaps even vaguely appreciated some of the basic processes fundamental in the modern concept of linear or evolutionary time, processes which today we would include in the scientific concepts of variation, adaptation and the relationship between structure and function. And this some five to six hundred years before Christ.[11]

On the other side of the world the Egyptian civilization was

11. P. Fothergill, *Historical Aspects,* pp. 9-10; Tye Tuan Chen, "Twenty-five centuries before Charles Darwin," *Science Monthly,* 29 (1929), 49.

in the last stages of its decline. In the sixth century B.C. Nebuchadnezzar toyed with the possibility of invading the Egyptian empire during the reign of Amasis. Though he did not carry out the plan, the Egyptian world soon fell to the Persians under Cyrus the Great. Somewhere during this era the *Legend of Creation* was composed. The version we have today dates from around 300 B.C., but in it we find a number of ideas about the origin of the world and the concept of linear time or evolutionary progress which "are not so far different in nature and significance from those of more recent and of Western thought."[12] The *Legend of Creation* speaks, for instance, of a divine and intelligent creator, of water as the primitive source of all living beings and, most important, of creation expressed as a process of becoming actual through a series of stages. For the Egyptians, creation was both an evolving, unfolding process and an epigenetic development or growth. Once shorn of its mythological garb, these ideas bear a great similarity to our modern idea of linear, evolutionary time and process.[13]

While the cyclic concept of time dominated almost everywhere, with only an occasional hint of a linear view, the Grecian soil of hard logic and scientific observation proved to be the most fertile environ for the germinating linear view. About the same time that Confucius was composing his *Yi-Chang*, Thales and his students were developing an interest in the origin of the universe and the laws which govern its functioning. This led to the formulation of several ideas quite fundamental to later evolutionary thought. Thales, for instance, suggested that water was the original substance from which all life came.[14]

12. G. J. Dudycha, "Ideas of Origin among the Ancient Egyptians and Babylonians," *Science Monthly*, 32 (1932), 269.

13. P. Fothergill, *Historical Aspects*, pp. 9-10.

14. Andrew G. van Melsen, *From Atomos to Atom* (Harper & Row Torchbook, 1960), pp. 12-13. Also P. Fothergill, *Historical Aspects*, pp.

Another of the early Ionians and possibly a student of Thales', Anaximander, seems to have turned the course of Greek thought on the origin and development of our universe into a more fruitful, though still speculative path. Out of the infinite, boundless space all things evolved, and to it all would eventually return. Within this cycle, Anaximander claimed heat and cold, water, air, earth and fire came in a definite sequence. He went on to speculate that the earth was at its birth a mixture of dust and water from which came the plants, animals, and finally man, again in a definite order and sequence. Some scholars even maintain that Anaximander had some idea of natural selection and adaptation to the environment, elements that are very important in our modern idea of evolution. Even if this claim is not valid and despite the fact that he retained a basically cyclic concept of time, it is still the great achievement of Anaximander that he rejected the cosmogonic myths of the past and accepted a real development and linear movement in nature. With him we encounter the first real speculations about evolutionary time.[15]

For Anaximander the boundless infinite was indescribable. But his successor in the schools of Miletus, Anaximenes, believed it could be identified with air because this permeated all things. Anaximenes is often said to have been the first Greek to propose the idea of the spontaneous generation of living forms from primeval slime, though some scholars would give the credit to Anaximander.[16]

As Darius, the King of Kings, began to extend his influence into the land of the Ionians and particularly its center at Miletus where Thales, Anaximander and Anaximenes lived, the Ionians became restless. Even as the early Ionian philoso-

---

12-13. What we know of Thales comes to us second-hand from Aristotle, and so we cannot really appraise his importance and contribution.

15. P. Fothergill, *Historical Aspects,* p. 13.

16. *Ibid.,* pp. 13-14.

phers spoke of the origin of all things from the primordial water, air, or infinite, the Persians were gaining control of the city. Before they could solve the problem of how all things emerged from the primordial substance, the city of Miletus was sacked and those who escaped deportation and enslavement fled north to Ephesus.

The philosophers of the later Ionian school were actually physicists. One of their primary concerns was the articulation of a distinction between matter and energy, a distinction which ultimately would make an important contribution to the mechanistic sciences of the nineteenth century where the scientific concept of evolution and linear time germinated. Only the seeds of the evolutionary and linear world vision were planted by the Greeks, Egyptians, and Chinese; germination would require some two thousand years.

After Miletus was razed in 494 B.C., Heraclitus tried to solve the question of how all things proceeded from the primordial stuff. He came to see the world as a conflict of opposites in which the world is at once a unity and multiple. Not satisfied with water or air as the primordial substance, he claimed that fire was the ultimate source of all things. Because it burned steadily, it was one; because it was in constant motion, it could also be the source of all things. *Panta rei,* all things are caught up in a flux of constant change in which there is a reciprocal exchange between unity and multiplicity. Fire becomes moist by condensing; it changes then into water and finally earth. The cycle is completed when the earth changes back into water and then fire. As for man, Heraclitus taught that he also was composed of these three elements and was involved in the process of reciprocal exchange in which something is added and something taken away in every change. For Heraclitus, changes were dynamic even though any evolution of species was inconceivable. Even with the negative note attached to the Heraclitan flux, his admission of a true and dynamic change in nature would eventually form a basic element in the germination of the science of evolution and linear time.[17]

Heraclitus believed that *to be* meant *to change*. The threat of change, as we have seen, is one of the prime reasons why men have favored a cyclic interpretation of time. One of Heraclitus' contemporaries saw this very clearly and violently opposed the admission of change as real. Change for Parmenides is the illusion, reality must be unchangeable. That two contemporary thinkers should reach such contradictory views can be traced to the fact that Heraclitus was an experimentalist who accepted the perceptions of his senses while Parmenides was an idealist for whom sense perceptions were illusions. The result of these diametrically opposed views gave new impetus towards solving or at least clarifying the concept of change and its true nature.[18]

Empedocles was the first philosopher to accept the challenge of Parmenides. The answer he gave may strike us as very fanciful if not imaginative, but it approached the essence of reality enough to merit for Empedocles the title of "Father of the concept of evolution." To explain the nature of change and motion, Empedocles claimed that these were due to two forces, love and hatred, or perhaps more generally, the cosmic forces of attraction and repulsion, which act on and form the four primeval elements of fire, air, water and earth. In a constant tug-of-war where first love and then hatred carry the tide, Empedocles described the whole history of our universe and the development of life. The early universe, he believed, was a formless conglomeration of the four elements, which slowly separated from each other under the influence of the forces of repulsion. At this point life arose by spontaneous generation from the earth's bosom. Trees were cast forth from

17. *Ibid.*, pp. 14-15. Also A. G. van Melsen, *op. cit.*, p. 13.

18. P. Fothergill, *Historical Aspects*, p. 15; A. G. van Melsen, *op cit.*, pp. 13-17.

the earth's lifeless depths by repulsion long before the sun had achieved its proper and final form. Limbs, tails, eyes, heads and arms of animals were likewise spewed forth into the air where the attraction of love brought them together in haphazard combinations. (In this way, Empedocles found a handy solution to those mythical monsters, half human, half animal, which people Greek history and folklore.)

In this fanciful explanation we can find half buried, or half uncovered, one of the most basic concepts of modern evolutionary theory, the idea of natural selection and the survival of the fittest. In the world of Empedocles, ill-formed monsters had to die out because they could not adapt to the requirements of the environment. Other animals which were better suited for life on this earth managed to survive.

The origin of man was claimed to be similar to that of the animals. Thrown from the bowels of the earth by fire and the forces of repulsion, man's limbs and organs slowly came together by chance attraction. Lacking the power of speech and any sexuality, these various parts were gradually drawn together to form man and woman. Once animal and human sexuality evolved, sexual reproduction was possible and there was no longer any need for the earth to generate men and animals spontaneously as it did in the beginning.

Essentially the views of Empedocles are quite similar to those of modern evolutionary thought, provided we disregard the fanciful and picturesque presentation. Yet even in their germinal importance, these ideas were so crudely conceived and so without any scientific support, that neither Empedocles nor anyone else in the pre-Darwinian world could appreciate in the least their pregnant implications.[19]

A third member of the later Ionian philosophers has been described as a universal scholar. An able philosopher and physical theorist, he was also a sincere biologist who very likely

19. A. G. van Melsen, *op. cit.*, pp. 23-25; P. Fothergill, *Historical Aspects*, pp. 15-17.

performed actual dissections. He was also, it seems, a dedicated and observant traveler. Aristotle, his great critic, paid him the compliment of admitting he had thought about everything. Though we could hardly call Democritus an evolutionist or advocate of linear time, he was the first thinker to suggest that whole organs were adapted for certain specialized purposes.

Here, as with other elements that would eventually contribute to or foreshadow certain aspects in the scientific concept of evolution as we know it today, we are dealing with naive and rough ideas. From these seeds, modified, purified of their superstitions and finally rooted in scientific experiments, has emerged a kernel of truth, eternal and valid. The scientific theories proposed today as an explanation of the origin of life from non-life are much more exquisitely detailed and far better grounded in experimental evidence, but their spark can be traced back to Democritus and others many centuries ago.

With the death of Democritus around 400 B.C., Greek philosophy and science entered a new era. The Ionian philosophers had laid the foundations of medicine, biology and scientific speculations unencumbered by mythologies. For natural events they sought natural explanations based on observation and experimentation, primitive as these might have been. In their approach to nature they were whole men, thinking as scientists or physicists and as philosophers at the same time.

The Sophists carried the individualism of the Ionians to its extreme, much to the detriment of the experimental and observational sciences. Since man was the measure of all things, as Protagoras put it, there was no need for objective explanations of natural phenomena. What was the use of disputing about questions which could be viewed from a number of different standpoints, each just as valid as the other?[20]

20. P. Fothergill, *Historical Aspects,* pp. 17-18.

They influenced Socrates and Plato in the sense that neither spent much time with scientific or biological questions. Platonic thought is completely engrossed in the cycle of time, for time is only a "moving imitation of eternity," of the timeless.[21] The role of the archetype in this cyclic imitation of the timeless Beyond we will only mention here as we will treat it in some detail when we take up the question of original sin and the fall of man.

While Plato emphasized the divine origin of man to the point where one wonders if we really belong to this world of physical being, Aristotle stressed man's relationship and roots in the animal world to the point where one wonders how man could possibly possess an immortal spirit. Aristotle viewed the animal and plant world as being set out in a definite series of levels or grades of being. He was thus the first to suggest the idea of what became one of the most influential formative ideas behind the success of scientific evolutionary linear time, the "Great Chain of Being." Among the scholars there is no agreement as to whether Aristotle would admit any evolution or movement from one step of the Great Scale of Being to another, that is, whether he would admit the possibility of species mingling and evolving. Yet it would seem more likely that, with his total involvement in a cyclic conception of time, he would not be inclined towards an evolutionary development, for that would imply a linear progress in time. "Indeed time itself seems to be a sort of circle."[22]

Later when the Stoics and Epicureans strengthened Aristotle's concept of man's kinship with animals, they implicitly

21. Timaeus, 37d. See also C. Tresmontant, *Hebrew Thought*, pp. 17-38 and A. E. Taylor, *Introduction to Plato's Timaeus*, as well as his *The Mind of Plato* (Constable, 1922; Ann Arbor, 1960) and *Plato, the Man and His Work* (Humanities, 1952; Meridian, 1956), and Toulmin and Goodfield, *op. cit.*, pp. 42-54.

22. *Physics*, 4:14. A. G. van Melsen, *op. cit.*, pp. 25-44. P. Fothergill, *Historical Aspects*, pp. 18-33. Werner Jaeger, *Paideia* (Oxford University Press, 1939), Vol. I.

strengthened a position absolutely essential for any idea of the evolution of man from the animal world. But in all the speculations and philosophies of primitive societies as well as of the Greeks, Egyptians, and Babylonians, we find an overwhelming cyclic approach to time and nature. Though we may find hints of an evolutionary or linear understanding of time and nature, the overall impression is one of a world vision that is *almost totally cyclic and thus anti-evolutionary*.

For the Greek philosopher, primitive man, and all outside the pale of Judaism, *the symbol of time is the circle*.[23] There is, however, one early culture in which the cyclic view of time did not prevail. *For biblical Judaism the symbol of time is the arrow*.

Basically Oriental in their mentality, the Hebrews were not inclined to speculation and philosophical discussions. In fact, they had a strong aversion towards any philosophical system and preferred the world of concrete experience and personal encounter. As shepherds, and later as farmers, the Semites were greatly concerned with fertility and the whole process of growth. Unlike the Greek philosophers, who avoided all manual labor as ill-befitting the cultured man, the Hebrews daily encountered the world of nature with its constant change, growth and maturation. Greek contemplation and Hebrew contemplation arise from their conceptions of time, and these are worlds apart. While contemplation for the Greeks entailed the exclusion of all activity and action, the Hebrew saw in contemplative detachment "a consciousness capable of enclosing history within the grasp of a single thought [which] would have to be eminently active, creative, taut."[24]

Underlying the whole of the linear approach to time taken

23. O. Cullmann, *op. cit.*, pp. 51-52.
24. William F. Lynch, *op. cit.*, pp. 59-65.

by the Hebrews is the revelation of a creation, fall and future redemption of mankind. If there was a beginning and is to be an end to this world, how could they view history as an eternal cycle of repetitive events or as a mere ritual imitation of a mythic archetype? This is not to say that the cyclic concept of time did not influence the Hebrews at all. However, the essential and fundamental view of the Hebrews saw human history as a line traced from the moment of creation and fall, through the mid-point of the Messiah to the pleroma at the end of the world. History, for the Jews, had a beginning and it will have an end: it is directional, with certain unrepeatable and unique stages. The individual moments or stages along this line flow and mature one out of the other. In this way, the prophet of the biblical era was the man blessed with the wisdom necessary to see in which direction events would flow. It was not his task to predict an arbitrary future event, but to interpret the "signs of the times."

It was not only because of the creation-fall-pleroma sequence, but even more because of the center or mid-point of history, the coming of the Messiah, that the Hebrews accepted a linear concept of time. As the awareness of the covenant increased and the biblical revelation deepened, so the awareness of creative time with its sense of moments or stages in a cosmic process or maturation became more and more acute.[25]

After the period of the Babylonian exile, when the Hebrew world came into closer contact with the Greek world—and particularly, as we will see, during the early Christian era—a dipole tension arose between the Hellenic and Hebraic worlds, between the cyclic and linear concepts of time. Words were necessarily borrowed from the Greek, but in the process they were thoroughly modified and altered to fit the linear

25. C. Tresmontant, *Hebrew Thought*, pp. 33-34. Also W. F. Lynch, S.J., *op cit.*, pp. 59-65.

view of the Judaic world. A typical example can be found in two words which the Greeks commonly used for time. When the Greek used the word *kairos,* he meant a moment in time which is especially favorable for some undertaking, a point in time of which one has long before spoken without knowing its actual date. For the Hebrew and early Christian the same word meant the time of a definite maturing, "the time of a harvest" or the "time of fruit." When the Greeks spoke of *chronos,* they were referring to time as an abstraction, in its problematic character. For the biblical tradition, *chronos* meant rather the time of a genesis or childbirth, "the time for her delivery had arrived." Particularly when the coming of the Messiah was spoken of, this word was used with the nuance of a growth and maturation which the world and mankind would have to undergo before the Messiah could come, "when the fullness of time had come." The Hebrew and Christian saw the world's growth and development as part of a process of movement towards the divine but not, as the Greeks did, as a striving to reach the timeless.[26]

In all truth we can say that the Judaeo-Christian and Greco-Roman appreciations of time were totally and insolubly opposed to each other. For the Hebrew time was the necessary and good mark of progress, for the Greek it was the sign of eventual death and degradation, a curse and enslavement. Redemption for the Greek consisted in escaping from the eternal circular course of time. For salvation to be worked out through divine action in the course of temporal events would be impossible to the Greek mind. Redemption could come only if we were transferred from our enslavement to circular time in this world into the blessed existence in the Beyond which is *timeless,* total simultaneity in which past,

26. C. Tresmontant, *Hebrew Thought,* pp. 17-38. O. Cullmann, *op. cit.,* pp. 37-50.

present and future are one moment. The Hebrew concept of salvation is just the opposite. Heaven in the biblical view is *endless time,* world without end![27]

Later developments make it even clearer how diametrically opposed to each other the biblical and Greek views of the world are.

The first heresy of the Christian era revolved around just this point of the two conceptions of time. The marks of early Christian Gnosticism have been classified in a number of ways, but "in the last analysis, they may all be traced to the Greek, and so to an un-biblical concept of time." The Gnostics rejected the Old Testament as the salvation history of God's action within time, Docetism ultimately rejected the action of Christ within time, and all early Gnosticism rejected the primitive Christian eschatological hopes "whose characteristic distinction in terms of time between the present and the future age is replaced by the Greek metaphysical distinction between this world and the timeless Beyond."[28]

It is also no accident that among the theologians of the second century none fought Gnosticism with such acuteness as did Irenaeus, who with unyielding consistency carried through the time line of redemptive history from the Creation to the eschatological new creation. Down to the theologians of the "redemptive history" school in the nineteenth century, . . . there has scarcely been another theologian who has recognized so clearly as did Irenaeus that the Christian proclamation stands or falls with the redemptive history, that the historical work of Jesus Christ as Redeemer forms the mid-point of a line which leads from the Old Testament to the return of Christ. Therefore also no theologian of antiquity grasped so clearly as Irenaeus the radical opposition which emerges between Greek and Biblical thinking as to this point, namely, the conception of time. Irenaeus is the theologian of

27. O. Cullmann, *op. cit.,* pp. 52, 62-63; C. Tresmontant, *ibid.,* pp. 31-38.
28. O. Cullmann, *op. cit.,* pp. 55-56.

antiquity who understood the Greek world in its innermost nature, and yet undertook no such violent reductions and reinterpretations of the New Testament message as were practiced, not only by the Gnostics, but also by the Alexandrian scholars Clement and Origen.[29]

But the matter is not as simple and clear cut as we might at first suspect. There were gray zones in both worlds of thought. While the Greeks were certainly imprisoned in the eternal circle of time, their genius did grasp certain elements of the linear and evolutionary perspective.[30]

The same gray zone of alien influence can be seen in the Judaeo-Christian pattern of thought, for the Hebrews and Christians were not untouched by their contacts with the Hellenic world. This is quite evident in the question of early Christian gnosticism. Despite the linear conception of time so essential to the biblical revelation and so clearly delineated by Irenaeus, Basil, Gregory of Nyssa and Augustine, the cyclic concept of time did make inroads into the Christian mentality. The influence of lunar and stellar cycles on human events, for instance, was accepted in part or whole by a number of Fathers and Doctors of the Church. Ptolemy in the second century, Thomas Aquinas, Roger Bacon, Dante and others accepted without question the theory that the cyclic periods of the stars exercised a definite controlling influence over human events in the mass. These ideas, which became very popular in the twelfth century, were later worked into a whole systematic cosmology. For most Christians the concession of the periodic influence of the stars and heavenly bodies was limited to an instrumental role within the eternal linear plan

29. *Ibid.*, pp. 56-57.

30. R. C. Zaehner, *Matter and Spirit: Their Convergence in Eastern Religions, Marx, and Teilhard de Chardin,* (Harper & Row, 1963), *passim.* O. Cullmann, *op. cit.,* p. 51. Perhaps this may be traced to contact with the Iranians, who outside the Judaeo-Christian milieu seem to have followed a linear conception of time.

of the Creator, but for others this cyclic influence became more and more a cosmic force inherent in the world itself.[31]

One of the fundamental questions that came up in the early days of the Christian Church was the problem of how to approach the biblical writings: the question of interpretation. Neither the formulation of this question nor all its implications were clear to the scholars of early Christianity. Today we can formulate the question in a number of ways. What should be the value we place on the literal interpretation of the biblical writings? Are there different literary styles in the Bible? Is the Bible meant to teach us only certain divinely revealed truths and moral principles which man must accept if he is to fulfill his vocation as a human being, or can we consider the Bible as revealing also certain facts about science and secular knowledge? In even simpler terms, the question comes down to the distinction or lack of distinction between revelation and divine inspiration. We are only now working out the answers to this basic question. In the early centuries of Christianity, the appreciation of the complexity of the Bible emerged very slowly. While all saw in the Bible primarily a collection of divine messages concerning God's self-revelation as Creator and Giver of grace, an understanding of its more pragmatic message of how men can achieve supernatural life was very clouded, simply because there was a confusion of purposes attributed to the Bible by various readers.

In attempting to understand the full message of the biblical writings, two great schools of scriptural interpretation developed in the early Christian community: the allegorical school with its center in Alexandria, and the literal school located in Antioch. Over the years a number of those who insisted on

31. M. Eliade, *Cosmos and History,* pp. 141-47.

the allegorical interpretation of the biblical narrative, especially the first chapters of Genesis, carried the practice to extremes. These excesses led to a number of theological errors and heresies. As a result, the Christian community slowly came to favor more and more the completely literal interpretation of the sacred writings. This literal interpretation was given an important qualification by Augustine in the third century when he pointed out that the Bible is not a book of science; it was written to tell us "how to go to heaven and not how the heavens go." But this qualification was more often than not ignored for a number of reasons: the lack of scientific facts about the origin of the earth and man, the lack of literary criticism as we have it today, among others.[32]

Even in their groping, the early Fathers managed to suggest some very interesting ideas about the origin of the universe and man, interesting not so much for their scientific content as for the link they indicate between the Hebrew and Greek worlds. The scientific ideas about the origin of the world and man which some of the early Fathers picked up from the Greek world fitted perfectly the mentality of the Christian world with its thorough commitment to salvation history.

Trained, in many cases, in the secular universities where Greek philosophies were studied, the early Fathers tried to reconcile and synthesize their religious beliefs with the world views and philosophies prevalent in the culture they set out to convert. To present to the Greeks and Romans the revealed truths of a covenant rooted in a loving creation (and man's consequent vocation) by the only true personal God meant

32. "Allegory, Allegorical Interpretation," Joh. Geffcken, *Encyclopaedia of Religion and Ethics,* ed. James Hastings (Scribner's Sons, 1955), I:327-31; "Alexandrian Theology," W. R. Inge, *op. cit.,* pp. 308-19. Also E. C. Messenger, *Evolution and Theology,* p. 17.

that the early apologists had to build a bridge of understanding between the two worlds. Biblical thought and the Hebrew culture in general had no native philosophy or science; they had only a revealed message, a covenant to proclaim. What would be more natural for them to do than to accept those scientific and philosophical elements within the Greek culture which would complement and support the essential religious truths of revelation? Naturally the elements and scientific explanations they adopted were not those based on a cyclic concept of time since such would be alien to the Hebrew message. What the early Fathers of the Church did adopt from the Greek world, it seems, were just those evolutionary ideas which we have traced in our discussion of the Ionian and post-Ionian philosopher-scientists. (But this trend did not last, for the interest in Greek thought soon shifted to the cyclic elements within the work of Plotinus (205-270?) and other Neoplatonic writers of the third and fourth centuries.)

Quite early in the history of Christian thought the theologians of the Alexandrian school proposed a symbolic interpretation of the six days of creation mentioned in Genesis. They believed that the creative act of God was instantaneous, but that Moses and the rest of men found it so difficult to understand this unique moment of creation that they elaborated an explanation in which they could spread the creation out over six days and thereby make it more understandable.[33]

This symbolic interpretation was opposed by Ephrem and Basil the Great, the earliest members of the Antioch school, which taught a strict literal interpretation of the biblical narratives. Born in 306, Ephrem spent most of his productive life in Edessa after being ordained a deacon by Basil the Great. His commentaries on Genesis clearly adopted the idea

33. E. C. Messenger, *ibid.*, p. 17.

of the spontaneous generation of living beings from the active powers of the earth.[34]

The literary activities of the three Capadocians, Basil the Great, his brother Gregory of Nyssa, and his friend Gregory of Nazianzus, cover the last third of the fourth century, when allegorical interpretation was falling into disrepute.[35] Basil (331-379) was well educated, having studied in the academies of Athens and Constantinople before he became bishop of Caesarea. According to reports, Basil met Ephrem some time in 370 and it is quite likely that they exchanged ideas about the interpretation of the Genesis narratives, for shortly after that Basil wrote a series of homilies or explanatory sermons on the first chapters of Genesis. In these texts, which have come down to us in their entirety, the spontaneous generation of eels, field mice, frogs, gnats and flies, and a very clear causal relationship between the birds and reptiles, are proposed with such clarity and insistence that despite the scientific naiveté surrounding them it does not seem amiss to say, as a number of scholars have, that Basil would feel quite at home in our post-Darwinian world. By a simple extension of his statements about the origin and development of the world over a period of time much longer than the six days of which he spoke, an extension which in no way does violence to his basic thought, it is not hard to see why many scholars consider Basil as one of the great Christian forerunners of Darwin.

"Let the waters bring forth abundantly moving creatures that have life," it is said, "and fowl to fly above the earth in the open firmament of heaven." Why do the waters give birth also to birds? Because there is, so to say, a family link

---

34. Ephrem, *Explanatio in Genesim, Opera,* ed. Roman, 1737, I:18, 24 and 80. Also E. C. Messenger, *Evolution and Theology,* pp. 17-18.

35. J. H. Srawley, "Cappadocian Theology," in: *Encyclopaedia of Religion and Ethics,* III:212-17.

between the creatures that fly and those that swim. In the same way that fish cut the waters, using their fins to carry them forward and their tails to direct their movements round and round or straightforward, so we see birds float in the air with the help of their wings. Both are endowed with the property of swimming, their common derivation from the waters has made them of one family (Homily 8).

These homilies of Basil's stirred up a good deal of controversy and discussion, mainly because the people could not adjust to the change from an instantaneous creation as taught by the Alexandrian theologians to the explanation given by Basil, where there was a real succession of works spread out over six days of twenty-four hours each. Nor could they understand in his explanation how there could be a real evening and morning before the sun was actually created on the second day.[36]

The dispute became so heated and widespread that eventually Peter, the bishop of Sebaste and a brother of Basil, appealed to another brother in the family, Gregory, to settle the question. Gregory was bishop in Nyssa and a much more critical theologian than the more pastorally-minded Basil. Basil's sermons had stirred up a good deal of confusion which the technical theologian would now have to explain in scientific language that would satisfy both the experts and the ordinary layman. Thus it was that Gregory of Nyssa came to write his *Apologetic Treatise on the Hexameron* ("hexameron" means six days).

Gregory first stressed that his brother Basil had been primarily a pastor and that his explanations of Genesis and creation were presented in homilies intended for simple and uneducated people. Hence, he felt, it was quite natural that these sermons were not as accurate and precise as some theo-

36. E. C. Messenger, *Evolution and Theology*, pp. 19-22.

logians would have liked. Gregory then attempted to present Basil's views in more precise theological terminology. Gregory's genius in this explanation was that he blended the best elements in the allegorical interpretations of the Alexandrians and the strict literalism of Ephrem and Basil into a more complete and satisfying interpretation of the Genesis account.

In his *Treatise* we find the first attempt, and a quite successful attempt at that, to harmonize the instantaneous creation of all things in the beginning of time "potentially and in their causes" with the subsequent working out of this creative decree as time passed. After creating all things in their potencies in the beginning, God allowed not a fresh and distinct creative act on each subsequent day of the six, but rather "the development or unfolding of individual things from their causes or principles, according to a fixed and necessary order of succession."[37] Gregory expressed his thought very succinctly when he wrote, "All things were in the first Divine impulse of creation virtually. They existed as it were in a kind of spermatic potency sent forth for the genesis of all things, for individual things did not then actually exist."[38]

As for the origin of man, Gregory was also more specific than his brother had been. He taught, for instance, that in some way or other the whole human race existed from the very beginning of creation in the Divine will. But he also pointed out that the natural order of succession made it necessary for man to appear only after the plants and animals had come into being, since the rational form of life can only originate in a sensitive or animal organism which in turn presupposes a vegetal form of life. Messenger maintains that this clearly implies than man went through a vegetal and then animal

37. *Ibid.*, p. 23.

38. *Apologetic Treatise on the Hexameron*, in Migne, *Patrologia Graeca*, vol. 44, col. 77.

stage in the course of his development from the virtual creation in the beginning to his actual appearance later in time. He points out that Gregory expressly says that man derives many of his attributes from animal life. Or as Gregory himself put it, "the vital power blended with corporeal nature according to a certain succession. First it infused itself into a nonsentient nature, then it advanced into the sentient world, and finally ascended to intelligent and rational beings."[39]

While Basil and Gregory were the great Doctors of the East who dealt with the specific question of the origins of the universe and mankind in terms that foreshadowed the evolutionary view, another and ultimately much more influential advocate of this view appeared in the West in the person of Augustine, bishop of Hippo in Africa and the "Father of Western Theology." Augustine adopted the basic ideas suggested by Gregory with a few modifications. For instance, while Augustine admitted the idea of a simultaneous creation of all things in the beginning, he believed this was an actual creation of inorganic or non-living things and a potential creation of all living forms. Thus, unlike Gregory, who applied the idea of potential creation to all things, Augustine would limit the evolutionary creation to animals, plants, and man.

When Augustine set about explaining how God created all things simultaneously and virtually in the beginning, he coined a new phrase, *rationes seminales,* which has been given several different translations by scholars, "seminal natures," "seminal principles" and "seminal reasons." What Augustine meant by this phrase has been disputed, but it now seems that his seminal principles were *active powers or principles* which, given the proper conditions and time, would actualize themselves in new species and forms ultimately leading to Man.

39. Gregory of Nyssa, *De Anima et Resurrectione, P.G.,* 46:59. See also E. C. Messenger, *Evolution and Theology,* pp. 131-44.

These active powers or principles were placed in created nature when God created all things, not actually but in their potencies in the beginning of time.[40]

Regarding the creation of man, Augustine categorically affirmed that the complete, active virtuality of the body of Adam, and generally of the whole human race, was present among the causes created at the beginning of time.[41] He believed that when Adam actually appeared on the scene, he most likely appeared as an adult. In Augustine's explanation, however, it would not matter at what age Adam actually appeared since this would be in accord with his virtual and potential (causal) creation at the beginning of time. In explaining the function of these causal principles, Augustine said that theoretically they could have operated in two ways. God could have created a single seminal principle that would then have directly determined the manner in which Adam actually came into existence, or he could have reserved to himself a choice among several seminal causes which, when one was actuated, would result in man appearing as a child, an adolescent or as an adult. Augustine seems to have preferred the second hypothesis, though he does not exclude the first or give any indication that he thought the second theory more in keeping with the Genesis account.[42]

One important result of the acceptance of a simultaneous creation of all things in potency was the distinction that could then be made between God's creative word at the beginning of time ("God rested on the seventh day from all his works which he made") and his conservation of the universe ("My Father and I work until now"). This distinction was very crucial in the early days of Darwinism, though recent considera-

40. *Ibid.*, pp. 40-55.

41. Augustine, *De Genesi ad litt.*, VI. See also E. C. Messenger, *ibid.*, pp. 160-78.

42. *Loc. cit.*

tion of the concept of creation within an evolutionary perspective has transcended the problem, as we will see in our final chapter.

With the dominating image of Augustinian thought in Western theology, the idea of potential creation became quite common in the Church by the end of the fourth century. Indicative of this is a letter written by Pope Anastasius II to the bishops of France at the end of the fifth century. The French bishops at that time were troubled by the belief of some of the faithful that the souls of children as well as their bodies were generated by their parents. To solve the problem, the bishops appealed to the pope who assured them that:

> Before the order and arrangement of all creatures according to their species, as shown in Scriptures, [God worked] potentially and causally—something that cannot be denied— in the work pertaining to the creating of all things at once. From this work, when finished, he rested on the seventh day. Now, on the other hand, he works visibly in the work pertaining to the course of time until the present. . . .[43]

While the passage may be a bit obscure in some respects, it seems clear that the pope considers the idea of a potential and causal creation of all things in the beginning with their actualization later in time as being perfectly orthodox. The document, of course, is not an infallible pronouncement, but it does give an indication of a view apparently quite common in the Church at that time.[44]

Later ages were not at all productive of any advances in the linear concept of time nor man's understanding of his origins, though it seems that the view of absolute evolution as proposed by Augustine and Gregory of Nyssa prevailed as

---

43. Henricus Denzinger, *Enchiridion Symbolorum,* ed. C. Bannwart & J. Umberg, 24th edition, Barcelona, 1946, #170.

44. E. C. Messenger, *Evolution and Theology,* pp. 56-58.

"the common opinion of the Fathers, at least up to the eighth century and probably to the end of the twelfth."[45]

45. Canon Dorlodot, *Darwinism and Catholic Thought* (Benzinger, 1922), p. 151. In summarizing his study of evolutionary thought among the early Christians, Dorlodot said, "Some authors explicitly profess the theory of absolute natural evolution of living things in the sense of St. Gregory of Nyssa and St. Augustine. Others repeat more or less in their entirety the assertions of St. Basil; lastly, there are some who remain silent on the matter, and limit themselves to expounding the order of appearance of the different creatures, and the meaning of the six days of the Hexameron. But we have not been able to find a single Christian writer previous to the scholastic period who opposes the theory, or who endeavors to regard the *rationes seminales* of St. Augustine simply as material or passive powers, as later writers endeavoured to do" (*op. cit.*, pp. 68-69).

CHAPTER 2

Aquinas to Erasmus Darwin

As the age of scholastic philosophy dawned, the situation began to change. During the twelfth and thirteenth centuries the Arabian philosophers, particularly Avicenna and Averroes, introduced the thought of Aristotle into the west by way of Spain. Until this silent invasion, the dominant philosophy in Europe had been that of Plato and the Neoplatonists. Most systems of thought go through periods of growth and senescence, and at this time Neoplatonism was suffering a period of unfruitful stagnation. Confronted with the excessive idealism generated by the decadent Neoplatonism of the tenth, eleventh and twelfth centuries, Albert the Great and Thomas Aquinas turned to the philosophy of Aristotle for a contact with reality that would bring philosophy and especially theology down from the ethereal realm of idealistic speculation. In adopting Aristotle as a guide to the world, the scholastics were only following the lead of the scientists who had already rejected Plato's concept of the universe in favor of the Stagirite. But since Aristotle was a man of synthesis and based his philosophical speculations on his scientific observations and theories, the impact of his thought on the scholastics encompassed a whole world vision.

As we noted in the first chapter, Aristotle was basically anti-evolutionary. The immutability of species and of the substantial form in the Aristotelian hylomorphic theory is essential to Aristotle's view of physics and the natural world. It is also the root of his philosophical thought. Thus when Aquinas adopted the Aristotelian synthesis, with its physics and philosophy, he made a step that rendered his philosophy of nature hopelessly static. Even though, due to his Christian mentality, his metaphysical conception of nature was dynamic in that it saw the whole of creation as involved in an irresistible upward movement towards God, Aquinas' interpretation of Augustine's *seminal principles* betrays the influence of the static physics of Aristotle.[1] Augustine had been very definite in explaining his seminal principles as active creative powers or potencies residing within all matter. Aquinas found this difficult to integrate into the immutable substantial form of Aristotelianism and thus modified Augustine's explanation so that they became passive potencies.[2]

One of the most important elements in the birth of scholasticism is found in the contrast between Albert the Great and his pupil, Thomas Aquinas. Until Albert's time, the scope of human knowledge was such that one man of genius could hope to master it all. From the time of Paul the apostle to the days of early scholasticism, constant efforts were being made by Christian scholars to harmonize the Judaeo-Christian revelation with the scientific and philosophical knowledge of the secular world. This synthetic bond reached a critical stage with Albert the Great, who happened to be a very fine biologist and student of nature as well as a keen philosopher and theologian. The story is often told of how Albert used to interrupt his travels to parishes within his diocese of Ratisbonne to study the habits of the tiny ant lion or to examine some unu-

1. Joseph F. Donceel, *Philosophical Psychology*, 2nd edition (Sheed & Ward, 1961), pp. 62-63. E. C. Messenger, *Evolution and Theology*, pp. 49-55.

2. Thomas Aquinas, *De Potentia*, q. 4, art. 2, ad 2. Also *Summa Theologiae*, I, q. 91, art. 2, ad 4.

sual plant along the path. It was a different situation with his prize pupil at the University of Cologne, for Thomas Aquinas was so engrossed in the philosophical and theological realms that he had no time for the natural sciences. Perhaps this was due to a deeper penetration into the realities of theology and philosophy than his master was capable of. Perhaps it was also due to the explosion of learning that followed the foundation of the great universities of the Middle Ages.

But cut off from contact with living science, the theologian-philosophers began to brew their own arm-chair speculations about the world of nature. To make up for their lack of an up-to-date and living scientific picture of the world, the scholastics had to rely on their own cosmologies, erected on an up-dating of Aristotle's physics achieved without the benefit of experimentation or observation. They ended up in the same pit as their Neoplatonic predecessors. Theology and philosophy were cut off from the world of experience and direct observation. The scientists made the same dichotomy, but they recovered from it much quicker, only to find the theologians and philosophers so isolated from reality that communication was practically impossible. In the years that followed, the factors favoring a complete separation of science, philosophy and theology, with an inability to communicate, were compounded.

In the previous chapter we touched on the importance of biblical interpretation in the history of evolutionary thought. It might be well to add that all Christians before the Reformation followed a literal interpretation of the Bible, though a figurative interpretation was permitted within certain bounds defined by the Church. After the Reformation, Catholics continued this view down to the present with ever greater precision about just what is to be interpreted figuratively in terms of a literary style or technique and what must be taken literally. The Protestant world, on the other hand, adopted a policy of approaching the Bible from a strictly literal view-point. This policy they were able to maintain with increasing difficulty down to the publication of Darwin's *Origin of Species* in 1859. In the scientific discoveries that led up to 1859, the Protestant world found a tension between the sciences (which they supported wholeheartedly) and the literal interpretation of the Bible (which they had maintained with equal vigor). As a result of a number of scientific discoveries culminating in the *Origin of Species,* the Protestant world was split, not along denominational lines, but along the lines of two approaches to the Bible: the Fundamentalist and the Modernist views. After 1859 the Fundamentalists or Evangelical Protestants held firm to an absolutely literal interpretation, while the Modernists or Liberal Protestants accepted a literal and figurative interpretation within limits defined by the individual.[3] The development of this split, and particularly of the scientific discoveries behind it, we will take up shortly as it will add a clearer perspective to our history.

As we have already noted, a tension and, one might even say, an incongruous juxtaposition developed in the Western world as the Greco-Roman cosmology and philosophy with its predominantly cyclic outlook infiltrated the linear mentality of the Judaeo-Christian culture. The archetypal pattern of thought in the Christian mind is quite different from that conceived within the cyclic context of the Greek philosophers and primitive societies of the pagan world. For the Christian, the imitation of Christ means a *personal* encounter which in

3. Raymond W. Murray, *Man's Unknown Ancestors* (Bruce, 1943), pp. 339-44. John A. O'Brien, *Evolution and Religion* (Century, 1932), pp. 28-44. On the fundamentalist interpretation of the Bible and the fundamentalist movement in general, see Franklin Hamlin Littel, *From State Church to Pluralism, A Protestant Interpretation of Religion in American History* (Doubleday, Anchor, 1962); Winthrop Hudson, *The Great Tradition of the American Churches* (Harper & Row, 1953; Torchbook, 1963); and Winthrop Hudson, *American Protestantism* (University of Chicago, 1961).

no way lifts the burden of responsibility from the individual. This imitation of Christ must also be worked out within society and more specifically as an essential to achieving the fullness of time, the pleroma. Nowhere in truly Christian spirituality is the imitation of Christ and the saints conceived as a magical ritual imitation of an eternal archetype which would liberate us from the burdens of an essentially evil and time-bound world.

Some observers might be inclined to read into the sanctoral and temporal cycles of the Roman liturgy and the sacraments the overtones of a cyclic view of time. Superficially it seems that the constant repetition of the liturgical year, moving as it does through Advent, Christmas, Epiphany, Lent, Easter, Pentecost and the time after Pentecost, may seem to be just a Christian expression of cyclic ritualism. And because the sacraments are said to repeat the actions of Christ by which a person is sanctified (that is, the Mass and reception of Communion is said to be a bloodless repetition of Christ's sacrifice on Calvary and the Last Supper), we might tend to see in the sacraments nothing more than a reincarnation of the ritual imitation of the gods practiced by the pagans.[4] But the resemblance is only superficial. While the liturgical year appears cyclic, it is basically linear: for it is a sacramental, concrete but mystical point of contact with Christ *within a temporal world*. Like the sacraments which bring us into a personal encounter with Christ, the liturgical year extends the mystery of God's incarnation in this world of time and matter which began but did not end with Bethlehem.

The liturgical year and the sacraments are archetypal in

4. Such is the interpretation suggested by Mircea Eliade in his *Cosmos and History*, pp. 23, 59, 143, etc.: "The liturgy is precisely a commemoration of the life and passion of the Savior. We shall see later that this commemoration is in fact a reactualization of those days." It is that, but it is also more the *extension* of the incarnation in a linear time. See, for instance, Eduard Schillebeeckx, *Christ, the Sacrament of the Encounter with God* (Sheed & Ward, 1964).

form, but the eternal pattern is not in the timeless age in the beginning. It lies rather at the end of this world, in the age to come, in that world without end which will begin when this world is purged of evil and sin during the apocalyptic second coming of Christ. The liturgy and sacraments are the means by which the Christian is personally incorporated into the mystical body of Christ. Unlike redemption for the Greeks which implied a liberation from time, the Christian redemption is fulfilled by a personal eschatological incorporation into Christ *achieved only at the end of this world, in the fullness of time*. The Greek heaven is timeless, it has no beginning, no end; the Christian heaven indeed has no end, but it does have a beginning. The Platonic archetype would liberate us from time and personal responsibility, it looks to the Golden Age in the past; the true Christian typology achieves itself in the perfection of the human person by direct loving encounter with the Divine—it brings the fullness of time, and looks more to the future than to the past.[5]

Nevertheless the similarities are there and pose a danger when imperfectly understood. When the basic principles are once properly understood, as for instance Irenaeus understood them, the Christian becomes consciously aware of the problems involved in careless and shallow integration of Greek and Christian thought patterns. Such an awareness was not always the case, as we can see in many instances in the history of Christianity.

As the awareness of the Christian message deepened and science groped its way towards the birth of Darwinian evolution, the contrasts and tensions between cyclic and linear views became stronger and more perplexing.[6] At the peak of

---

5. O. Cullmann, *op. cit.*, pp. 22-33, 51-68. C. Tresmontant, *Hebrew Thought*, pp. 17-38.

6. William Irvine, *Apes, Angels, and Victorians* (McGraw Hill and Meridian, 1955), *passim*. Herbert Wendt, *In Search of Adam* (Houghton

the middle ages, cyclic and astral theories began to overwhelm the historical and eschatological views of the authentic Christian tradition.[7] Popular in the twelfth century, they became an integral part of the systematic thought of the scholastics in the thirteenth century, especially after the Arabian philosophers, Avicenna and Averroes, became popular in the universities.[8] Albert the Great, Aquinas, Roger Bacon and Dante, the intellectual giants of the thirteenth century, accepted the belief that the cycles and recurrent patterns of world history were controlled by the stars. In the Christian tradition, this influence was seen as subject to the will of God, being merely his instrument in guiding the course of history. But as times changed and the sciences, especially the new-born astronomy, lost contact with theology, this astral influence was viewed more and more as a natural force inherent in the universe. As the science of astronomy began to replace the astrological treatises of earlier ages, the cyclic theory was brought down out of the heavens and made immanent in our cosmos, in nature.[9] Thus we have the works of Cardanus (1501-1576), Giordano Bruno (1545?-1600), Tycho Brahe (1546-1601), Kepler (1571-1630), and Campanella (1568-1639).[10]

Parallel with this demythologizing and naturalizing of the

Mifflin, 1956; Collier, 1963) has a fascinating account of the conflict between linear and cyclic conceptions, in which the novel-like narrative in no way lessens the factual and valid character of the material presented. Cf. also his *The Road to Man* (Doubleday, 1959; Pyramid, 1962).

7. Pitirim Sorokin, *Social and Cultural Dynamics, II* (American Book Co., 1937-1941); also Pierre Duhem, *Le System du monde* (Paris: A. Hermann, 1913-1917), and Lynn Thorndike, *A History of Magic and Experimental Science* (1929-41).

8. L. Thorndike, *op. cit.,* I:455ff. P. Sorokin, *op. cit.,* p. 371, and P. Duhem, *op. cit.,* V:223ff.

9. P. Sorokin, *loc. cit.;* M. Eliade, *Cosmos and History,* pp. 143-45.

10. Arthur O. Lovejoy, *The Great Chain of Being: A Study of the History of an Idea* (Harper & Row Torchbook, 1960), pp. 86, 100-121, 249. H. Wendt, *In Search of Adam,* pp. 130-36, 284.

cyclic concept of time went a similar expansion and development of the linear concept of time. Conceived, as we have seen, in the biblical mind and tentatively explored by some of the early Fathers of the Church, the linear idea of history really began to assert itself in the seventh century. That Mircea Eliade should find strong indications of linear history in the writings of Albert the Great and Aquinas is not surprising, but it is not in these two that he found the best expression of linear time during the thirteenth century. The linear progress of history "appears in all its coherence, as an integral element of a magnificent eschatology of history, the most significant contribution to Christianity in this field since St. Augustine's," in the *Eternal Gospel* of Joachim of Flora.

Joachim's interpretation of history is completely biblical, linear and eschatological in character. He saw the history of the world as divided into three eras, each inspired and directed by a different person of the Trinity. Each of these three eras reveals a new dimension of the divine in the context of cosmic history, and this progress allows humanity to perfect itself in stages until it finally arrives, under the direction of the Holy Spirit, at absolute spiritual freedom.[11] During the late sixteenth and early seventeenth centuries, when astronomy was coming into its own, Francis Bacon (1561-1626) and Pascal (1623-1662) pushed the linear concept further along the path towards final acceptance. At the opening of the eighteenth century, Leibnitz (1646-1716) had already found in the linear and progressive concept of history the basis for a faith in the infinite progress of mankind and the world towards perfection.[12] The century of "enlightenment" only strengthened the idea.

Picking up certain threads of the Judaeo-Christian tradi-

11. See M. Eliade, *Cosmos and History*, p. 145.
12. H. Wendt, *In Search of Adam*, pp. 85-86. M. Eliade, *Cosmos and History*, pp. 145-46.

tion, Hegel (1770-1831) proposed a philosophy of history in which every historical event was a manifestation of the Universal Spirit. For the biblical mind, "as for Hegel, an event is irreversible and valid in itself inasmuch as it is a new manifestation of the will of God—a proposition really revolutionary . . . from the viewpoint of traditional societies dominated by the eternal repetition of archetypes."[13] The role of Karl Marx (1818-1883) was to bring this concept of history down out of the clouds and naturalize it in the socio-economic progress of mankind. Kant (1724-1804), Goethe (1749-1832), and finally Herbert Spencer (1820-1903) added argument after argument to the linear structure. Of course, the key figure, as we will see, is Charles Darwin, whose *Origin of Species* (1859) proved to be the turning point in the dialectics between cyclic and linear time.[14]

The conflicts that arose as a result of these general developments are quite informative both for the relationship between science and theology and for the gradual emergence of the scientific idea of evolution.

The growth of the natural sciences began with mathematics, astronomy and physics, then chemistry, and finally the biological sciences. In that same order we can trace the conflicts between science and theology to their culmination in the Darwinian controversy of the mid-nineteenth century.

The first critical blow to the cyclic cosmology came with the Copernican and Galilean denial of the geocentric theory in the sixteenth and seventeenth centuries. Here was the first scientific challenge to the literal interpretation of the biblical

13. *Ibid.*, pp. 147-49.
14. *Ibid.*, pp. 149-50; H. Wendt, *In Search of Adam, passim*. On the social implications of evolution, see Richard Hofstadter, *Social Darwinism in American Thought* (Beacon, 1964; American Historical Association, 1944); and Vincent C. Hopkins, "Darwinism and America," in *Darwin's Vision and Christian Perspectives,* ed. by Walter J. Ong, S.J. (Macmillan, 1960).

texts.[15] Coupled with the proof of a spherical earth resulting from the voyages of the explorers of that time, Christians should have been reminded of Augustine of Hippo's warning that we should not turn the Bible into a science textbook. In theory, the Protestant world before Darwin was generally committed to a literal interpretation of the Bible, word for word as it was written. In theory, the Catholics were not as tightly constrained to this literal interpretation. And yet in practice there was little difference in the way the two groups responded to the new scientific ideas. Habits of thought are hard to break, and when a person has been conditioned to think of the Bible and Aristotle as *the* ultimate authorities in all matters it is not easy to introduce a new and contradictory idea, even with solid evidence.

When Copernicus and Galileo proposed the idea that there were more than seven planets, that the earth and other planets revolved around the sun, and that the sun itself had spots on its surface, the response was quite clear. The revered Aristotle "the Master of those who know," said nothing about there being more than seven planets, therefore there were only seven planets. The seven-branched candlestick in the Tabernacle, the seven golden candlesticks of the Apocalypse and the seven Churches of Asia offered more than enough biblical proof for the Christian that Galileo was proposing heresy. That the sun should have spots on its surface was also impossible, for Aristotle had proven that the heavenly bodies were perfectly pure. A Jesuit, Christopher Scheiner, who was brash enough to claim he discovered the sun spots before Galileo, was told by his Provincial:

I have read Aristotle's writings from end to end many times, and I can assure you I have nowhere found anything similar

15. J. O'Brien, *Evolution and Religion*, pp. 66-89; A. Lovejoy, *op. cit.*, pp. 121-43; Giorgio de Santillana, *The Crime of Galileo* (Univ. of Chicago, 1955); Arthur Koestler, *Sleepwalkers* (Macmillan, 1959; Grosset & Dunlap, 1963). (Koestler is more critical than Santillana.)

to what you describe. Go, my son, and tranquillize yourself; be assured that what you take for spots on the sun are the fault of your glasses, or of your eyes.[16]

Theoretically, Catholics were in a much better position to accept and reconcile the findings of science with their faith than the Protestant world, but in reality they proved themselves just as obstinant in clinging to literalism as any one. Aristotle and the Bible; but it was more than a conflict between religion and science. As Professor David Starr Jordan noted,

The real essence of conservatism lies not in theology. The whole conflict is a struggle in the mind of man. It exists in human psychology before it is wrought out in human history. It is the struggle of realities against tradition and suggestion. The progress of civilization would still have been just such a struggle had religion or theology or the churches or worship never existed.[17]

In the seventeenth century a very important discovery was announced by the Reverend John Lightfoot, doctor of divinity, eminent Hebrew scholar, a Westminster divine and one time Vice-Chancellor of Cambridge University. After a most careful and detailed study of the biblical chronologies, Lightfoot announced that "man was created by the Trinity on October 23, 4004 B.C., at nine o'clock in the morning."[18] A Sunday morning, of course! Bishop Ussher followed this up by determining the exact date of the great flood of Noah, 2348 B.C.[19] These dates were commonly accepted in the Christian world, so much so that even as late as 1925, William Jennings Bryan cited them during the famous Scopes "Monkey Trial" in Dayton, Tennessee, much to the merriment of non-

16. Louis T. More, *The Dogma of Evolution* (Princeton University Press, 1925), p. 99.

17. David Starr Jordan, *Footnotes to Evolution* (Appleton, 1902).

18. J. O'Brien, *Evolution and Religion*, p. 93.

19. R. Murray, *op. cit.*, p. 346.

Fundamentalists in the court and the whole scientific world.[20]

4004 B.C. and 2348 B.C. are pretty definite dates for the creation and flood. When only the Roman Empire was known to civilized man (Europe, a bit of North Africa and Asia), and when recorded history went back only a relatively few centuries, the problem of these dates was almost non-existent. The same could be said for a literal adherence to the "universality of the flood" which supposedly covered the face of the earth and wiped out all mankind and life except that aboard the Ark. But even in those early days there were some questions stirred up.

Augustine of Hippo was a practical bishop, and while his people were generally uneducated he himself had studied in the great universities, so that such problems were not unknown to him. In his *City of God,* he touched on these questions and offered some amusing solutions which apparently satisfied the Christian of the fourth century. After the deluge ceased and Noah had released his hoard, God used a number of means to assure the distribution of the animals once more over the face of the earth. For animals like the frog there was no problem since they could be generated spontaneously from the mud and slime left by the flood. Domesticated animals were also no problem for Augustine claimed that men took these along with them when they explored new lands, islands and continents. But how the wolves and other wild animals reached the islands was a more serious problem. If the island were close to shore, perhaps the animals could have swum out to them. Or if the island was too far to swim to, the first men to land on their shores might have captured wild animals and transported them to the island so they could have something to hunt in their new home. (And when the situation really got pressing, angels could always be called in to drop the wild animals off on the distant shores.)

20. Jerome Lawrence and Robert E. Lee, *Inherit the Wind* (Random House; Bantam, 1955). See also H. Wendt, *In Search of Adam,* pp. 424-27.

Augustine's solution was generally acceptable for Christians until the Crusades began. When the age of the explorers dawned shortly after this, Marco Polo, Columbus, Magellan, Vasco da Gama and others pushed the ends of the world even further into the distance, reaching across seas and oceans to increase the problems of a literal interpretation of the flood narrative. Most Christians still believed that the waters of the deluge had covered the whole surface of the earth, even though this seemed pretty fantastic. The new discoveries called for new solutions. One Jesuit missionary in the West Indies, Joseph Acosta, gave the matter a lot of thought as he prepared his *Natural and Moral History of the Indies,* published in 1590. He was dissatisfied with Augustine's explanations:

> Who can imagine that in so long a voyage men would take the paines to carrie Foxes to Peru especially that kinde they call "Acias" which is the filthiest I have seene? Who woulde likewise say that they have carried Tygers and Lyons? Truly it were a thing worthy the laughing at to thinke so. It was sufficient, yea, very much, for men driven against their willes by tempest, in so long and unknowne a voyage, to escape with their owne lives, without busying themselves to carrie Woolves and Foxes, and to nourish them at sea.[21]

Indeed the discovery of America placed quite a strain on the theologians. It was a real shock for these people, who had firmly held for ages the literal interpretation of Genesis. With the special approval of the Bishop of Salzburg, Abraham Milius tried to solve the dilemma of the universality of the flood and the new lands by returning to the spontaneous generation theories of the early Greeks. "The earth and the waters, and especially the heat of the sun and of the genial sky, together with that slimy and putrid quality which seems

21. Joseph Acosta, *Historia natural y moral de las Indias* (Seville, 1590). The old English translation given here is from the London, 1604 edition cited by J. O'Brien, *Evolution and Religion*, p. 97.

to be inherent in the soil, may furnish the origin for fishes, terrestrial animals, and birds."[22] Milius was very much puzzled by animals he found in the New World which were not to be found near Mount Ararat. The migration of animals that could swim or fly was understandable, but the others posed a real problem. And Augustine's answer was no answer at all for an intelligent man of the seventeenth century.

The question of the flood was further complicated by some supposedly innocuous pieces of rock that seemed to mock our world of plants and animals: the fossils. Aristotle was the first writer to mention these plant and animal-like formations in stones. An interesting curiosity, but not really important, was his judgment. Many years later people still collected fossils as amulets, charms, or trinkets. In the late fifteenth century, however, Leonardo da Vinci, whose mind ranged over so many fields, found the explanations offered by his contemporaries not only unsatisfactory but also very naive. In fact, he found their explanations positively irritating:

> They say that these shells were formed in the hills by the influence of the stars; but I would like to ask them where in the hills today are the stars now forming shells of distinct ages and species? And how can the influence of the stars explain the origin of gravel which occurs at different heights in the hills and is composed of pebbles rounded as by the motion of running water? Or how can such a cause account for the petrification of various leaves, sea-weeds and marine crabs in the same places?[23]

The debate over fossils soon became quite heated as various scholars offered their explanations. "Working models which the Creator either approved or rejected as he laid his plans

22. Abraham Milius, *The Origin of Animals and the Migration of Peoples* (Geneva, 1667). Cited by J. O'Brien, *Evolution and Religion,* pp. 97-98.

23. H. Wendt, *In Search of Adam,* pp. 10, 12, 83. Cf. H. B. Glass, *et al., Forerunners of Darwin* (Johns Hopkins Press, 1959), pp. 12-16.

for creating the world," was one proposal. But another scholar disputed this, "No, they are plans and models for some future creation." "Mere sports of nature"—the stones simply took on their peculiar formation under the action of some "occult internal principle which originated from the heavenly bodies," others maintained. Some opinions were not so appreciative or optimistic about these harmless pieces of stone. For some they were instruments of the devil, tricks which would arouse and mislead man into proud curiosity about the mysteries of nature. Others were kinder, perhaps, when they blamed the fossils on God who placed them in the strata of the earth in order to bring human curiosity to naught or merely to mimic the world of life in the mineral kingdom. Some even waxed poetic over the fossils: "Porous bodies petrified by a 'lapidifying juice' or produced by the tumultuous movements of the terrestrial exaltations."[24]

Even more serious than fulminations against fossils, telescopes and "atheistic" scientists in general was the question stirred up by the discovery of the North American Indians. Since most Christians, Protestant and Catholic alike, believed that all mankind had descended from the three sons of Noah, Shem, Ham and Japheth, they had traced the Caucasian and Mongoloid races back to Shem and Japheth. The Negro, of course, took his origin from the accursed Ham, who mocked his drunken father and was punished with "the foulest colored skin." This accounted for the whole human race, at least till Columbus stumbled on the Indians. Where to fit them in the picture was an enigma. Isaac de la Peyrere, a Calvinist scholar of the mid-seventeenth century, suggested that God had created a race of "gentiles" along with the animals and before Adam. These pre-Adamites, he believed, were really not human beings, and in fact had died out long ago everywhere except in the New World. Many religious leaders fought

24. J. O'Brien, *Evolution and Religion*, p. 93. H. Wendt, *ibid., passim.*

this explanation. Given the mentality of the day, it allowed the Spaniards and others to enslave the Indians as sub-humans with neither dignity nor rights. Pope Julius II had to make a very definite statement that the American Indian was just as much a descendant of Adam and Eve as was the European, but his 1512 pronouncement had little effect on the common mentality of the day. Later the same literal interpretation of the Genesis account of the flood would allow the American colonists to abuse the Negro since he was "accursed by God."[25]

As the world approached the time of the Darwinian explosion, the questions became more and more pressing. The search for Adam and the ante-diluvian man began to concern the scholars, and many controversies developed among the scientists.

The scientific method and the individual sciences began to blossom during the period of the Renaissance, that period covering the fourteenth to sixteenth century in Europe which saw a gradual and often painful transition from the medieval to the modern world. The work of Copernicus and Galileo, Kepler and Newton, contributed greatly to the advance of astronomy and physics. The biological sciences, which would ultimately become the focus of the conflict between the evolutionary and cyclic concepts of time, emerged much more slowly. Like the progress of the other sciences, the advance of biology hinged on experimental work. Even in the thirteenth century dissection of the human body was possible, even if not commonly practiced. William Harvey (1578-1657), one of the first and greatest of the anatomists, contributed such important details to our knowledge of anatomy and physiology that he is often thought of as the pioneer and father of these biological sciences. Actually the birth of anatomy as a biological science seems to occur somewhat earlier with Vesalius (1515-1564). The other science which would ulti-

25. R. Murray, *op. cit.*, pp. 7-8, 344-49.

mately contribute major evidence leading to the success of the linear concept of time, embryology, had its foundations laid by Malpighi (1628-1694), a physician in the papal court. The first real embryologist since Aristotle, Malpighi studied in the minutest detail the development of the chicken embryo.[26]

Explorations, new discoveries, and the rapid advances in the art of printing books with movable type led to a flood of biological writings in the seventeenth and eighteenth centuries. This outburst of activity is interesting from two angles. In it, we can see not only the winding thread of germinal ideas which eventually matured in the truly scientific concept of evolution, but also a wide variety of wildly imaginative speculations about the origin of life and man. Two quite natural groupings emerge in this era, aside from the strict naturalists (who culminate in Buffon): the purely speculative writers like Diderot and de Maillet; and the philosophers of nature like Bacon, Descartes, Leibnitz and Kant. The contributions and importance of these two groups we will deal with in turn before taking up Kant, the only one of the age who accepted the evolutionary concept of time. The true naturalists were the great classifiers of the centuries just before Darwin: Edward Wotton (1492-1555), Konrad von Gesner (1515-1565), and Cesalpino (1519-1603), Pope Clement VIII's physician and a lively botanist. There was also John Ray (1627-1705), the famous English preacher and amateur biologist who set out the Great Chain of Being in all its splendor and detail as a proof of the wisdom and majesty of the Creator who had arranged his creation so magnificently. Carolus Linnaeus (1707-1773) has been one of the most influential of the naturalists. We are indebted to him for the binomial system whereby every animal and plant can be defined scientifically as belonging to a definite genus and species. The Great Chain of Being and the immutability of natural species were the two

26. P. Fothergill, *Historical Aspects,* p. 60.

great dogmas of pre-evolutionary days. But these were already being challenged. The greatest of the naturalists, George Louis Leclerc Buffon (1707-1789), befriended a poor abbé from Picardy, Jean Baptiste Lamarck, but he also made his own personal contribution to the emergence of scientific evolution:

> . . . almost everything necessary to originate a theory of natural selection existed in Buffon. It needed only to be brought together and removed from the protective ecclesiastical coloration which the exigencies of his time demanded. . . . It is a great pity that his ideas were scattered and diffused throughout the vast body of his *Natural History* with its accounts of individual animals. Not only did this concealment make his interpretation difficult, but it lessened the impact of his evolutionary ideas. If he had been able to present his thesis in a single organized volume, it is possible that he himself might have argued his points more cogently and perhaps seen more fully the direction of his thought.[27]

On the all important question of man, Buffon thought that the ape was only a degenerate form of man, since it seemed to possess so many vestigial organs, now no longer used. The orang-utang he placed closer to man than the monkeys in his scale of being, though he felt God had used the same basic plan for both man and the monkey. In the purely theoretical sphere, Buffon was undoubtedly the foremost biologist of the eighteenth century, a man possessed of the greatest wealth of ideas and a man whose influence reached far into the centuries after his death.[28]

The speculative writers of this pre-Darwinian era indulged in all sorts of science fantasy, even though they claimed to be very scientific in their labors. Many of their ideas were simply

27. H. Wendt, *In Search of Adam*, p. 50.
28. *Ibid.*, pp. 78-79, 175-85; A. Lovejoy, *op. cit.*, pp. 268-78 *et passim;* P. Fothergill, *Historical Aspects*, pp. 44-47.

reincarnations of the ancient Greek mixture of science and fantasy. In this respect they really do not belong in the main line of preparation for Darwin. Duret, Oken and Diderot are among the more prominent figures in this group, but the most influential seems to have been Benoit de Maillet (1656-1738). This very original and creative thinker wrote a book, widely read in the mid-eighteenth century, which he entitled *Telliamed,* adding the impressive subtitle of *Discourses Between an Indian Philosopher and a French Missionary on the Diminution of the Sea, the Formation of the Earth, the Origin of Men and Animals, etc.* By inverting his name, de Maillet was able to carry on the role of a sincere Christian truly horrified at the preposterous and novel ideas uttered by his fictitious eastern sage, Telliamed.

Duret had already suggested that leaves falling in the autumn turned into birds if they happened to settle on land or fish if they fell into the sea. Despite such anecdotes as the attraction exerted on mermen by the wooden figureheads of sailing ships (which de Maillet undoubtedly picked up in some seaside tavern), he did strengthen the force of an evolutionary or linear approach to the world and time. Loren Eiseley has summed up his influence:

He made one of the first fumbling attempts to link cosmic to biological evolution; he anticipated a greater age for the world; he recognized the true nature of fossils and suspected that some fossil plants "exist no more." He termed a fossil quarry "the most Antient Library in the World"; he had an idea of a planet evolving by natural forces. He even grasped dimly the principle of the successive deposition of strata. He is not, of course, the original author of all these separate ideas but he picked them up, combined them in his own cosmological theory, spread them and made them widely accessible. . . . He noted amphibious species such as otters and seals which he rightly observed are in some manner transitional half-world creatures moving from one medium to another. In one passage, he is already debating the significance of a phenomenon which was still mystifying the naturalists of Darwin's time; namely, that "in small islands far from the Continent, which have but appeared a few Ages ago at most, and where it is manifest that never any Man had been, we find Shrubs, Herbs, Roots and sometimes Animals. Now you must be forced to own, either that these Productions owed their Origin to the Sea, or to a new Creation which is absurd."

In effecting the transition from sea to land, De Maillet, in one passage, and without elaboration, strongly hinted at what really amounts to mutation and preservation through natural selection.[29]

Another concept which played a vital role in the birth of scientific evolution was also anticipated by de Maillet when he suggested that acquired characteristics might be inherited. This belief was later advanced by Lamarck in the first scientific exposition of evolution. Along with Darwin's theory of natural selection and de Vries' mutation theory, it ultimately formed the basis of early scientific evolution.

Among the speculative philosophers, the place of Charles Bonnet (1720-1793) is crucial in more than one way in the dialogue between evolutionary and cyclic mentalities. He appeared on the scene just at the time when evolution was beginning to receive serious consideration from thinkers all over Europe, and as a result was stirring up the vehement and fearful antagonism of the religious world. "Only a kind of godlessness could invent such dreams" as were being proposed by de Maillet and the other forerunners of scientific evolution who questioned the stability of natural species.[30] Like de Maillet, Bonnet had to recognize that there must be something to the theory of evolutionary development, but to admit

29. Loren Eiseley, *Darwin's Century* (Doubleday, 1958; Anchor, 1961), pp. 33-34.

30. See *Forerunners of Darwin: 1745-1859*, ed. Bentley Glass, Owsei Temkin, and William Straus (Johns Hopkins, 1959), p. 231.

this would be to shake the very foundations of the Christian world. Unlike de Maillet, who chose to create a fictitious character as advocate for his own belief in evolution, Bonnet tried to "synthesize" the two views, fixity of species and evolutionary development: If we cannot escape the reality of evolutionary development, perhaps we can remove its fangs by eviscerating the idea; if we cannot deny evolution, and still want to save the fixity of species within the Great Scale of Being, perhaps we can reduce this evolutionary development to the simple unveiling or unrolling of something already present.

A short time before Bonnet, Leibnitz had suggested that the perfection of this "best of all possible worlds" allowed for no gaps or leaps in nature. Animal species may be subject to modifications but there could be no arbitrary or chance mutation that was not already provided for in the original scheme set out by the Creator. "The entire future of the world is contained in its present, completely planned in every detail."[31] Evolutionary changes could be explained as the unfolding of a *preformed* pattern. For Leibnitz and his followers, any suggestion of the possible transformation of lower animals into higher forms was viewed as "insolent presumption." Every form of life developed in keeping with the pattern of its eternal archetype.

Like other believers in the "preformation theory," Bonnet tried to find experimental evidence for the theory. Chopping worms and polyps into a dozen pieces and watching them come back together, chopping and rechopping again till the poor worm died of exhaustion; observations of virgin birth or parthenogenesis among the plant lice, as well as the scientific theories of others, led Bonnet to the formulation of a theory which seemingly allowed for evolution but basically rejected it to save the Christian faith.

31. H. Wendt, *In Search of Adam*, pp. 85-95.

Evolution, he maintained, was simply a jack-in-the-box, an unwinding of all the realities actually present in our ancestors since the beginning of time. Evolution was not any real development of something new but merely the actualization of the primordial mythic archetype. If aphids could reproduce without any sexual union, here was proof enough that every female contained not just a fully formed tiny individual in each egg within her ovaries, but also the fully formed germs of all her descendants down to the end of time. This encasement of all one's descendants in the body of the parent Bonnet saw as ordained by nature to the production of ever more perfect types, and ultimately, man. The evolutionary sequence or unwinding of this preformed germ began with the union of the basic elements of fire, air, water and earth. It continued through all the stages of fish, amphibian, reptile, mammals and man, just as the atheistic evolutionists of Bonnet's day claimed. But actually there was no real change or evolution of species, merely the unfolding of a predetermined, preformed plan. An embryo could evolve in the true sense into a child and finally into an adult, but the evolution of species was another thing entirely.[32]

The third group of pre-Darwinians comprises that of the philosophers of nature, particularly those of the German school. Except for Emmanuel Kant, who worked as a scientist in his youth, none of the natural philosophers could be called biologists. However, they were very much concerned with the phenomena of nature and with interpreting these within a comprehensive explanation of the world and life. Here again, while individual thinkers were able to grasp such realities as natural selection, survival of the fittest, and adapta-

---

32. *Ibid.*, pp. 88-91, 124; *Forerunners of Darwin: 1745-1859* contains numerous references to Bonnet, but gives his surname as Charles, while Wendt gives it as Jacques de Bonnet. Cf. P. Fothergill, *Historical Aspects*, pp. 45-46.

tion, none of them could work them into an integrated and complete world vision. In philosophical circles another very important factor was slowly taking shape. As man became more and more disillusioned with scholastic philosophy and ever more devoted to the world of nature, a shift in emphasis became apparent.

In the past, classical philosophy had erected whole systems of thought on the concept of *essences* or *beings:* neat pigeon-holes, categories that were immutable and eternal since they were rooted in the archetypal patterns of a Golden Age. As man found his way through the Renaissance and the Age of Enlightenment, he became more and more fascinated with the concept of *becoming.*[33] This growing awareness and recognition saw that, "contrary to the postulates of a certain *philosophy of being,* there is more being, more reality in movement than in rest."[34] Until man recognized this fact, it would be totally impossible for him to reject the fixity of species patterned on a Platonic *eidos* and accept the evolutionary origin of animals and man. Hence this philosophical shift is most important in preparing the way for the ultimate acceptance of scientific evolution.

Another of the more significant contributions to the birth of scientific evolution was made by the philosophers of nature in the hundred or so years just before Darwin. Out of the efforts of these men there came the articulation of a philosophical premise known today as mechanism. Behind every scientific approach to the phenomena of this world has always been a thinking man. Every time a scientist looks into a microscope, he implicitly makes certain philosophical acts of faith. He believes that there is a consistency between what he observes under the microscope and similar animals studied

33. P. Fothergill, *Historical Aspects,* pp. 51ff; *Forerunners of Darwin: 1745-1859,* pp. 268, 275, 325, 436-37.
34. Ignace Lepp, *Authentic Morality* (Macmillan, 1965), p. 52.

by other scientists; he assumes that there are certain logical, rationally analyzable "laws" evident in the phenomena he studies. He further presumes that he can discover by observation these consistencies and deduce some meaning from them. Over the centuries two main philosophical systems have sparked and illumined man's reading of nature. The oldest, and until the seventeenth century also the most popular philosophical view, was that of *vitalism*. This philosophical option assumes that the phenomenon of life is made possible by some force which is neither chemical nor physical, a principle of life or *psyche*. This vital force is not subject to observation, though it is responsible for a living being reacting the way it does. Mechanism, on the other hand, believes that the phenomenon of life can be explained entirely by explaining the operations and reactions of a plant or animal's physical and chemical components.[35]

Aristotle has been commonly accepted as the founder of the vitalist tradition which prevailed among philosophers, scientists and theologians until well into the seventeenth century. He saw three basic types of *entelechy* or life principles: a plant (vegetative) psyche, an animal psyche and a rational psyche. Each of these forces was sufficient on its own level to maintain the vital processes of the plant, animal or human matter which it animated.

René Descartes gave the mechanistic view its first real acceptance just about the time the American colonists were landing on our east coast. Descartes was a contemporary of Kepler and Galileo. Instead of publishing his treatise on the cosmogony of the universe, and antagonizing the Church

35. Jacques Loeb, *The Mechanistic Conception of Life,* ed. Donald Fleming (Harvard University, Belknap Press, 1965); Hans Driesch, *The History and Theory of Vitalism* (London, 1914). Loeb and Driesch were two of the greatest figures in the vitalist-mechanist debates of the early twentieth century. (The Loeb publication is a reissue.)

authorities by debunking the Bible as a text of science, Descartes rewrote the basic ideas and included them in his *Principles of Philosophy* in 1644. Here he managed to ignore God's direct causal action by concentrating on purely natural causes as an explanation of the creation of our world. Along with this purely natural explanation, Descartes introduced his dualistic approach to science by denying the psychic character of animals and plants. These, like man's body, were only mechanical clocks which could be taken apart and analyzed.

The battles that arose over vitalism and mechanism were hot and furious, especially since mechanism seemed to eliminate or weaken the concept of God as Creator. Living things, for the mechanist, were simply more complex than non-living things. Ultimately, neither side won and both schools of thought have now merged in the organismic biology of recent years (which we will take up later).

Shortly before Descartes resurrected the mechanistic thought of Democritus, another natural philosopher, Francis Bacon (1561-1627), made his contribution to the birth of scientific evolution by questioning the stability and permanence of species in nature for the first time in the history of human thought.[36]

The mechanistic philosophy of Descartes laid the ground for scientists who would eventually study the history of our earth. It ultimately gave that study the purely materialistic bent so evident at the time of Darwin and Huxley, but it was the only way, perhaps, for the world of science to avoid the danger of explaining everything with supernatural, unprovable forces. Descartes was no evolutionist, but there were many implications in his dualistic thought that caused strong reactions among other philosophers of nature, particularly Leibnitz (1646-1716). This German philosopher played a

36. P. G. Fothergill, *Historical Aspects,* p. 52; *Forerunners of Darwin,* pp. 36-38.

major role in the emergence of scientific evolution. Not that he was an evolutionist. Far from that, he was a staunch advocate of vitalism, the fixity of species and the Great Chain of Being. Still his defense of the preformation theory contributed in a negative way to the emergence of evolutionary thought.[37]

The most important among the philosophers of nature was Emmanuel Kant (1724-1804), the German philosopher. Kant accepted the Cartesian separation of body and soul, though he did not agree that man and other living beings were mere mechanical clocks which could be perfectly and completely explained by chemical and physical laws. In a way, Kant's position is a mediation between vitalism and mechanism. He rejected the naive supernaturalism of the vitalistic approach to nature, and denied the naive teleology or purposiveness of nature, but at the same time pointedly emphasized that every organism possesses a formulative principle which inanimate things do not have. Even as he rejects the extremes of vitalistic teleology (which can be reduced to preformation evolution), Kant is very careful to point out that a purely mechanistic approach to life is incomplete. Thus Hans Driesch, one of the great protagonists of the vitalist-mechanist debates in the early twentieth century, called Kant a "dynamic teleologist."[38]

Kant's distinction between body and soul and his articulation of the mathematical and experimental approach to the study of living beings enabled the sciences of psychology and biology to go their separate but very fruitful ways. The elimination of supernaturalism and teleology allowed the biologists and geologists to concentrate on natural explanations for the growing awareness of changing and evolving species.[39] Here

37. P. G. Fothergill, *ibid.*, pp. 52-53; *Forerunners of Darwin, passim.*

38. Hans Driesch, *op. cit.*, p. 87.

39. For an interesting comment on the re-instatement of teleology in recent times, see S. O. Waife, "In defense of teleology," *Perspectives in Biology and Medicine,* 4:1 (1960), 1-2.

Kant played a major role, for he was the first to suggest, in strong terms, that the Great Chain of Being was actually a phylogenetic history, and evidence for the serial evolution of species.[40]

Fothergill has summed up this period of human thought just prior to the emergence of scientific evolution as an age in which both theoretical and practical biology began to recognize and accept the mutability of species. Parallel with this development was the shift from the idea of "being" to the concept of "becoming." Both advances were absolutely essential for the emergence of scientific evolution.[41]

40. For fuller comments on Kant, see P. G. Fothergill, *Historical Aspects,* pp. 53-58; H. B. Glass, *op. cit.,* pp. 200-11, *et passim;* John C. Greene, *The Death of Adam* (Iowa State University Press, 1959; Mentor paperback, 1961), *passim;* H. Wendt, *In Search of Adam,* pp. 137-43; Toulmin and Goodfield, *op. cit.,* pp. 129-134.

41. P. G. Fothergill, *ibid.,* pp. 57-58.

CHAPTER 3

Scientific Evolution

The era of scientific evolution dawned, strangely enough, in the quiet English village of Breadwall, near Derby, and in a long poem with the odd name of *Zoonomia*. The author was a versatile, eccentric country doctor named Erasmus Darwin (1731-1802), who loved to explore every land and every topic of human interest by visiting the exciting museums now bursting at their seams all over England. Tied pretty much to his desk and medical practice, Dr. Erasmus Darwin nevertheless managed to read just about every tome available in the libraries, thanks to his voracious reading habits.

Two writers from widely variant fields contributed much to the development of Erasmus Darwin's ideas on evolution: David Hume and Adam Smith. Smith was a Scottish political economist of nationalistic bent. His *Enquiry into the Nature and Causes of the Wealth of Nations* (1776), the Bible of the Whigs, the British liberals, suggested that the motive force behind human development was a free competition among the many different tendencies of mankind. For Smith, economic competition with its struggle for survival was the basis for all human advancement. Dr. Darwin logically asked if the same principle could be applied to all nature? His answer was a simple affirmative. David Hume was likewise a Scotsman, but his interests lay more in the fields of philosophy and history. Following much the same logic of the natural scientist, Hume felt that there should be a consistency in the functioning of things. If societies, civilizations, political institutions and man's own personality grow and evolve, then why not other phenomena as well?

When Erasmus Darwin welded these two ideas together, the result was the two-volume *Zoonomia or Laws of Organic Nature* (1794-96) and the posthumous *Temple of Nature*. Both these works received little attention from the scholars of the day, nor did they stir up the fuss and furor created by Lamarck a few years later in France. Darwin was certainly provocative and original enough to deserve some controversy. He suggested such new and startling ideas, in a scientific presentation, as evolution by natural and sexual selection, protective adaptation, inheritance of acquired characteristics, and even the evolution of mankind. "There is hardly an idea and hardly an invention in the world today that Erasmus Darwin did not father or foresee, from the philosophy of Bernard Shaw to the phonograph of Mr. Thomas Edison, from eugenics and evolution to aeroplanes and submarines, from psycho-analysis to antiseptics."[1] The trouble was Dr. Darwin preferred rhymed verse to the more intelligible and clear prose of common scientific writing. To discern what the eccentric doctor was getting at sometimes took more than a bit of literary perspicacity as, for instance, when he proposed the idea of evolution in nature:

> Where milder skies protect the nascent brood
> and earth's warm bosom yields salubrious food;
> Each new descendent with superior powers
> of sense and motion speeds the transient hours;
> braves every season, tenants every clime,
> And Nature rises on the wings of Time.[2]

1. Hesketh Pearson, *Doctor Darwin, A Biography* (Toronto and London: J. Dent, 1930), p. vii (Preface).
2. *Temple of Nature,* Canto II, 11, lines 31-36.

Hence without parents, by spontaneous birth,
rise the first specks of animated earth.
From Nature's womb, the plant or insect swims,
And buds or breathes, with microscopic limbs.
Organic life beneath the scoreless waves
Was born and nurs'd in ocean's pearly caves;
First forms minute, unseen by spheric glass,
Move on the mud, or pierce the watery mass;
These, as successive generations bloom,
New powers acquire, and larger limbs assume;
Whence countless groups of vegetation spring,
And breathing realms of fin, and feet, and wing.[3]

Erasmus Darwin and Lamarck (in France) were unfortunate enough to propose the scientific idea of evolution at a time when the revulsion of people everywhere to the excesses of the French Revolution made the idea of social evolution "morally reprehensible." Lamarck was labelled "the French atheist," and Erasmus Darwin was left to gather dust on the shelves of libraries as religious orthodoxy with the beauty of the Great Chain of Being was restored to its throne.[4]

In one of those strange twists of fate, Lamarck, the poor abbé who had been a tutor to Count Buffon's son, was to befriend another down-and-out young scientist by the name of Georges Cuvier. Through the patronage of Lamarck, Cuvier obtained a minor position at the Jardin des Plantes in Paris, 1794. Cuvier was quite the opposite of his patron in appearance: Lamarck a shy and quiet botanist gradually losing his sight and Cuvier a frail body topped with a wild mop of shaggy red hair, flashing eyes, the explosive voice of a demagogue and the vehement arms of a rabble-rouser. In the meetings with his older patron and senior members of the staff,

3. *Ibid.*, Canto I, lines 247-50, and 295-302. Cf. P. G. Fothergill, *Historical Aspects*, pp. 62-68. H. Wendt, *In Search of Adam*, pp. 114-19, and 235-39. J. C. Greene, *op. cit.*, pp. 169-71.

4. L. Eiseley, *Darwin's Century*, pp. 46-54.

Cuvier soon made his presence felt. A strong advocate of the Linnaean stability of species and the sacred *status quo* of orthodox science, Cuvier nevertheless made one of the most vital contributions to the birth of evolutionary science when he not only established but also thoroughly organized the whole science of paleontology. His brilliance and intuitive discernment allowed him to reconstruct the skeleton of a whole unknown animal from just a bone or two. His Law of Correlation, deduced from this ability, stated that the organs and structures of an animal are so closely correlated and integrated that one has to examine only a few parts and the whole structure is evident to the shrewd observer. Comparative anatomy and paleontology had been only a minor department at the Jardin, but Cuvier made it the most important, far overshadowing all the others, even those headed by his patron Lamarck and by Geoffroy Saint-Hilaire.[5]

The lines of battle were drawn when Cuvier approached Lamarck with his idea that the whole kingdom of the animals could be classified on the basis of four general plans: the vertebrates; the insects, spiders and crustaceans; the molluscs; and the worms, starfish, sponges and infusoria. This was a modification of the Linnaean concept of one general plan of creation, but it retained the immutability of species with no genetic relationship between the animals within the four groups. Lamarck informed Cuvier, only an assistant in anatomy at the time, that he preferred evolution as an explanation rather than the arbitrary plans of creation determined by Cuvier. But the upstart found support among the other professors of the Jardin, and more important, among the members of the Directory who had replaced the Jacobins in the government.

5. Fothergill, *Historical Aspects,* pp. 68-78; H. Wendt, *In Search of Adam,* 145-66; Donald Culross Peattie, *Green Laurels* (Garden City, 1938). This last mentioned work is a delightful and scholarly account of the Lamarck-Cuvier-Saint-Hilaire era.

Cuvier's opposition to the idea of evolution grew stronger as he received promotions that finally placed him in a position to rid the Jardin of all those brash enough to support the evolutionary theory. A formal debate ensued between Cuvier and Saint-Hilaire during which Cuvier was challenged to explain how it was that the simpler animals preceded the more complex, and how or why certain animals were now extinct. These two questions had to be answered if Cuvier was going to maintain the immutability of biological species successfully. To explain the extinction of certain animals, Cuvier proposed a *theory of catastrophism*. This theory claimed that at the end of each geological period nature experienced a catastrophe of world-wide dimension, a "flood" which wiped out every living thing. Nature and God then created a whole new series of plants and animals, each time following Cuvier's four basic plans. The debate ended in a draw and the rise of Napoleon eased the tensions at the Jardin. Saint-Hilaire, since he was the emperor's special favorite, took off for Egypt to gather fossil remains as the French armies conquered the world. Cuvier stayed at home to become an advisor for the Imperial University and head a committee of scholars charged with setting up universities on the French pattern in all the lands conquered by Napoleon. In Egypt Saint-Hilaire uncovered a number of transitional forms which did not fit at all the catastrophic schema of Cuvier. More and more he was convinced that Cuvier was wrong and the evolutionary interpretation the only valid answer, but Saint-Hilaire was not the popular demagogue Cuvier was. He knew nothing, in his cynicism, of how to wean an audience or how to use ridicule and oratorical tricks to divert the audience to the conclusion he proposed. To meet Cuvier, now recognized throughout Europe as "the pope of bones," in a public debate and defend the case for evolution, Saint-Hilaire was not the man.

That lot fell to Jean Baptiste Lamarck, the man who had befriended Cuvier and taken him under his wing. The little abbé from Picardy had patiently and diligently examined all the fossils brought back by Saint-Hilaire and listened to all his wild but fascinating explanations of how these animals had evolved. Slowly he welded the facts and evidence into a comprehensive and consistent evolutionary theory, the first complete scientific explanation of evolution in the history of mankind. As Lamarck poured over the fossils from Egypt, he became convinced that in nature there was no such thing as a species, there was only a whole series of minute variations. As a typical son of the Revolution, he assumed that new conditions in the environment make new demands of the creature living in that changing environment. Just as man has to adapt to evolving social pressures, so animals, in the long history of nature, had to adapt to their environments. This influence along with the growing animosity of Cuvier towards the evolutionary theory, led Lamarck to compile his *Philosophie Zoologique*, which he published in 1809 at the age of sixty-five. Six years later he published the first of his volumes on *Invertebrate Zoology*, restating the basic laws of evolution with more precision. Before he stated his explanation, he first formulated his official position:

> what we describe as the system of animals and plants is a genealogical tree, a line of ancestors. Species have no hard and fast limits, they blend into one another, proceeding from simple Infusoria right up to humanity. The fossil forms of organic life are the genuine and actual predecessors of our present forms.[6]

To explain this evolution, Lamarck proposed two laws in his 1809 work, which he expanded into four in the work on invertebrates. Those basic laws could be summarized best as claiming that:

1. Life, by its own force, tends continually to increase the

6. H. Wendt, *In Search of Adam*, p. 161.

volume of every living body and to extend the dimensions of its parts, up to a limit which it imposes.

2.   The production of a new organ in an animal body results from a new need (*besoin*) which continues to make itself felt, and from a new movement which this need brings about and maintains.

3.   The development and effectiveness of organs are proportional to the use of those organs.

4.   Everything acquired or changed during an individual's lifetime is preserved by heredity and transmitted to that individual's progeny.[7]

The battle was set. The decisive engagement came when Cuvier sat in on one of Lamarck's lectures. The lecture was one of Lamarck's favorites, and dealt with what he thought was a perfect example of evolutionary change as a response to environment. In the Illyrian Alps, certain caves contained a type of salamander which had apparently lost its sight because it did not need or use this in the darkness of the caves. Lamarck described how this creature regained its sight when exposed to light for any length of time.

Cuvier's patience was short, as was his social finesse. Tactlessly, he interrupted Lamarck's lecture to launch an attack not on Lamarck's science, but on his person. At the time Lamarck was nearly blind and had to be guided around the Jardin and University by his devoted daughter, Cornelie. "If that is so, Monsieur Lamarck, one can only conclude that you, too, have made no use of your eyesight, and have consequently lost it!" Silence. Cuvier pressed the point, "If you used your eyes a little more, you would get a better idea of nature, instead of indulging in obscure fancies." Laughter replaced the silence, and then desertion as Cuvier suggested that the students quit wasting their time and adjourn to another hall where he would give them a spectacular demonstration of his

7. H. Graham Cannon, *Lamarck and Modern Genetics* (Manchester University Press, 1959), pp. 51-52.

Law of Correlation. Lamarck was left alone with his daughter.

Towards the end of his life, the socialists began to influence French political life. Their leading theoreticians, Saint-Simon and Fourier, turned to Lamarck hoping he would permit them to use his evolutionary theory in support of their political philosophy. But Lamarck was now blind, discouraged, and too disillusioned to take up the fight again. Cuvier was victorious, the Law of Correlation was established and since this was obviously valid, the implication was that Cuvier's unproven theory of catastrophism and the special creation of each individual immutable species was just as valid and true.

Lamarck died penniless, blind and ignored. But death did not end his misfortune, for the man chosen to deliver his eulogy for the French Academy was none other than his antagonist, Cuvier. The personal vendetta was crowned when Cuvier deliberately mistranslated Lamarck's basic concept that the needs created by the environment caused animals to develop and evolve new organs. In the eulogy, Cuvier translated "need" *(besoin)* to mean wish. Thus the animal *wants* to fly, so he develops wings; the animal *wants* to swim, so he develops fins and a tail. The ridicule was perfect, and Lamarck's theory of evolution was totally disgraced. In later years, another injustice has been dealt Lamarck by the oversimplification of textbooks which have reduced his evolutionary synthesis to the simple statement that animals inherit the characteristics acquired by their parents, a statement that can be easily ridiculed.[8]

Lamarck died in 1829, the first man to propose a complete and detailed scientific explanation of evolution, a man who made a very valuable and lasting contribution to systematic biology.

8. Cannon gives a fair and valid, though somewhat colored, history of the treatment received by Lamarck at the hands of Cuvier, in his book cited above.

The story of Charles Darwin has been told often and well by scholars and writers who have spent years studying his life and works. Hence we would suggest only the briefest sketch of this central figure here and refer the reader to the popular and scholarly studies.

By now it should be evident that Darwin's theory of the evolutionary origin of species did not suddenly and unexpectedly appear on the stage of human thought. It was, in fact, only the logical flowering of a thought long germinating on European soil. There is one last link we must mention in our historical sketch, and that is the work of an English geologist who later became one of Darwin's strongest supporters and closest friends.

In the early 1830's, just after Lamarck's silent demise, Charles Lyell published a masterpiece on geology. He totally rejected the catastrophism of Cuvier and restored the "uniformist theory" of an earlier age, but solidly updated and revised in the light of his own observations and studies. He pointed out that universal catastrophes in nature simply did not exist. Instead the crust of our earth was subject to a slow, tedious process of gradual changes; mountains, rivers, valleys, lakes, deserts and coastlines all were subject to purely natural forces of erosion by the wind, water, frost, ice and rain. The crust of the earth slowly cooled and as it did, like any cooling object it contracted, slowly lifting up ridges and mountain ranges. These mountains, in turn, were subjected to the forces of erosion. But this suggestion of a uniform history of our earth, besides eliminating the need for Cuvier's "supernatural" catastrophes, also indicated that the earth was much older than the sixty thousand years or so allowed by Cuvier.

This view of the history of our earth posed several questions for the inquiring mind of Charles Darwin (1809-1882), a retiring country squire and naturalist. If our earth has undergone so many slow changes in the course of millenia, then might not the animals and plants have undergone a similar gradual evolutionary change?

Darwin was only twenty-two when he accepted the position of naturalist on the *H.M.S. Beagle* which was about to depart on an expedition to chart the unknown coasts of South America and the islands of the Pacific. On this voyage, the young Darwin had a world of leisure and the opportunity to spend many hours and days on the coastal lands of South America where he could collect many unknown and interesting specimens. He was impressed by the prolific nature of life in the tropics, and even began to wonder about the chances for survival in such a world. The *Beagle* rounded Cape Horn and entered the Pacific. About six hundred miles off the western coast of South America, Darwin discovered a thriving laboratory of evolution, the Galapagos Islands.[9] This small group of islands, totally cut off from the mainland and in some cases isolated even from each other, swarm with examples of evolution. The huge land-bound tortoises were slightly different on each island; finches not only differed from those on the mainland but also from island to island, and even on the same island. These could be classified on the basis of their beaks' sizes and shapes, which were adapted to feeding on different types of seeds and food. Darwin observed; his log book was packed with details and facts, and his mind puzzled: how to explain such diversity?

In 1837 the *Beagle* returned to England and Darwin went back to his country home. The following year, as he tried to organize all the information gathered on the expedition, Darwin read a new and startling book by the English political economist, Thomas Malthus, *An Essay on the Principle of*

9. William Beebe, *Galapagos: World's End* (G. P. Putnam's Sons, 1924); Lincoln Barnett, "Enchanted Isles," *Life Magazine*, 45 (Sept. 8, 1958), 56-69; I. Johnson and E. Johnson, "Lost World of the Galapagos," *National Geographic*, 115 (May 1959), 680-703.

Population. Malthus maintained that the rate of human reproduction increased in a geometric progression (2, 4, 8, 16, 32, etc.) whereas our capacity for increasing food production rose in a straight arithmetic progression (2, 4, 6, 8, 10, etc.) Such a situation, he thought, could only end in a struggle for food and, ultimately, for existence and survival itself.

Besides the evidence collected on the voyage of the *Beagle,* the influence of Lyell and Malthus, we must note Darwin's experimental observations. The man was a devoted experimental biologist, working on worms, pigeons, and a variety of plants and animals. He made a careful study of the pigeons raised by the English landlords and country squires. He knew that all the fancy varieties of pigeons had originated from the common wild pigeon and so tried to trace their genealogies. His studies of the origins of cultivated plants was another factor contributing to the final emergence of his theory. The data was there, the question was how to arrange it into a single consistent and logical system. Darwin worked carefully, even too carefully at times. In 1842 he wrote, for his own information only, a "brief" thirty-five page sketch of his theory of evolution. Two years later, it had become an "essay" of some two hundred and thirty pages. He discussed this paper with his friends Lyell and the botanist Joseph Hooker, but still did not publish anything. Discussions and correspondence continued, reaching out to the American botanist Asa Gray among others. Views and opinions were received joyfully, for Darwin longed for acceptance in his own shy way. They were worked into his swelling manuscript, and the more that work expanded the further into the future did Darwin project its publication. Fifteen years passed, for Darwin persisted in his effort to gather every single scrap of evidence to work into his all-embracing theory of evolution, a theory which he strove to make as convincing as possible.

The turning point came in 1858 in the form of a letter and

abstract from Alfred R. Wallace (1823-1913), a naturalist who had been spending considerable time in Malaya.[10] Wallace thought Darwin would be just the right man to offer some friendly and critical comments on his paper. He also suggested that Darwin pass it on to Lyell for his comments. The essay was a stunning blow to Darwin, for it contained the very essence of all he had written in the past twenty years but had not yet published: *the evolutionary origin of species through natural selection.* Darwin was astounded and bewildered, but he was convinced that Wallace had preceded him and therefore had the right to publish first. What had actually happened has happened time and again in science: the simultaneous discovery of some phenomenon by two or three men working completely independently. Only the insistence of Hooker and Lyell could persuade Darwin that this was a joint discovery for which both he and Wallace should receive credit. On July 1, 1858, Wallace's paper and an abstract of Darwin's unfinished tome were presented to the Linnaean Society of London under the joint title: *On the Tendency of Species to Form Varieties; and on the Perpetuation of Varieties and Species by Natural Means of Selection.*

Wallace's letter had been a shock to Darwin, and a very necessary shock if this methodical, ponderous thinker was ever to have his manuscript ready for publication. Darwin recovered from the blow and hurriedly put the finishing touches on his work, leaving out some evidence and details which he wanted to add but could not at the moment for lack of time. *On the Origin of Species by Means of Natural Selection* reached the book dealers of London in November of 1859 and immediately sold out its first printing. A dull, dry tome, crammed with scientific data, the results of experiments and observations, the book nevertheless became the center of

10. Loren C. Eiseley, "Alfred Russel Wallace," *Scientific American,* 200 (Feb. 1959), 70-82.

one of the greatest and most violent ideological controversies in the history of mankind. Darwin himself was the shy country squire; he disliked the noise of debate intensely and so retired to his estate in Down where he continued his experiments on earthworms and plants. In the debate forum, Thomas Henry Huxley and Joseph Hooker took on all challengers, and the debate between Huxley and Samuel Wilberforce, Bishop of Oxford, rivals any in the history of science. *The Origin of Species* made only a passing reference to man's place in the evolution of nature. It was twelve years later that Darwin published his second work, *The Descent of Man.* But the "ape question" stirred all of England.

More and more Huxley came to the forefront as "Darwin's Bulldog," a Saint George of science out to slay the perfidious and naive doctrine of special creation. The crucial confrontation took place in the auditorium of the University Museum at Oxford. On the right, Bishop Wilberforce, an eminent natural scientist and a learned divine; on the left, Thomas Huxley; and in the audience an eager array of bishops, puritanic clergy, aristocratic Tories quite unwilling to count apes among their ancestors, professors of all persuasions, students, and ladies of noble birth.

Huxley was in the middle of his statement of Darwinian evolution when Wilberforce rudely interrupted to pose a question: "I should like to ask you whether you really believe that your ancestor was an ape. If so, I should be interested to know something else. Did that ape come into the family on your grandfather's or your grandmother's side?" If you cannot face the evidence and cannot answer the logic of the opponent's arguments, then attack him as a person. The same tactic Cuvier used with Lamarck, but this time a bulldog was the opponent, not a feeble blind professor. Huxley gleefully replied that he would not be ashamed to have a monkey as an ancestor though he would be "ashamed to be connected with a man who used great gifts to obscure the truth."[11] This encounter and the many that followed both on the continent, in England and America, right down to the Scopes Monkey Trial of 1925 in Dayton, Tennessee, make for some of the most delightful and entertaining episodes in the history of ideas, though we cannot tarry over them.[12]

There is often serious misunderstanding of Darwin's concept of natural selection. As a natural mechanism which could explain the origin of new species, Darwin suggested 1) that all organisms produce more offspring than they actually need to keep the species going; 2) that because of this overpopulation, there is a constant struggle for survival among the individuals within a population; 3) that these individuals differ in many small ways and as a result, some are "better-fitted or adapted" than others to survive in this struggle for life.

Overproduction is obvious to any one who has walked through the woods in the spring, stood under a maple tree in June, or looked at the shallow waters of a spring pond. An oyster produces over a hundred million eggs in a single spawning; a fern plant fifty million reproductive spores in a year; puffballs, billions of spores; a mustard plant nearly three-quarters of a million seeds; mice, rabbits, and all life . . . That only a few of the winged seeds of the maple can survive is obvious: there is only so much soil, so much room, so much sunlight, so much water. And because each of these seeds is slightly different, some have advantages the others do not have. The same applies to animals. In a brood of mice, some have thicker coats of fur, some are a bit faster, some a little stronger. Survival of the fittest is the logical conclusion. Natural selection and the survival of the fittest can best be expressed in the classic phrase of Arnold Toynbee, "challenge and response." The environment and overproduction offer a

11. H. Wendt, *In Search of Adam*, pp. 259-64.
12. William Irvine, *op. cit.*; H. Wendt, *op. cit.*; L. C. Eiseley, *Darwin's Century*.

challenge to which the individual responds in the struggle for survival.[13]

One of the most serious weaknesses in the Darwinian theory of evolution, a weakness overlooked by Wilberforce and others, was that it failed completely to explain *how* traits originated which made an individual better or poorer adapted, and how they were handed on from parent to progeny. Scientists of later years would answer that question.

Darwin summarized his evidence for evolution and natural selection in five categories: 1) evidence from the breeding of animals and plants; 2) geographic distribution; 3) the fossil record; 4) homologies or similarities in organs; and 5) evidence from embryology and rudimentary organs. Of course, our evidence today is much stronger and more detailed than it was for Darwin a hundred years ago, but it does follow the same general pattern with some important additions contributed by biochemistry and physiology. All of this gives us volumes of evidence as to *what* has happened in the evolution of life. This *what* of evolution must be sketched before we can deal with the *why* or *how* of evolution.

THE WHAT OF EVOLUTION

The term "evolution" has about as many meanings as there are people who use the word. However, we may reduce the confusion by limiting ourselves here to a few basic views. In 1959 a convocation of scientists from all over the world was sponsored by the University of Chicago to celebrate the one hundredth anniversary of the publication of Darwin's *Origin of Species*. During the proceedings, fifty of the world's leading experts on evolution worked out a definition which contains

13. Practically any high quality high school or college biology text contains a summary of the facts and mechanisms of evolution. We would highly recommend, for a brief summary, the Biological Sciences Curriculum Study texts referred to in this work.

the essence and heart of what today the scientists mean by evolution:

> Evolution is definable in general terms as a one-way irreversible process in time, which during its course generates novelty, diversity, and higher levels of organization. It operates in all sectors of the phenomenal universe but has been most fully described and analyzed in the biological sector.[14]

Two elements are vital in this definition: first, the acceptance of evolution as a scientifically established fact, and secondly, the application of that fact to all levels of observable reality.

Let us begin with the second element and simply point out four main areas on which study of the evolutionary character of nature has been focused. On the broadest and least known level we can talk of an evolution of the pre-stellar and stellar universe, of a physical cosmogony or *cosmogenesis*. We can speak also of the evolution of our earth's crust, of a geological evolution or *geogenesis;* and of the evolution of plants and animals on that crust, of an organic evolution or *biogenesis*. Finally, we can speak of human evolution as the latest stage of organic evolution, or as it is commonly referred to, *anthropogenesis*.[15]

Cosmogenesis

Scientists have only recently begun to explore the evolutionary history of our universe.[16] In their search for answers

14. *Evolution after Darwin,* ed. Sol Tax (University of Chicago, 1960), III, p. 107.

15. Remy Collin, *Evolution* (Hawthorne, 1959), pp. 11-13. Cf. Theodosius Dobzhansky, *Genetics and the Origin of Species,* 3rd ed., (Columbia University Press, 1951), p. 11. Scientists are agreed on the *fact* of evolution, but certainly not on its *mechanics*.

16. G. J. Whitrow, *The Structure and Evolution of the Universe* (Harper & Row Torchbook, 1959). This is an excellent summary, particularly

to the question of what happened in the beginning, they have been greatly aided in recent years by such giants as the 200-inch Palomar and the 100-inch Mount Wilson light telescopes. Since 1840 when the first daguerreotypes were made of the moon and, ten years later, of a star, astronomers have been perfecting their apparatuses for photographing the heavens. This has now reached the point where telescopes are specially constructed for photographic work only. When this technique of photography was linked with the knowledge of the physical chemist, the astronomer obtained a new and most valuable tool for his exploration and understanding of space. The physical chemist made his contribution when Gustav Kirchhoff, in 1859, learned that the spectrum of light emitted by any burning object is a characteristic of the density, chemical constitution and temperature of the source. When this knowledge was complemented by the development of color photography, the scientist could begin the task of analyzing the density, chemical make-up and temperature of the stars in our heavens. Bright-line or emission spectra, given off by a hot gas of low density, and the dark line spectra which a cool gas gives off in a characteristic pattern of black bands (due to wave lengths that are absorbed), have allowed the astronomer to chart the secrets of our heavens. Work with visible light rays has now been supplemented with the radio telescopes such as the giant dish antenna of Jodrell Bank in England and Goobang in Australia, which analyze the high frequency radio (sound) waves emitted by burning stars.

Three theories have been suggested by the astronomers to explain the creation of the universe: the "steady-state," "big bang," and "pulsation" hypotheses. All three theories agree on one essential point, namely, that all the galaxies we know

the final chapter. See also Remy Collin, *op. cit.*, pp. 18-23; David Bergamini, *The Universe* (Time: Life Nature Library, 1962), and the recent question of quasars summarized in *Time*, 85:21 (May 21, 1965), 72.

are expanding and receding from each other. This fact, drawn from observations of the "red shift" or spectrum shifts to the lower "red" frequencies because certain stars are moving away from us faster than others, and the widely held belief that stars differ in their ages, are both incorporated into each of these three theories.

The "steady state" theory claims that the universe has been expanding at a constant rate ever since the beginning. As matter spreads out from the hypothetical center of our universe, it remains at about the same concentration, new matter being constantly created to fill the voids left by the expanding galaxies much as you would add new ink spots to a balloon as you blow it up. In this theory, the galaxies will never return to the hypothetical center, nor was there any great "explosion" in the beginning. The "big bang" theory claims that the universe began with a gigantic explosion after which the galaxies slowed down to a steady rate of expansion. Unlike the steady state theory, this view maintains that all the natural atomic elements were created in the first half hour of the explosion, with no new matter being created after that. The "pulsating" theory claims that all matter is now in a state of expansion, flying apart from a previously compact center. This expansion will eventually slow down, stop and begin to reverse itself as the mutual gravitational pull of its parts is exerted. This reversal will ultimately lead to a mass so tightly compacted that it will again explode and expand. In this pulsation explanation, matter is neither created nor destroyed, it is only rearranged. It would also be possible, in this theory, for the universe to be eternal, a belief Thomas Aquinas found in no way contradictory to the Christian revelation. The recent discovery of "blue galaxies or quasi-quasars" lends much weight to a combination of the "pulsation" and "big bang" theories, though it does not rule out the steady state explanation conclusively. There are many pieces missing in our understanding of cosmogenesis. For instance, it was only quite recently that the discovery of the "blue galaxies" allowed scientists to calculate the time-span for a single expansion of the universe according to the pulsation theory as approximately eighty-two billion years. Our own universe is approximately fourteen billion years old. And the existence of anti-matter in our universe, also a recent discovery, has opened a whole new perspective and area for exploration.

As for the origin of our own planetary system and the earth, one of the most popular and satisfying explanations is that proposed by Kuiper in the early 1950s. It assumes that the sun and all our planets were formed from a cloud of primordial gases, such as we can observe many places in outer space. This very thinly distributed gas was slowly drawn together by gravitational forces into an ever tighter mass. Kuiper assumes, on scientific grounds, that there is always some movement in a gaseous mass, and that this could easily, by mere random whirling, give a general whirling movement to the whole cloud. This movement would, as it became faster and more rotational, cause the mass to flatten out. The greater concentration of matter, in "lumps," would occur in the center with the matter on the outer reaches being more scattered. As the central mass condensed, it became incandescent. Our sun was the result. Its heat would drive the last traces of free gases from our system. The planets nearer the sun would be compact and solid, though they would never reach the incandescent state of our sun because their gravitational forces would not reach that critical stage. The outer planets would remain larger and in a more gaseous, less compact state.

Geogenesis and Biogenesis

Anyone who has stood on the edge of the Grand Canyon, driven through Bryce and Zion National Parks or even along the highways cutting through the Appalachian, Smoky or Rocky Mountains has seen the absorbing fingerprints of geogenesis and the evolution of our earth's crust. The geologist is a professional student of this history, and while he may be primarily concerned with the sedimentary effects of primeval seas, the wrinkling and folding of the earth's crust as mountain ranges came into existence, and the forces of volcanic, glacial and erosive activity, he knows that within the layers he studies is contained not only the history of the earth but also the history of life. Between the layers of sedimentary rock and in the compressed dust of long extinct volcanoes are sheltered the fossil records of the history of life. Biogenesis is intimately interwoven with geogenesis, the history of life with the history of our earth's crust. For this reason we might well view these two histories together as we explore the *what* of evolution.

Dust settles on the earth every day, and as each minute layer builds up beneath our feet another page is imperceptibly added to the surface history of the land. In the past, the geologist could only study the layers of the earth much as a boy scout examines the layers of a tree trunk to determine its age. Today he has more sophisticated tools to help him put together the pieces of his puzzling history: aerial photography, comparative studies involving such projects as the Molehole and Antarctic expeditions, electronic sounding devices, seismographs, etc. Most helpful to the geologist and the paleontologist in their combined efforts to decipher the history of the earth and life are certain tools developed by atomic physicists and chemists. The rough estimates of age made by the geologist working from the strata of the earth, such as one sees in Grand Canyon, are now supplemented with much more accurate and precise dating by radioactive elements.

The radioactive carbon dating is based on the fact that all living things contain a quantity of carbon of which a definite percentage is the heavy, radioactive isotope, carbon 14, which can be detected and measured with sophisticated versions of the Geiger counter. Since this radioactive carbon decays at a definite known rate—one-half the radioactive atoms present decaying every 5,560 years—we can measure the amount still present, compare it with the total amount of carbon, and thereby determine the age of a fossil with very small percentage of error up to the age of twenty-five thousand years. With less accuracy, this method can be applied to fossils dating back forty thousand years. A similar measurement can be carried out on the decay of radioactive potassium to argon, an inert gas, for fossils and deposits dating from a half a million to several million years old. Beyond this age, and working in the range of two hundred million years to several billion, we can measure the long-range radioactive clocks such as uranium 238 and 235, and thorium.[17]

To sketch the story of our earth and of life let us use the evidence known to the geologist and the paleontologist. Since we are dealing with millions and even billions of years, we might find a simple comparison illuminating and helpful. Rather than talk about enormous numbers which have little meaning to us, we can draw a scale between the history of our world and a "hypothetical year" in which fourteen million years would equal "one day," and one hour equal about 550,000 years.[18]

17. A popular but clear and accurate discussion of the uranium, carbon and fluorine dating methods is given by Ruth Moore, *Man, Time, and Fossils* (Knopf, 1961), pp. 237-402. On the potassium method, see Garniss H. Curtis, "A Clock for the Ages: Potassium-Argon," *National Geographic*, 120:4 (1961), pp. 590-92.

18. The idea of comparing the history of evolution with a calendar year is suggested by Raoul Plus in an essay, "Prime Jeunesse," in *L'Actualite . . . et Nous* (Paris: Spes, 1952), pp. 9-10, and in the more recent B.S.C.S. publication, *Biological Science: an Inquiry into Life* (Harcourt, Brace & World, 1963), pp. 682-83.

There are a number of excellent surveys of the evidence for evolution. Among these we would particularly recommend: Ernst Mayr, *Animal Species and Evolution* (Belknap Press, Harvard, 1963); Julian Huxley, *Evolution: the Modern Synthesis* (Wiley & Sons, 1964); Edwin H. Colbert, *Evolution of the Vertebrates* (Wiley & Sons, 1958); Alfred Sherwood Romer, *The Vertebrate Story*, 4th ed. (Wiley & Sons, 1959); Paul Amos Moody, *Introduction to Evolution* (Harper & Row, 1953); P. G. Fothergill,

January 1 to November 16: The Pre-Cambrian Era

Five billion years ago, as the crust of our earth slowly congealed and the steaming vapors of the atmosphere condensed on the still warm rocks, the biosphere came into existence. Today the atmosphere that surrounds us is composed of oxygen, nitrogen, carbon dioxide, water vapors and traces of a few other gases. In the early days of the Pre-Cambrian era it was quite different. For one thing the high temperature would not permit certain of these gases to remain free in the atmosphere: oxygen at high temperatures spontaneously combines with hydrogen to form water. The nitrogen would combine with hydrogen to form ammonia. Both would combine with other elements in the crust of the earth. On the primitive earth the atmosphere was a combination of methane (CH_4), ammonia (NH_3), water vapor and nitrogen gas.

Scientists today theorize about the origin of life by natural causes from this primitive atmosphere. But they do more than just theorize. In 1953 Urey and Miller were successful in forming amino acids, the building blocks of all living organisms, under conditions that closely simulated those we believe existed in the beginning of our earth. In a flask they boiled water. The vapors were then carried to another apparatus where they were mixed with methane, ammonia and hydrogen. Electrical charges, to simulate the violent storms of those early days, were introduced into the gaseous mixture. Later ultraviolet light rays were used to simulate the energy of the sun. After only a week of constant operation, the solution had turned red. When analyzed, it was found to contain a variety of amino acids.

Other experiments have produced interesting and complementary results. Dr. Calvin and his students at Lawrence

---

Evolution and Christians (Longmans, London, 1961); and Raymond Nogar, *The Wisdom of Evolution* (Doubleday, 1963). Other valuable works will be referred to in the notes.

Radiation Laboratory have used gamma radiation on the same mixture of gases to produce amino acids and sugars. Later work from this laboratory has shown that some of the compounds necessary for life, some proteins, lipids, fatty acids, and sugar phosphates, can be formed in water at room temperature with a catalytic agent (DCDA). Sidney Fox of Florida State University has been able to form amino acid chains similar to those found in living cells by simply heating a soup of amino acids for a time. Thus the origin of life as suggested in 1924 by Oparin, a Russian scientist, has been confirmed. At least we now know of several ways in which the building blocks of life might have been synthesized under purely natural conditions.

We have no evidence, either direct or indirect, of the earliest forms of life which emerged from the thin hot soup of amino acids, sugars, phosphates, etc. that covered our earth five billion years ago. Undoubtedly the progress was excruciatingly slow as our comparison with a year's time would indicate, for this covered ten and a half months of our "year." However, we can theorize about the stages that must have occurred during that tedious evolution: the development of the ability to replicate structures, to maintain organization and to produce or utilize "food." The appearance of cells with distinct nuclei was certainly an important step in the evolution of life.

As the seas became separated by barren stretches of rock, the oceans also cooled. The waters sheltered the evolution of minute bacteria, fungi and algae, some of which could produce their own food by photosynthesis. The bacteria and blue-green algae were to end up in blind alleys, for both lack an organized nucleus even to this day. There were other microscopic plant-animals, the flagellates, which were not stymied. Blessed with a nucleus and some form of photosynthetic catalyst, these little animals became the ancestral stock from which has come the whole menagerie of higher life. Over the bridge of colonial flagellates, colonies of one-celled animals with a whip-like appendage for swimming similar to the *Volvox* and *Eudorina* of today's ponds, the evolutionary stream passed on to primitive sponges with their loosely associated individuals, the earliest jellyfishes and polyps, which were the first to possess a mouth and stomach, and on to the gutless flatworms—the proud possessors of the first real nervous system and brain. From here evolution meandered through the true flatworms, giving rise to segmented worms and the mollusks with a true body cavity, the simple annelids, ancestor to the earthworms and later insects, and finally the primordial echinoderms. It was this last animal, the ancient ancestor of our modern starfish and sea urchin, that scientists believe formed the original stock from which has come the line of the vertebrates, the higher animals with an internal skeleton: fish, frog, snake, bird, mammal and man. While most of the living forms in this primeval sea were very small, some did develop into good-sized organisms. The kelps, or brown and red seaweeds (algae), attained a length of five to six hundred feet as they reached up from the ocean floor to the surface and sun.

Towards the end of this first era, the climate became cool enough to allow glaciers to form on the land masses. Over eons, these eroded to barren rock, chiseling, grinding, cracking away the solid mass to produce gravel, and finally soil.

The Paleozoic Era

November 16 to November 25: The Cambrian period

Very roughly six hundred million years ago is the age set by scientists for the opening of the Cambrian period. Rocks from this period have yielded a wealth and variety of fossil remains, algae, fungi, bacteria, and even the first spore-forming plants. The lands were still barren, but as the seas warmed the variety and number of plants and invertebrate animals increased almost geometrically. Shrimp-like arthropods were found in abundance among a population which contained representatives of every major phylum of animals except that of the chordates, or animals with internal skeletons. One of the arthropods, the trilobite, was so successful that its varied species accounted for sixty percent of the population. Some of these trilobites were a foot long. And their success was not short-lived: their descendants can be found in fossil deposits for the next three hundred million years.

During this period two great troughs of water cut North America from north to south in the area of the present Rockies and Appalachians. Connecting these two great seas was another body of water flooding the central states.

November 25 to December 1, 6 a.m.: The Ordovician period

When the Ordovician period opened some five hundred million years ago, the seas along the continental shores swarmed with marine algae. The climate was warmer and the United States had become a cluster of islands surrounded by great coral and algal reefs. In the fresh water streams and rivers appeared the first indications of fish. These jawless and primitive fish eventually found their way to the seas where they fed on a variety of marine life, the first clams and starfish, nautiloid mollusks—the ancestors of today's squids and octopuses. With seventy percent of the United States under water, volcanic activity and the heavings of the earth crust slowly lifted the mountains of New England from Maine to Alabama.

6 a.m. December 1 to December 3: The Silurian period

Four hundred twenty-five million years ago the Ordovician opened into the Silurian age. The earth became generally cooler, but the volcanic activity continued in Maine and New

Brunswick. Most of the eastern coast had slipped once again under the salty seas. The continents were low land masses, except for the gentle rise of the Vermont mountains which left a salt basin some 100,000 square miles over the midwestern states. Today much of Michigan, New York and Pennsylvania shows the evidence of this inundation in the salt mines under Detroit and other cities. On the land a few primitive plants appeared, club mosses mainly. The fish line had advanced so that towards the end of the period sharklike fish only a few inches long, the acanthodians, had made their entrance. Some of the early scorpions and millipeds ventured onto the land, but for the most part both animals and plants remained in the safety of the sea where the invertebrates continued to evolve and radiate.

December 3 to noon of December 7: The Devonian period

The Silurian period lasted only twenty million years. The Devonian which followed it is named for the Devonshire region of England where geological evidence of the period is very abundant. The age was marked by broad tidal marshlands whose shores bore great cone-bearing trees and spidery exotic plants, the first forests, the first liverworts, horse tails and ferns. The climate was generally warmer than in the Silurian and the range of climates more varied. The eastern coast from Canada to North Carolina was now dry land, but the area of the Rockies was under water.

Besides the various types of spiders and the first wingless insects, whose fossil remains we have uncovered in Devonian deposits, a most important "missing link" appeared during this period. The early fish had evolved a broad spectrum of forms, and among these was a very important primitive fish now known to the scientists as the Crossopterygians. While one branch of the early fish continued to develop and expand the traits of typical fish, and eventually evolved into our modern bony fish (teleosts), a second branch developed some interesting and new traits. One sub-branch, the Dipnoi or lungfish, was the first vertebrate group to evolve an internal nasal passage which would permit the animal to breathe air without opening its mouth. Along with this important step towards the land animals, the Dipnoi had paired fins with prominent fleshy lobes. These, scientists believe, were the first step towards the formation of paired limbs with a supporting internal skeleton. Today we have only three species of lungfish extant, one in central Australia, one in the Nile valley, and the third in western Paraguay. Here these primitive fish live in the mud flats, where they depend greatly on a pair of lungs which developed off the pharynx. But even with these important qualifications, scientists do not reckon the lungfish in the direct line leading to all land animals.

Their vote falls rather on a "cousin" of the lungfish who during the Devonian period evolved even further along the line with a much more progressive skeleton within its two pairs of fleshy lobed fins. In almost every respect the skeleton of the typical crossopterygian is very close to that of the earliest amphibians to which they gave rise. For a long time scientists believed the crossopterygians were extinct. But then in 1939 a strange fish turned up in the market place of East London, South Africa. A large, deep-bodied fish, almost five feet long and covered with large, bluish scales, the animal was a real curiosity. No one knew quite what to make of it and certainly the fish peddlers did not suspect what a priceless find it was. When a zoologist from a nearby college was called in to examine the now stuffed specimen he could not have been more surprised if he had bumped into a dinosaur. After the second World War, expeditions were organized and a number of living specimens were found of this very important ancestor of the amphibians, now known as a coelacanth. Actually it represents a side branch of the *typical* crossopterygians, all of which are now extinct after having given birth to the amphibian form.

The Devonian period lasted from 405 to 345 million years ago, a scant four and a half days in our comparison, though a very critical time in the history of evolution since it witnessed the advent of land animals with backbones, the first amphibians.

Noon of December 7 to December 12: The Carboniferous period

The next sixty-five million years would have delighted the heart of a Florida devotee, for the earth had an undisturbed tropical climate from Iceland and Greenland to the tip of South America. Tropical seas were everywhere and swamplands likewise. On the shores of these warm seas appeared the first known mosses, seed ferns and conifers, the cone-bearing ancestors of our pines. Insects flourished. Dragon-flies with two and a half foot wingspread glided through forests of club mosses a hundred feet tall. Giant cockroaches scurried about the damp shores and watched the lush vegetation sink into the muck of the marshes where after millions of years of pressure and heat it would be transformed into coal and petroleum. Fish flourished in an inland ocean two thousand miles wide; most of the central states and California were covered by this sea. Here, in the first half of the Carboniferous period —the Mississippian—appeared the first reptiles, though in the second half of this period—the Pennsylvanian—amphibians were the dominant form of animal life on land.

December 12 to December 15, noon: The Permian period

Violence around the world brought an end to our tropical paradise. Over a few million years, the climate changed drastically. Mountain ranges were flung up and the great seas dried to dust. The area from Kansas to New Mexico became a salt desert, as did large areas of Germany and Russia. Glaciers blanketed much of the southern hemisphere, Africa, South America, and Australia. The ancient plants died off and the great seed ferns and club mosses became extinct. Amid all the chaos, another important milestone occurred in the evolution of the animals. As the amphibians struggled for supremacy on the land, they ran into one insurmountable problem during this period of upheaval. Because they had to return always to the sea to lay their eggs, the amphibians found it increasingly more difficult to keep up the fight as the marshes, lakes, and seas yielded to deserts and young mountains. The origin of the reptiles is very confused and indistinct, yet once they appeared, they quickly superseded the amphibians. The Permian period, which lasted some fifty million years, closed the Paleozoic Era.

The Mesozoic Era

December 15, noon, to December 19: The Triassic period

The Mesozoic Era has only three periods, the first of which lasted about fifty million years, from 230 to 180 million years ago. Once again the earth returned to the tropic and subtropic climates that dominated the Carboniferous period. The land areas continued to increase and the Appalachian mountains were now reaching their peak development. The forests slowly lost their strange and weird appearance as cone-bearing trees, pine and fir, became more common. During this age we find our first evidence of cycads, a tall tree with unprotected seeds like the pine, but combining oddly enough the characteristics of the earlier tree ferns and the palms. Only one of these early trees has survived to the present, the ginkgo or maidenhair tree, which frequently graces the sidewalks of our larger cities after being rescued from splendid isolation in the courtyards of the Chinese emperors.

Among the animals, similar advances were being made. The reptiles were reaching their high point with the appearance of the dinosaurs. Some of these progressive reptiles returned to the sea where they would later evolve into sea monsters in every sense of the word. Somewhere in this world of egg-laying reptiles appeared some pre-mammalian reptiles from which in the next period would emerge the true mammals, our remote ancestors.

December 19 to December 22: The Jurassic period

This period from 180 to 135 million years ago is the first half of the "Age of the Dinosaurs." All over the world the climate became quite temperate; forests of conifers and cycads flourished as did the dinosaurs. Here and there, though, new and important forms of life evolved. From deposits of this period we have our first evidence of flowering plants and the first mammals. Both these advances made very inauspicious beginnings. The tiny mammals were hardly noticed among the monstrous dinosaurs and for their first hundred million years they would remain just as inconspicuous. What gave these little creatures the eventual advantage was a number of newly evolved characteristics. Besides a number of important skeletal changes, the mammals had the advantage of giving birth to live young which they nursed. The reptiles had to rely on the quite unpredictable chances of laying eggs which were then left in the hands of the fates. Reptiles, unlike the mammals, are very sensitive to changes in the climate for they have no control over their body temperature. Protected from the cold by a mechanism which kept their body temperature within a comfortable range, and by a coat of hair, the mammals had advantages their much larger contemporaries could not compete with in the long run.

In geological deposits of the late Jurassic we have fossils of some of the classic dinosaurs: *Brontosaurus,* the long-necked, long-tailed vegetarian giant who weighed between thirty and fifty tons and stretched out some eighty feet from the tip of his nose to his tail; *Stegosaurus,* much smaller— only twenty feet from nose to tail—but nicely armored with heavy bony plates and a tail tipped with three massive and bony spikes which could be swung against any adversary.

Two evolutionary branches contended for supremacy in the air, the pterosaurs, small dinosaurs whose forelimbs had so specialized that they could soar over the shallow Jurassic seas and swoop down on the lagoons to snatch up fish in their long beaks, and the ancestor of all birds, the *Archeopteryx.* The fossils we have of Archeopteryx are complete down to the smallest feathers. A small bird, about the size of a modern crow, the Archeopteryx is a true intermediate form between the reptiles and the birds. How did wings evolve? On this question the scientists have posed two possible answers. Some scientists believe the evolution of forelimbs into wings came as a result of reptiles running on the ground and using their forelimbs as aids. Gradually through adaptation and natural selection, animals evolved which could fly. Another possibility has been suggested, this being that some reptiles had the habit of climbing trees and then gliding to the ground or another tree. Again natural selection and adaptation slowly led to the true birds.

December 22 to December 27: The Cretaceous period

The Cretaceous period closes the Mesozoic as well as the "Age of the Dinosaurs." It lasted from 135 to 63 million years ago.

The climates were varied and some of our modern mountains began to rise from the seas, the Sierra Nevada, Andes, Himalayan, and Rocky mountains in particular. The central states up through Canada were covered by a shallow sea that reached down over all Mexico, Florida and the Gulf states.

Between the surging Rockies and the edge of the California coast another sea stretched a narrow arm north and south. The flowering plants now comprised a wide variety as they gradually began to dominate the conifers, and in the lagoons and seas appeared the first teleost fish, the bony ancestors of our more common fish today.

The dinosaurs reached their peak during this period and then suddenly disappeared, why, no one seems to know. *Elasmosaurs* in the sea played the role of traditional sea monsters. With streamlined bodies sixty feet long, their sinewy necks with sixty vertebras, they glided through the waters in true serpentine fashion. *Triceratops,* a rhinoceros-like dinosaur twenty-five feet long and weighing six to eight tons, with its dangerous armored head plate and three massive horns, roamed North America. On the land *Tyrannosaurus rex,* tyrant king of the flesh eaters, towered twenty feet tall.

Just why the dinosaurs became extinct is somewhat of a mystery. Undoubtedly it was a complex play of a variety of causes: the much smaller and more agile mammals, ferocious insectivores, preying on the dinosaurs' eggs, a dramatic shift in the climates (though this occurred over millions of years, time enough for the dinosaurs to adapt), a change in the vegetation patterns as a result of the new mountain ranges, etc. But in the end the dinosaurs yielded to the mammals and evolution continued on towards man.

The Cenozoic Era

The Cenozoic Era covers roughly the last sixty-three million years—in our comparison, from about noon of December 27 to New Year's Eve. Scientists have divided it into two periods, the Tertiary and Quaternary, with a number of subdivisions or epochs as follows:

Period	Epoch	Began	Beginning in our "Hypothetical Year"
	Recent	Recorded history—a few minutes	
Quaternary	Pleistocene	3 million +	c. December 31, 6:30 p.m.
	Pliocene	13 million	c. December 31, 1:30 a.m.
	Miocene	25 million	c. December 30, 5:30 a.m.
	Oligocene	36 million	c. December 29, 4:00 a.m.
	Eocene	58 million	c. December 27, 8:00 p.m.
Tertiary	Paleocene	63 million	c. December 27, noon
Cretaceous		135 million	c. December 22

There is a real danger of getting lost in all the details of the plant and animal evolution during this period, for which we have a wealth of information. We prefer not to run that risk because for the average reader the details of this era are not important or vital for an understanding of evolution as we know it today. But rather than leave this as a blank in our sketch, perhaps we could limit ourselves to two pieces of evidence drawn from this time, namely the evolution of the horse and the elephant.

In the early Eocene epoch, around sixty million years ago, a small four-legged creature browsed among the trees and grassy plains. About the size of a fox terrier, eleven inches high at the shoulder, *Eohippus (Hyracotherium)* had three toes on his hind limbs and four on his forelimbs. This ancestor of the modern horse gave rise to two groups, one of which became extinct while the other evolved into *Miohippus,* a browser like *Eohippus* but better than twice his size, measuring twenty-four inches at the shoulder. *Miohippus* had lost the fourth toe of his forelimbs in the process of evolution and was a little faster afoot. Six different branches emerged from the *Miohippus* population which lived at the end of the Oligocene and beginning of the Miocene. During the Miocene the first grazing horses appeared in several of the lines, most of which became extinct over the years. *Merychippus* in this epoch was almost twice the size of his grandfather, *Miohippus*. The evolutionary spread continued and during the Pliocene several distinct groups of horses grazed on the plains of North America. Some of these migrated across the land mass that connected Alaska and Siberia, into Europe and Asia, while others wandered down into South America. Those in South America did not survive the Pleistocene and died out. Finally during the Pliocene the modern-type horse with but one toe per foot evolved in North America. These recent ancestors of our horses spread to all continents except Australia. Despite the fact that the ancestors of the horse family originated and flourished in North America to the point where in the Pleistocene it was represented by ten or more families in this area, it disappeared from our continent in prehistoric times while surviving in Eurasia, returning to the Americas only with the European colonists.[19]

The history of the elephant is equally well documented by fossil remains. The story begins during the late Eocene in northern Egypt where *Moeritherium* roamed, a creature only about two feet tall and with only the lightest hint of a trunk. His descendant, *Palaeomastodon,* had a fair trunk complete with tusks. With his "cousins," he invaded India and later Eurasia, until finally during the Miocene the elephant family reached North America. The *Triophodon* which reached North America stood eighty-two inches high. Because of his teeth and jaw characteristics, scientists think he was not the direct ancestor of our elephants today. This claim to glory seems to rest on the *Gomphotherium,* which was wide-spread during the Miocene and Pliocene. Among the many forms of elephants now extinct, this one may have evolved into both the mastodons and the modern elephants. No proboscidians, as the elephant family is known, are native now to the Americas, though four types lived in what is now the United States dur-

19. George G. Simpson, *Horses* (Oxford University Press, 1951; Anchor, 1961).

ing the Pleistocene, and mastodons inhabited South America during the late Pliocene and Pleistocene. The mastodon hunted by the earliest Indians stood about nine and a half feet tall. As it roamed the forests of Canada and the United States its coat of long coarse hair protected it from the chill blasts of the Ice Ages. The woolly mammoths were a bit smaller; their range covered all the northern hemisphere from Siberia and Alaska (where we still find their frozen remains) to Europe (where they "posed" for cave paintings) and North America.[20]

A number of general trends or "laws" can be seen in the fossil record we have just reviewed, and these we should mention. Throughout the history of fossils we can note a tendency to move from simple to more complex forms, a tendency for the phyla or biological groups to evolve into specialized and distinct types or species, and a trend towards greater size. Along with these trends we find that a period of rapid evolution and diversification (adaptive radiation) generally follows the birth of a phyla. The evolution of phyla often is closely related to important migrations that result from changes in the climate and topography, and the isolation that results from such migrations is vital in the evolution of species and other groups. The creative instability of unspecialized forms is easy to note in the fossil record. Only those animals which are small in size, few in number generally, and unspecialized in their characteristics retain the capacity for further evolution. Finally, the scientists speak of Dollo's law, which tells us that once a regressive trend has been established in a certain evolutionary group it is irreversible. Thus the disappearance of the dinosaurs, the atrophy of an organ like the appendix in man or the dwarf lines of certain animals are processes which cannot be reversed.[21]

The fossil record is much like a gigantic picture puzzle, all

20. A. S. Romer, *op. cit.,* pp. 280-84.
21. R. Collin, *op. cit.,* pp. 55-56.

in a jumbled chaos. It is the task and love of the paleontologist and comparative morphologist to make sense and order out of the jumbled pieces. In this attempt, the scientists work on the assumption that there is an order and logic in nature, a consistency rooted in the similarities between all animals and plants, between their structures, their functions and their component elements. All animals and plants are composed of cells and all cells are composed of organelles, structures which are consistent and quite similar throughout the kingdoms of life. In his study of evolution, the scientist is interested in these micro- and molecular structures and functions just as much as he is in the larger and more obvious pieces in the puzzle. Let us begin with the larger pieces.

If God had created each individual species separately, there would be no reason for animals to show any consistent pattern or correlation between organs and structures that have a similar function. However, we do find both in the fossil record and in the animals today certain patterns. The animals naturally fall into certain groups or phyla, each with similar systems of organs for digestion, reproduction, locomotion, etc. The groupings based on similarities can be and are carried through classes, orders, genera and species.

Some similarities occur in structures that are alike in their purposes but have arisen from widely different sources. Thus the wing of an insect, of a flying dinosaur, a bird and a bat are similar. An insect's wing has no internal skeleton and therefore is only *analogous* to the other wings mentioned. The wings of the bat, the pterodactyl, and bird all have the same basic pattern in the internal skeleton which has modified from the basic forelimb. The *homologous* structures found in these wings and in the arm of a man and the leg of a horse indicate a common ancestry in descent, more or less remote depending on the similarities.

The homologies now traced in every organ system of the

vertebrates (animals with an internal skeleton) offer some of the most convincing evidence in favor of the evolution of animals. Homologies can be traced in the nervous system, in the brain structure, in the excretory, circulatory, digestive and reproductive systems, as well as in the skeletal system. All of this converges on one fact: the reality of evolution. The evolutionary development of the kidneys, of the brain, and heart have been worked out in the finest details. The fish, for instance, have a two-chambered heart. The amphibians which are one step higher and later in the evolutionary history have evolved a three-chambered heart. The reptiles have a basic four-chambered heart, but the separation of the two ventricles is not complete, a small opening still connects these two chambers: a "three-and-a-half-chambered heart." The birds as a side branch and the mammals as the main stem and culmination of evolution show the greatest complexity in their circulatory system, with a full four-chambered heart.[22] Similar studies have been carried out in tracing phylogenetic relationships among the invertebrates, the worms, insects and crustaceans.

Additional evidence for the reality of evolution has come in recent years from the biochemists and physiologists. These scientists have, for instance, confirmed the classification of animals drawn up by the morphologist. The comparative anatomist studies not only the bones, but also the organs and systems within the body in an effort to determine relationships between different animals and their origins. The biochemist and comparative physiologist study biochemical reactions in different animals and try to determine phylogenetic relationships. They can compare the enzymes involved in the

22. An excellent example of such studies of homologies is described by John Napier, "The Evolution of the Hand," *Scientific American,* 207 (December, 1962), pp. 56-62. Also see William K. Gregory, *Our Face from Fish to Man* (G. P. Putnam, 1929; Capricorn, 1965).

digestive and the nervous systems. More important, they have subjected the blood fluid of a whole range of mammals to precipitin tests. These are bio-assay tests in which serums from different animals are tested for antibody/antigen reaction. One of the reactions of an antibody is that it causes the precipitation of its protein partner, the antigen, in a very specific chemical reaction. Much like a key fitting a lock, each antibody reacts chemically with its antigen partner. If animals are within the same genus and species, they will react positively to the same antibodies. This, by the way, is the basis for our practice of immunizing shots for tuberculosis, poliomyelitis, etc. When the sera from animals not in the same family are tested for reactions, it is logical that the less closely related they are to each other the less their antibodies will interact. By such comparisons carried out with the utmost precision, scientists today have confirmed and clarified many areas of the phylogenetic history of the animals. We know from such enzymes and serum tests that man is a distinct biological species, closely related to the anthropoid apes, the gorilla and chimpanzee, but quite distantly related to the monkeys and other primates.[23]

Another strong argument for evolution has come from the study of oxyhemoglobin crystals taken from the blood of vertebrates. These crystals, like any crystal, have specific and distinct structures based on the structure and arrangement of the atoms within the basic molecule. With very precise techniques, they can now be arranged on the basis of similarities

23. Morris Goodman, of the College of Medicine, Wayne State University, has been very active in this research. See his papers on: "Serological analysis of the systematics of recent hominoids," *Human Biology,* 35:3 (1963), 377-424; "Man's place in the phylogeny of the primates as reflected in serum proteins," in *Classification and Human Evolution,* ed. S. L. Washburn (Viking, 1963); and "Immunochemistry of the primates and primate evolution," *New York Academy of Sciences Annals,* 102, art. 2 (1962), 219-34. For a popular summary, see Emile Zuckerkandl, "The evolution of Hemoglobin," *American Scientist,* 212:5 (1965), 110-18.

and differences in a taxonomical series identical with that indicated by the precipitin tests and comparative anatomy. Similar studies have also been carried out with enzymes and hormones.

Returning to the more classical evidence, let us proceed into an area closely related to the studies of the morphologist: namely, the field of descriptive and experimental embryology. Sexual reproduction is a very common phenomenon in the animal world, almost universal in fact. While the fertilized egg of any animal has the potential and ability to develop into an individual of the same species as its parent, we can again find a good number of similarities. All eggs, no matter what the animal may be, pass through a period in which the fertilized egg divides into many cells (Cleavage). The developing animal then enters the blastula stage in which it resembles a solid ball of cells. This soon develops a hollow center and then invaginates to form a double-layered gastrula stage. While the details may vary with the amount of yolk present, the overall pattern is very similar among all the animals. As the embryo develops, the earliest stages are very similar, so much so that it is impossible to tell a turtle embryo from a chicken embryo of the same age, a pig, cow, or rabbit from a human embryo.

Von Baer, a German embryologist of Darwin's time, has summarized the evolutionary trends of embryological development in four general "laws": 1) General structures and characters appear before more specialized ones; 2) the more specialized structures of all animals develop from the less specialized and more general forms; 3) as an embryo develops it departs more and more from the general traits and develops its own characteristics; and 4) the early embryonic stages of an animal resemble the young or embryonic stages of animals lower than it on the taxonomical scale, but they are not at all like the adults of these lower animals.

In the course of evolution many organs have lost their usefulness and become functionless. As a result, in many cases, these organs have been gradually reduced in size. Such vestigial organs are found in cave-dwelling fish, crayfish and insects whose eyes have been reduced and are totally sightless or absent. Traces of limb bones can be found in the whales and boas. "Scarce as hen's teeth" may be a joke, but chicken embryos do develop tooth buds which disappear without developing, though the ancestral birds did possess teeth. The toes of horses which we spoke of a while back are vestigial organs, having been reduced to mere splits of bone. Man has some ninety vestigial organs, including his appendix, the muscles for wiggling his ears (which a rabbit makes good use of), muscles in the scalp for raising the hair when frightened (cats are better at this than men), wisdom teeth, and a vestigial third eyelid left over from the cat, bird and frog.

Anthropogenesis

Having reached the Pleistocene some two to three million years ago, we can now turn our attention to the evolution of man proper.[24]

24. Besides those works already referred to, there are several excellent books on the evolution of man: Theodosius Dobzhansky, *Mankind Evolving* (Yale University, 1962); William Howells, *Mankind in the Making* (Doubleday, 1959); Gabriel W. Lasker, *The Evolution of Man* (Holt, Rinehart & Winston, 1961); Noel Korn & Harry Reece Smith, (ed.), *Human Evolution* (Holt, 1959); Ruth Moore, *Man, Time, and Fossils: The Story of Evolution* (Knopf, 1961).

The September 1960 issue of *Scientific American* contains nine articles summarizing our present knowledge of human evolution. These cover such topics as the evolution of tools, society, speech and cities, the agricultural and scientific revolutions, the distribution and present evolution of man. Dated, but still fascinating and useful reading, is Raymond Murray, *Man's Unknown Ancestors* (Bruce, 1943). Our account here is based on the papers read at the conference sponsored by the Wenner-Gren Foundation for Anthropological Research, held at the University of Chicago, April 2-4, 1965.

Our fossil record of man today is much more complete than it was at the time of Darwin. Many scientists have contributed years of effort to the search for fossil men, including the prodigious L. S. B. Leakey whose phenomenal "luck" in the past twenty years has added many details to our picture of man's history. This fossil history is now spread over thirty million years ranging from southeastern Africa and Egypt to India, Java and China, not to mention important finds of more recent man in Europe and Palestine. While the data we now have is very good and can be quite accurately dated by carbon 14 and postassium-argon methods, there are still some major gaps in our knowledge.

Besides the natural scarcity of fossils, there is another reason for these gaps, peculiar to man himself. As the early ancestors of man became more efficient in the use of tools and fire, as well as better skilled in hunting, the competition became just too much for their near relatives. Species closely related to man's ancestors, which in other circumstances would have been able to survive, were simply decimated when confronted with the superior and faster evolutionary rate of the pre-human stock. The evolutionary line leading to man exhibits a number of characteristics that would allow our ancestors the advantage when brought into direct conflict with related species. When one is more skilled with tools, has a better brain, is more skilled with the hands, and better adapted to stereoscopic vision, the advantage can be crucial for survival when the food supply is low.

Studies of comparative anatomy indicate that the human species belongs to the large grouping known as mammals. This class of backboned animals first came on the scene some seventy to a hundred million years ago when their transitional forms first began to give the more classical and highly specialized reptile forms real competition. Blessed with a more complicated cerebral cortex, better sense organs and a mechanism to regulate the body temperature, one particular branch of this mammalian family very quickly showed a tendency to specialize along certain lines. This group, called the Primates, seems to have concentrated all its energies on the greater development of the brain, its cerebral cortex (which is ultimately the seat of rational activity), and a highly complicated and coordinated system of communication with the outside world, the sense organs. The primate group includes the monkeys, apes and man, as well as those strange primitive forms which have survived down to the present in the tropical forests of Malaysia, Ceylon and Madagascar. The tiny goblin-like tarsier of Malaysia (and his fossilized relatives) is probably the starting point for the higher primates and man, while the relatives of the langur of Ceylon would seem to be the starting point for the side branch leading to all the simian forms except those of the New World.

Our evidence today indicates that man's ancestral stock emerged from the broad mainstream of primate evolution some thirty to thirty-three million years ago with *Propliopithecus,* a small gibbon-like creature. Fossils of this creature have been found in the Fayum region of Egypt, about a hundred miles inland from the present Mediterranean coast. Millions of years ago, this region formed the shoreline of a vast tropical jungle, teaming with a variety of primate forms. Between *Propliopithecus* and the next ancestral form of the human line we have a gap of some eleven million years for which we have no evidence.

The broad "cosmopolitan" genus of *Dryopithecines* ranged over Africa and Eurasia for some ten million years, roughly from nineteen to nine million years ago. Of course, in this time, many forms of the *Dryopithecines* evolved, some dying off after unsuccessful specializations, others surviving for many years. Remains of one form, *Proconsul,* which Leakey who discovered its remains near Lake Victoria, South Africa, would like to classify as a separate form, is included by most scientists within the dryopithecine group. *Proconsul* is neither human nor ape, though it has several characteristics of both modern groups. Abundant remains have now been found of the *Proconsuls,* ranging through a variety of sizes and forms, from that of a large monkey to one the size of a modern gorilla. The skull of *Proconsul* generally resembles that of an ape though it lacks the heavy brow ridge and a shelflike reinforcement behind the front teeth of the lower jaw, traits quite characteristic of modern apes. The limbs indicate that the animal stayed pretty much on the ground like man and the ape today. Tree-swinging gibbons apparently broke off the mainstream of the primates somewhere before this through a langur-type ancestor. *Proconsul's* gait seems to have been much like the modern ape's, occasionally erect but mostly using the arms for support. Certain characteristics of his arms foreshadow human traits.

Considering all the opinions of the scientists today, *Proconsul* seems to belong not at the dividing point of the two branches leading to man and the ape, but rather somewhere along the earliest stages of the ape line. We should, perhaps, point out here that when we talk of evolutionary lines we are not speaking of straight lines, but rather of a tangled bush with many intertwining branches, a bush on which we have only a few scattered reference points, difficult to interpret in the light of the whole picture.

Midway during the dryopithecine period, we have another group, apelike in their bodies and yet possessing almost human facial features: the genus *Ramapithecus.* Twelve to fourteen million years ago is the age assigned to the Ramapithecines by potassium-argon dating. The Siwalik Hills of northwest India yielded the first examples of this group, whose name is drawn from a local Indian god. Other examples of this form have been found by Leakey at Fort Terna in Keyna. Leakey's discovery is also dated at about fourteen million years and may belong to the same group.

Another creature, from the same period, has been found in a coal mine of Tuscany, Italy. Originally this creature, *Oreopithecus,* may have walked erect, on two legs, as he roamed the swamp forests ten million years ago. Characteristics of his face, teeth, and skull definitely would exclude this animal from both the monkey and ape families. But, at the same time, his resemblance to man is only vague and general. For these reasons, paleontologists have generally agreed that *Oreopithecus* occupied a position well off the more direct line leading to man.

Anthropologists today have sketched a picture of this era in pre-human evolution when proto-hominoids were spread all over southeastern Africa during the Middle and Late Miocene period. That picture could be summarized thus:

> They see our ancestors as hairy, tailless, and a little larger than present-day gibbons. They had mobile facial muscles and no "mental eminence." They had large interlocking canines and could only chew up and down.
>
> These creatures lived in bands of from 10 to 30, consisting of a very few adult males plus females and offspring. Each band is thought to have moved around in roughly defined territories but home base was a specific arboreal site where they built their nests.
>
> They were expert climbers and spent much of their lives in trees. On the ground they could stand with a semi-upright posture. They could walk on all fours and could run on their feet.
>
> Occasionally they would pick up a stick or a stone and use it as a tool. They may have reshaped such tools with their hands or teeth.
>
> Diet was largely vegetarian, supplemented by worms and grubs and sometimes small animals that were sick or injured and could not escape.
>
> Relations with neighboring bands were normally hostile

or at best neutral. Yet, Drs. Hockett and Ascher believe there was contact enough to provide for some exchange of genes [through inter-mating]. The proto-hominoids apparently did not have the power of speech.

Some of the descendants of the proto-hominoids had to move out of the trees and become erect bipeds. Geological evidence suggests that during the time period in question, climate changes thinned out the vegetation, leaving stretches of broad plains with only clumps of trees.

Some bands of hominoids stayed with the trees, and their descendants are today's gibbons. Other bands were caught in small, rapidly diminishing groves. Those whose physiques made it possible for them to go across open country to another forest survived. Those that could not do this died out.

The two scientists attribute the trick of carrying as essential to survival. Early carrying, they say, consisted of transporting some weapon and scavenged food. Carrying led to more locomotion on foot instead of all fours, so the hands would be free. Moreover, holding a weapon and taking food from where it was found to another spot for later consumption shows the development of foresight and memory.

Among the proto-hominoids the band leaders were the strongest adult males. Once they learned to communicate through language, however, this was changed. The oldest members of the group were valued because they had had time to learn more.[25]

A second enormous gap in our fossil record brings us down to about two million years ago, a jump of some seven million years for which we have no information. This blank period lies towards the end of the Pliocene and the beginning of the Pleistocene, an era which seems to have been very dry. As a result, the proto-hominoid primate population may have dwindled under the adverse conditions, only to erupt in rapid evolution as soon as conditions became favorable again. The

25. Charles A. Betts, "Man's Tree—A New Root?" *Science News Letter*, 87:22 (1965), 346-347.

immediate ancestors of man have been recently reclassified by the scientists into two groups. One of these apparently lived exclusively on vegetation and hence had a massive chopping and chewing apparatus. This gigantic jaw required very heavy muscles for support, and these muscles, in turn, required large areas for their insertion into the skull. The skull likewise had to be heavy in order to support all the extra muscle and the bones of the jaws. This left little room for the brain, as can be clearly seen in a picture of Leakey's Nutcracker Man, *Zinjanthropus,* whose skull shows no forehead at all. The other group was a tool maker and meat eater, somewhat smaller than modern man but very likely our direct ancestor. The first group is now generally agreed to include the *Paranthropus* remains while the true "south African ape-man," *Australopithecus, Homo habilis* and *pre-Zinjanthropus* comprise the second group. Professor Leakey would like to place one of his most recent finds, the "LLK man," in a third group, and see man as emerging from the competition and intermating of these three groups. But most scientists today feel that the evidence supports only two such groupings with the second leading to man, the first eventually becoming extinct.

One of the most exciting finds in this area is, like the LLK skull, still not thoroughly detailed. It was discovered by Leakey in the treasure-trove of the Olduvai Gorge, Tanzania, where he found the Nutcracker man, *pre-Zinjanthropus,* and *Homo habilis* remains. This find was unusual for it was the bones of a complete foot, the size of its big toe being the crucial bit of evidence needed to prove that these creatures walked upright as a rule. The date given this particular remain is 1,375,000 years ago, while the australopithecine group ranges from a million three quarters to three quarters of a million years ago. The australopithecines are a varied group, ranging from "near-man" types to those closer to the ape family. Some of the earlier and unspecialized types appear quite human, for instance, in the structure of their pelvic bones, teeth, foreheads, and brain pattern.

Despite their small brains, the australopithecines certainly possessed a culture which allowed technical developments to be passed on from generation to generation. The palate structure of *Zinjanthropus,* as well as his brain configuration, indicates the structures necessary for speech, one of the essentials for maintaining a culture, no matter how primitive. Even so, the question does arise as to when true man actually appeared on the scene.

> When does a "near-man" become a man? No one can make any sensible rule to follow. When talking or writing about these fossils it is necessary to use various noncommittal terms, like "early forms," "fossils," and so on. "Ape-man," "man-ape," or other such designations should be avoided because of their rather oversimplified connotations. When most of us speak of "man" or "humans" we think in terms of representations of living populations that we see here on earth today. Our type of man is a far cry from the australopithecines, so that when we emphasize the humanlike qualities of the latter we must not be carried away. The emergence of man as we know him today came gradually, and these early stages now under discussion were still quite removed from what we recognize today as characteristic of *Homo sapiens.* However, their closeness to man is emphasized by the fact that they are apparently separated from the apes by about 23 million years of separate evolution.[26]

The great Ice Ages began during the time of the australopithecines and came down to some thirty or forty thousand years ago, a period during which the great ice sheets advanced and retreated some four times. There is no evidence from fossil material that the australopithecines ever migrated out of southern Africa, but sometime about six or seven hundred

26. Hapton L. Carson, *Heredity and Human Life* (Columbia University Press, 1963), pp. 125-126.

thousand years ago some primitive groups did leave Africa and find their way into Asia.

The first remains of this group were found by one of those fantastic "chances" so common in the history of science. After Darwin published his *Descent of Man* in 1871, the discussions about the "missing link" became hot and furious. A Dutch doctor decided that the debate would only be settled when someone found the missing link, or that "ancient anthropomorphic subgroup" from which man had evolved. Dr. Dubois thought the most likely place to look for the missing link would be in the fossil-bearing layers of Trinil, Java, so in 1889 he resigned his job in Holland and persuaded the government to give him a position near the chosen spot. After two seasons of digging on the banks of the Solo River, he found the "Java man," *Homo erectus,* or at least a piece of his jaw, part of his skull, and a few teeth. The trouble was, Dubois' discovery did not settle the question; it only added more fuel to the fire. Dubois was so upset by the debate that he retracted his claims and buried the fossils in the dirt floor under his dining room table. There they remained till the 1920s when other scientists were able to convince him of their sincere interest in pursuing the search for early man. Very different from both the australopithecines and modern man, Java man had a very heavy, bony ridge above his eyes, a low, sloping forehead, and a protruding lower face with receding chin. His brain capacity was small though larger than that of the australopithecines.

The *Homo erectus* form was not confined to Java, however, for remains of this form have been found in China, the "Peking man," and in Algeria, the "Atlantic man," *Atlanthropus.* In 1961 Leakey uncovered the "Chellean man," who seems to belong to this general grouping also.

The heavy brow ridge of these early men seems to place them off the main line of human evolution though definitely still within the human family. This trait, along with others, seems to be the highly specialized development characteristic of a terminal group rather than a primary source. Still this group apparently lived in many areas of Asia, Africa and Europe between six hundred and three-hundred fifty thousand years ago when from their midst arose an even more specialized form, the Neanderthaloids.

Just before the last great advance of glaciers, Neanderthal man again shows a variety of forms, becoming more and more specialized and exaggerated in certain traits, such as the brow ridge, as time passed. Just before Neanderthal man passed from the scene some fifty thousand years ago, he had evolved into a massive, heavy bodied "cave man," barrel-chested and bull-necked, with slightly bowed limbs and a bulging low head. All these characteristics would indicate that Neanderthal man is not our ancestor but rather a side branch within the human family that died out when a more progressive "modern type" man appeared after his less specialized earlier forms.

Neanderthal man roamed over northern Africa, Europe and western Asia, living in the tundra areas along the edge of the glaciers that covered northern Germany, England and south-central Russia. An excellent hunter, he often used the skins of animals for clothing. His tools were rough but well made and his brain about the size of modern man's or slightly larger.

The mainstream of human evolution did not come through the later Neanderthaloids and our knowledge of that mainstream is very confused at present. A number of very fragmentary remains from Africa, the Middle East and Europe give us only hints of this non-pithecanthropine stock: Mount Carmel man, Kanam, Heidelberg, Ternafine, Swanscombe, Steinheim, Kanam and Fontechevade among others. The early history of modern type man, *Homo sapiens sapiens,* is more than vague though the later stages can be traced with more sureness. Ultimately Cro-Magnon man replaced the Neanderthaloid type completely, but whether through inter-marriage, conquest or decimation by disease we do not know.

Even more recently, about ten to eight thousand years ago, the large mammals which populated the Cro-Magnon world suffered a world-wide catastrophe. Whatever it was that brought the Pleistocene Epoch to an end, it also brought the extinction of the woolly mammoths, woolly rhinoceros, cave bears, giant wolves, reindeer and horses. With his environ-ment radically altered, man's life no doubt suffered a similar change, which closed the Neolithic period and opened our modern era.

It might be helpful to continue (or rather extend) our little comparison of cosmic evolution, this time taking only the course of human evolution. No one can say exactly when true man appeared on this earth, but it would seem from our pres-ent evidence that it was somewhere between 1,750,000 and 650,000 years ago. Arbitrarily, because it offers an easy com-parison midway between the maximum and minimum esti-mates of man's age, let us work on the scale of one "day" being equal to four thousand years, and human history reach-ing over the last million and a half years.[27]

Working on this scale, January 1st would find our ances-tors already able to walk erect and use the most primitive tools. Roaming in bands to hunt, these ancestors probably could not talk as we do, though they undoubtedly did com-municate with each other. Speech, as we know it, evolved gradually during the first three months of our "year." The

27. Our dating of the Pleistocene at three million years ago, rather than the one million years ago given by most texts, is based on the most recent findings by Leakey. These have led to a modification of the traditional dating for the Pleistocene and Ice Ages, agreed upon by the December 1962 meeting of the American Association for the Advancement of Science in Philadelphia.

origins of man's use of fire are lost to our view, but it would seem to have occurred somewhere in May or June with Peking and Java men. At first, fire was used for protection at night, for warmth and for driving animals in the hunt. Not until much later did man learn to use fire for cooking. Over the ages mankind evolved. During July and August, he continued to improve his tools and skill in hunting. All this time, the size of his brain was gradually increasing. Summer came and went, and the fall was well through its course when Neanderthal man finally appeared with a brain the size of modern man's, around November 1st. Our first indication of a religious belief can be traced to the burial sites of the later Neanderthaloids, dating around December 17th in our comparison. Such customs would indicate a belief in an after-life, one of the major steps in the process of hominization.

By December 24th of our hypothetical year, all the *non-sapiens* or primitive types of men had died out or been absorbed by the more modern and progressive Cro-Magnon man and his contemporaries. Agriculture began around December 28th, and the whole of our historical era, the brief six to eight thousand years for which we have records, is nestled in the last two days of the year. Socrates, Plato, and Aristotle were born about 9:00 a.m. on December 31st, Christ at noon and Columbus about 9:30 p.m. The final hour of December 31st, from 11:00 p.m. to the stroke of New Year's Eve, covers the whole of the nineteenth and twentieth centuries. Think what events are crammed into that final hour. And then let us stretch our imaginations back over the "year" it closes. Unbelievable in a way, but true!

THE WHY AND HOW OF EVOLUTION

Our readers have been very patient if they have not been irritated by the lack of answers to the why and how of the evolutionary history described above. A number of questions undoubtedly arose in the readers' minds as the story unfolded. How and why did the mountains come into being. Why did the climate of our earth fluctuate so much from tropical paradises to Ice Ages? How were the fossils formed, how do scientists interpret them and why are they arranged in the series outlined in biology texts? Even more fundamental is the question of how the new species and forms of animals evolved. The questions could be multiplied without end, but these are basic ones for which we will attempt only the briefest answers here.

The science of orgeny studies the birth of our mountains. It is, however, a very hypothetical science, particularly when it tries to explain the origin of our earth's crust. A number of theories have been offered to explain the origin of the earth's crust: the continental drift, the earth-expansion, the earth-contraction, and covections currents theories. None of them are proven nor does any one explain all the questions and problems of the crust's origin.[28] To examine these theories would take us too far afield, however it is generally agreed that there are four ways in which specific mountains and mountain ranges can arise. Most obvious is the volcanic action which is responsible for such peaks as Pelee, Vesuvius, the islands of Hawaii, Fujiyama and Kilimanjaro. A second mode of formation can be a hidden volcanic action where the molten lava builds up from underneath without breaking through to the surface. Such action would form dome-shaped mountains. Faults or sharp clean breaks in the crust of the earth may be another cause for mountains forming, while the folding of the crust along a slanting fault may pile one area of the crust on

28. L. U. de Sitter, *Structural Geology* (McGraw Hill, 1964), 2nd ed., pp. 485-502. Also see Arthur Beiser, *The Earth* (Time-Life Nature Library, 1962), pp. 81-104; and Lorus Milne and Margery Milne, *The Mountains* (Time, 1962), pp. 33-52.

top of another smaller area. All of this brings home the point that we cannot consider our land a static unchangeable reality. It is constantly undergoing changes; light granitic continents floating in a sea of molten and heavier basalt; erosion from water, wind, ice and rain; continents drifting apart, cracks and shifts occurring at points of weakness or faults. Further variations in the location of the magnetic and geographic poles of the earth can account, at least in part, for the wide variations in climates from the Ice Ages to the eras when Antarctica was a lush tropical paradise.[29]

The formation of fossils is much easier to explain than the formation of our earth's crust. Living things are very fragile, and dead animals and plants even more so. However there are three ways a living thing can leave its imprint in the history of our land. It can fall into tar pits such as we find in California and be preserved. Or it can sink quickly into the sedimentary mire of some tropical marsh and be gently turned to rock as it is pressed between the layers of muck. Or the same fate may befall it if it is preserved in the dry sands of a desert which are later changed gradually to sedimentary rock. Finally, an animal bone or the remains of a plant may retain its integrity long enough for minerals to penetrate its cells and replace the material, leaving for posterity a carbon copy of the original form. This is what has happened in the petrified forests of our western states.

Fossils, which are usually bones, are a veritable library of information for the skilled and observant paleontologist. To give just a few examples. By examining very carefully the surface of a bone, the scientist can often determine just where certain muscles were attached. From the characteristics of the point of insertion on the bone he can then tell the size and character of the long-perished muscle. If he has enough of these points of reference, the scientist can tell quite a bit

29. Milne and Milne, *op. cit.*, pp. 160-165.

about his prehistoric animal. From the size of the big toe and the formation of the pelvic bones, he can learn whether a primate walked on two legs or on all fours. From the bones of the jaw, he can ascertain the possibilities of an animal having the proper arrangement of tongue muscles necessary for speech. By comparing the bones of the skull and making endocasts of the cranium, he can learn much about the native intelligence of an animal and its phylogeny.[30] The bones of the skull are particularly instructive in determining phylogenetic relationships.[31]

When Darwin proposed his theory of natural selection, he had no idea what the mechanism was which produced the hereditary variations in a population on which his theory was based. It was not until some years later that Weismann suggested that the hereditary units were contained only in the germ cells, and only at the turn of the century that the great Mendelian experiments with heredity were rediscovered on the dusty library shelves. Only when the science of genetics developed, and not before, was it possible to explain the mechanisms behind natural selection. The geneticist came to the realization that the hereditary unit is carried in the chromosomes of the cell, and that these units are arranged in linear fashion on the chromosomes. Later it was learned by experimentation, in the 1930s, that mutations in these hereditary units could be caused by various agents: X-rays, ultra-violet light, chemicals. The scientists, working mostly with the common fruitfly, were also able to learn how certain genes—which govern specific and definite characteristics—can be linked to sex determination because they are on the sex chromosome. Chromosomes could naturally break during the replication process in cell reproduction, and then recombine in different

30. R. Murray, *op. cit.,* pp. 12-14; A. Beiser, *op. cit.,* pp. 142-143.
31. William K. Gregory, *Our Face from Fish to Man* (G. P. Putnam's Sons, 1922; Capricorn, 1965).

combinations. These facts and many more give the scientists of the twentieth century some idea of the mechanism behind heredity and the variations within a population.[32]

It was soon learned through studies of natural populations that evolution within a species can occur when mutations are isolated, either in time, by geography or by the impossibility of interbreeding between two different populations. This same process of mutations, isolations, inbreeding, and natural selection, it seems from our present data, can also function to produce new species and genera, gradually and over many years.

This sketch of scientific evolution has been most brief. We have only outlined the what and how of our evolving universe. Yet, it should be clear from even this brief skeleton that evolution is a scientific phenomenon of cosmic import. The birth of scientific evolution and its growing acceptance to the point of being the only explanation judged valid by the modern scientists has caused untold conflicts for those of us who have not been aware of the basic evolutionary ground of our Judaeo-Christian beliefs, both in the past and today.

32. Practically any good, up-to-date biology text will have a chapter discussing the mechanisms behind biological evolution. An excellent exposition of the general mechanisms can be found in the B.S.C.S. text, *Biological Science: An Inquiry into Life,* pp. 611-632. An excellent account of the evolution of man, with beautiful pictorial work and in a popular style, has just been released by LIFE Nature Library. Entitled *Early Man* and prepared by F. Clark Howell, this book gives a summary of all the very latest evidence and theories.

CHAPTER 4

The Ascending Spiral

Several facts should be obvious from what we have said thus far. For emphasis, we might note them here as a prelude to discussing the question they raise.

The cyclic conception of time has its roots in the world vision of the Greeks; the overall impression gained from tracing its history indicates that it is totally incompatible with modern scientific evolution.

The linear conception of time has its roots, on the other hand, in the revelation of the Judaeo-Christian world vision.

And thirdly, there has been, in the history of Judaeo-Christian thought, a strange and often incompatible juxtaposition, a harsh and tense mixing of an essentially linear theological vision with a contradictory cyclic philosophy and physics drawn from the pagan world.

If the cyclic conception of our world is not only contrary to modern science but also incompatible with the fullness of the Christian world vision, there are bound to be conflicts, as there have been in the past, when thinkers ignore the contradiction. In the past, when science was part of the cyclic world, and even during the transition surrounding the Darwinian revolution, it is easy to understand how theologians, philosophers, and even scientists could be innocently ignorant of the problem. Today there is a different situation. With our biblical and theological scholarship and the advances in scientific evolution, the problem should be obvious.

We must bring our theological, our philosophical and our scientific world visions into harmony. This does not mean a forced concordism. Rather it means, simply and plainly, facing the facts as they are:

1. The evolutionary character of our universe, our world and man is an undeniable reality.
2. The cyclic world vision is contrary to modern scientific knowledge and the whole biblical foundation of the Judaeo-Christian view.
3. Modern science has faced the evolutionary dimension; our philosophy and theology have not.

Our problem, then, is to explore the implications of the evolutionary dimension for our philosophical and theological positions. The evolutionary dimension has changed and deepened our scientific appreciation of the world we are part of. Introducing this same scientific and evolutionary philosophy of nature into our theological and philosophical approach to our world restores the basic linear orientation of the Judaeo-Christian revelation. It brings into focus, renews, deepens, clarifies, and makes relevant to modern man what has been truly the essence of the Judaeo-Christian belief from the very beginning. We are not suggesting the introduction of a foreign or alien element into our theology and philosophy when we urge the adoption of an evolutionary perspective, for scientific evolution is far more compatible and harmonious with the Christian revelation than any cyclic, fixist, static philosophy of nature could ever be. Theology and philosophy (metaphysics) have always been based on a philosophy of nature. In the past, because of the lack of scientific knowledge, man may have had to limit his synthesis of human knowledge, as Aquinas did, by unsuccessfully complementing a linear and dynamic theology and philosophy with a cyclic and fixed philosophy of nature. There is no reason in the world why today we should have to endure an agonizing, meaningless, senseless and *artificial* aggregation of incompatible elements in our attempt to understand better the world we live in.

In the simplest terms, what we are asking for is a modern and intelligible philosophy and theology which takes into account modern science.

Only a scientist, a man deeply committed to the reality of our evolving universe, can appreciate the all-encompassing, luminous dimension that evolution adds to hitherto disjointed and jumbled facts accumulated by the scientists. Only a scientist, a man deeply committed to the reality of the Judaeo-Christian revelation, can appreciate the all-encompassing, luminous perspective an evolutionary philosophy of nature adds to the often meaningless, irrelevant and jumbled catalogue of catechism dogmas. Such a man was Pierre Teilhard de Chardin, mystic, scientist, theologian, philosopher, and poet.

More than enough biographical sketches of Teilhard de Chardin have already been published so we will not burden the reader with repetition. There have also been more than enough "introductions" to his synthesis of evolution, science, philosophy and theology.[1]

What we would attempt here is neither a biography nor an

1. R. T. Francoeur, ed., *The World of Teilhard de Chardin* (Helicon, 1961); Claude Tresmontant, *Pierre Teilhard de Chardin, His Thought* (Helicon, 1959); Charles E. Raven, *Teilhard de Chardin, Scientist and Seer* (Harper & Row, 1964); Paul Chauchard, *Man and Cosmos* (Herder & Herder, 1965); Neville Braybrooke, ed., *Teilhard de Chardin, Pilgrim of the Future* (Seabury, 1964); Olivier Rabut, *A Dialogue with Teilhard de Chardin* (Sheed & Ward, 1961). These are among the better introductions to Teilhard's thought available in English. The best short introduction to both his life and thought is by John Kobler, "The priest who haunts the Catholic world," *Saturday Evening Post*, 236 (Oct. 12, 1963), 42-51. The most definitive biography available is Claude Cuenot's *Teilhard de Chardin: A Biographical Study* (Helicon, 1965). See also George B. Barbour, *In the Field with Teilhard* (Herder and Herder, 1965); Helmut DeTerra, *Memories of Teilhard* (Harper and Row, 1964).

introduction. We would rather propose an analysis of his view of our evolving universe in terms of the cyclic and linear conceptions of time discussed in the previous chapters. Teilhard's competence and reputation among scientists is outstanding and impeccable. Professor Hallam Movius of Harvard, in writing the obituary for Teilhard in *Science,* said he stood "a head and shoulder above those of us who are left here to carry on the work and to mourn the passing of a noble scholar and a great gentleman."[2] In the field of theology, Teilhard was also no mere amateur or dabbler. Theologians of the stature of Karl Rahner, Pierre Smulders, Henri DeLubac, Ernst Benz, Roger Troisfontaines and Georges Crespy have thought his theological insights of sufficient value to merit their efforts in book-length commentaries.[3] In the field of philosophy, the masterful study of Bergson and Teilhard by Madeleine Barthelemy-Madaule, articles by John L. Russell, and others indicate the depth of Teilhard's insights and their value for the professional philosopher.[4] Hence he was, of all the moderns, one of the few who could sketch a valid and balanced synthesis of modern knowledge, at least in its basic outlines.

As a scientist, as a philosopher, and as a theologian—in other words as a whole, integrated thinker—Teilhard de Chardin was well aware of the conflicts between science and religion on the question of evolution. He sympathized with the conflict even as he personally suffered from its conse-

2. See *Science,* 123 (1956), 92.

3. Karl Rahner and Paul Overhage, *Das Problem der Hominization* (Herder, 1963); Pierre Smulders, *La Vision de Teilhard de Chardin* (Desclee, 1963); Georges Crespy, *La pensée théologique de Teilhard de Chardin* (Editions Universitaires, 1961); Henri de Lubac, *La pensée religieuse de Teilhard de Chardin* (Aubier, 1963); E. Benz, *Schopfungs-glaube und Endzeiterwartung* (Nymphenburgen, 1965).

4. Madeleine Barthelemy-Madaule, *Bergson et Teilhard de Chardin* (Seuil, 1963); also see the four excellent articles on the philosophy of Teilhard by John L. Russell in the *Heythrop Journal* (from 1961 on).

quences. But his suffering was not at all passive. Belabored by repeated denials of permission to publish, accusations of heresy, and charges of being a pantheist or an atheist, he nevertheless saw clearly the root of the problem.

> The conflict dates from the day when one man, flying in the face of appearance, perceived that the forces of nature are no more unalterably fixed in their orbits than the stars themselves, but that their serene arrangement around us depicts the flow of a tremendous tide—the day on which a first voice rang out, crying to Mankind peacefully slumbering on the raft of Earth, "We are moving! We are going forward!" . . .
>
> It is a pleasant and dramatic spectacle, that of Mankind divided to its very depths into two irrevocably opposed camps —one looking towards the horizon and proclaiming with all its new-found faith, "We are moving," and the other, without shifting its position, obstinately maintaining, "Nothing changes, We are not moving at all."[5]

The "immobilists," as Teilhard called the one camp, may lack passion—for immobility has never inspired anyone with enthusiasm—but they do have common sense, habit of thought, inertia, pessimism and to some extent also, morality and religion with them. And yet there is some truth in the immobilist position. The cyclic conception of time cannot simply be discarded, nor can the mythic archetype of Plato be tossed aside as totally irrelevant and useless, just because we now recognize the fact that we live in an evolving universe. If the cyclic view of nature has been accepted by scholars and philosophers from Plato to Toynbee, there must be something of truth in it. There must be something of value in it. Perhaps the problem is that we have not seen the facts which suggest the cyclic conception in the proper light. Perhaps if we shift our stance, what appears to be totally and irrevocably cyclic may turn out to be part of a much fuller and more com-

5. P. Teilhard de Chardin, *The Future of Man* (Harper & Row, 1964), p. 11.

plete picture. Is it possible, for instance, that we can combine the best, the truth of the cyclic world vision with the pure linear view and thus come up with a deeper and more penetrating picture of the universe? Is it possible to combine the cyclic and linear in such a way as to preserve the truth of each and achieve, by their complementary contributions, a fuller synthesis of human knowledge than has ever been possible for man prior to the present century?

We are convinced that the only answer to this question is a ringing and firm, definitive Yes: *in an ascending and converging spiral.*

How can this synthesis be achieved? We would answer by calling to mind the analysis of evolution proposed by Teilhard de Chardin in his masterwork, *The Phenomenon of Man,* and in his numerous other works.

A scientist assumes that nature is consistent and logical. He looks for "laws" which are but the verbal expression of nature's logical consistency. Hence when scientists get together and discuss the relevance of their particular disciplines and their implications beyond the narrow range of their fields of specializations, the question is how to link the findings of various sciences together into a total, all-encompassing picture of nature. Science is always seeking a hypothesis which will embrace and explain all phenomena. Such a hypothesis is evolution, as we have seen, for it embraces all the realities of our world. "It operates in all sectors of the phenomenal universe but has been most fully described and analyzed in the biological sector."[6]

Teilhard was an expert in the field of paleontology and more specifically in the area of the mammalian fossils which populated our earth just prior to the appearance of man. As a paleontologist familiar with the evolution of life, he noted that as each new species of animal appeared it experienced a phase

6. *Evolution after Darwin,* ed. Sol Tax, II, p. 107.

of *divergence* during which the species developed all sorts of modifications and specializations, exploring all the possible forms that species could take. Once the species was established, certain branches began to *converge* and concentrate, so to speak, their evolutionary dynamism. Then, when the creative instability of the converging species reached a "boiling point," the species gave birth to a new species. This dialectic of *divergence, convergence and emergence* can be traced in the history of all biological species, including man (with some modifications as we will note shortly).

The question now is whether we can extend this dialectics of evolution beyond the biological sector to encompass all visible phenomena. Is the dialectics of biological evolution a process basic enough to be valid and instructive when extended to cosmogenesis, geogenesis, or anthropogenesis? Teilhard was convinced that it is, and formulated his now famous "Law of Recurrence" or the "Law of Increasing Complexity/Consciousness" as an articulation of this extension.

What does this mean? Let us retrace the history of cosmogenesis, geogenesis, biogenesis and anthropogenesis that we gave in the preceding chapter, this time with a slightly different approach.

Throughout the history of our evolving universe we can see a gradual, tedious, groping *trend towards greater complexity* in the organization of "matter" and *a growing consciousness,* freedom, spontaneity, or "spirit." Teilhard believes that all cosmic stuff can be viewed from two aspects. Looked at one way, everything in our world exhibits certain characteristics we would label variously as Matter, the Without of things, materiality, tangential or physical energy (which preserves what evolution has produced), materiality (dependence on others), or simply, complexity. Viewed from the other side, everything in this world expresses a certain amount of spontaneity in its being, freedom, consciousness, "spirit," or psychic energy (that which urges us on to higher levels of evolution).

This view of nature may seem strange to some. It may even seem like a crude form of panpsychism, a belief which maintains that everything has a psychic aspect, even the rock and mineral. Actually all Teilhard is doing is repeating, *in a modern context and in the evolutionary perspective,* a fundamental insight of perennial philosophy from Empedocles to Aquinas and down to the present day. This insight is the foundation of all philosophical thought: the analogy of being. The metaphysical principle of proportionality or analogy claims that all ontological perfections, such as being, unity, truth and goodness, are shared by all beings, each according to the level of its own existence. But as Donceel has pointed out in his text on *Philosophical Psychology:*

> the principle of proportionality has a deeper meaning. It refers not only to the transcendental attributes of being but to all the pure perfections. All beings derive from God. God is spirit, consciousness, life, intellect, love and liberty. Now every agent produces effects which resemble it—*"Omne agens agit simile sibi."* Therefore all God's effects, all beings, must be, in their degree, in their own way, spirit, consciousness, life, intellect, love and liberty. These are the ontological perfections implied by the principle of proportionality.[7]

Or as Thomas Aquinas put it, "Natural love is found not only in the powers of the plant soul, but in all the potencies of the soul, and indeed, in all the parts of the body, and universally in all things."[8] It might be well to add another comment from the philosophers to clarify this point before we try to apply it in the dialectics of evolution.

> The principle of proportionality seems, at first sight, paradoxical and opposed to common sense. Does it not entail

7. J. Donceel, pp. 14-15.
8. Thomas Aquinas, *Summa. Theologiae,* I-II, art. 26, q. 1, ad 3.

panpsychism?[9] Shall we say that a mineral possesses life and intelligence?

We must first remark that words should be given the meaning which they have in everyday usage. We shall not say that a mineral possesses life, because life means the perfection of immanence, at least in that degree which is found from plants upward. Likwise the application of the word "knowledge" begins only with the animal, and of the term "intellect" only with man. We only say that, since all beings are only being, and since being is common to all of them, there is in none of them an ontological perfection which is totally heterogeneous [foreign] to other beings. Aside from all terminological discussions, we must affirm that there is in the atom something which is to the intellect what the being of the atom is to the

9. Panpsychism is the designation given a certain *pre-Darwinian* analysis of created nature. Donceel has defined it as that system of thought which maintains: "Body and soul are but two aspects of one fundamental reality. The basic stuff of reality possesses two sides which always occur together: a psychic side and a physical side. What is true of all reality is also true of man; in him the psychic side is the soul and the physical side is the body. Now the perfect correspondence existing between mental and bodily events is easy to understand: they are fundamentally the same thing, looked at from different angles.

"This theory leads to impossible conclusions. If all reality possesses a physical and a psychic side, the Supreme Reality will not constitute an exception to this rule. Hence God has a body and He is extended in space. Spinoza, the greatest proponent of panpsychism, was led by the logic of his system to call space a divine attribute. A system which leads to such a conclusion is false" (J. Donceel, *op. cit.,* p. 343).

Working within the dynamic metaphysics of the Aristotelian-Thomistic tradition, Donceel would avoid the dangers of classical panpsychism by using the principle of proportionality. Conceivably one could defend Teilhard against the charge of being a panpsychist by invoking this principle of Thomistic philosophy. We feel, however, that this only skirts the real question posed by Teilhard. He is speaking in terms appropriate to an *evolving, four-dimensional world vision.* He is *not* speaking either of body-soul, or of the physical and psychic in terms of a fixed and pre-Darwinian philosophy. He is working and thinking in a totally new dimension. See our comments, somewhat dated now, in: "Evolution and 'panpsychism' in Teilhard de Chardin," *American Benedictine Review,* 12 (1961), pp. 206-219. Also our comments in Chapter Four of Part Two in this work.

being of a spirit. This formula is above reproach and contains nothing paradoxical. God is only life, spirit, intellect and love; yet He sees in Himself, as a very imperfect participation of Himself, the being of the atom. Would that be possible if the atom were entirely heterogeneous [alien], entirely "alterius rationis" to life, intellect and love? This principle destroys the basis of agnosticism and provides us with the only means of escaping it. It opens the way to the real intelligence of beings which understands the lower ones by means of the higher. The most material determinations are, in their intimate core, nothing but participations of thought and of love.[10]

Teilhard sees all cosmic phenomena as possessing two sides, much like two sides of a single coin. "Since the stuff of the universe has an inner aspect at one point of itself, there is

10. Pierre Scheuer, "Notes on metaphysics," *Cross Currents,* 7 (1957), p. 344. In an article for the *International Philosophical Quarterly,* 5 (May, 1965), 248-266, "Teilhard de Chardin: Scientist or Philosopher," Donceel seems to equate Teilhard's concept of the Within with formal or final causality and the Without with material or efficient casuality. He also cites several times from Kant in support of his equations in a way that we would not agree with. In fact, we believe that such attempts to fit Teilhard into Thomistic categories, even with a subtle Kantian flavor, are basically distorting his insights. It is interesting to note that Claude Cuenot (*op. cit.,* pp. 12-13) has traced the influence of Pierre Scheuer, a professor of philosophy, who greatly influenced Pierre Charles, later a professor at Louvain. Charles had a great influence on Teilhard's philosophy and was "thoroughly anti-Kantian." "Though he was to remain long imbued with scholasticism, *Teilhard soon left behind the categories of the Thomistic synthesis and the methods inherent therein . . .* "

In commenting on the relationship and possible causal connection between the scholastic analogy of being and the concept of evolution, Schoonenberg points out *the essential difference* between the scholastic view of nature and the evolutionary philosophy of nature proposed by Teilhard when he notes that no matter how close the principle of analogy *seems* to come to the evolutionary concept, it is still "without the element of time and movement, more or less like a frozen fountain" (*God's World,* p. 11). Thus, keeping in mind Cuenot's comment about Teilhard's indebtedness to Scheuer (whom Donceel quotes) through Père Charles, along with Schoonenberg's comment, we prefer to see this discussion as an enforced dialogue between two distinct world visions.

necessarily a *double aspect to its structure,* that is to say in every region of space and time . . .: *coextensive with their Without, there is a Within to things.*"[11] In looking at things in our world, Teilhard gropes to find appropriate terms to express something we are all aware of. His groping is not always successful, and so we would simply list in two columns the terms he uses at various times.

Side A	Side B
Matter	Spirit
materiality	spirituality or personality
dependence on others	being-in-oneself
pluraity or multiplicity	unity
complexity	consciousness, love, centreity, spontaneity, liberty, freedom
physical energy	psychic energy
tangential energy	radial energy

But do not be deceived. Teilhard is not simply putting the Great Scale of Being in more modern terminology. He is not simply rephrasing the philosophical principle of proportionality and analogy. *He is adding a new dimension to it. He is changing the fixed and immutable scale of being, with its analogous sharing of ontological perfections, into a dynamic and evolving process.* This makes all the difference in the world!

In looking at our evolving universe as a process of ever increasing complexity and consciousness, Teilhard can trace the dialectics of evolution. Actually, if we follow the implications of his law of recurrence to their limit, we can easily see how he could come to equate all cosmic evolution with a process of centration in which things become centered on themselves, more free, and more conscious or spontaneous. He could then see cosmic evolution as the process by which

11. P. Teilhard de Chardin, *The Phenomenon of Man,* p. 56.

the human personality *emerges from* the limitations or dependence on materiality, as the process of amorization whereby all things are drawn on to ever higher unions, unions which perfect and complete the component elements. For Teilhard cosmic evolution is equated with personalization, centration (ultimately on Christ the Omega), amorization, and hominization, or the emergence of man as a fully mature, loving and human person perfectly integrated and in harmony with the whole universe and with his Creator.

Let us trace, then, the dialectics of evolution on the various levels.

Whether we follow the steady state theory with its supposition of a constant creation of new matter or the "big bang" theory which maintains that all matter was created in the first half hour of our universe's history, all scientists agree that the thirty-two or more subatomic particles are very short-lived. Photons, neutrino, sigma$^+$ and antisigma$^+$, XI and anti-XI, XI$^-$, Mu$^+$, Pl$^+$, and K$^+$, as well as the more commonly known electron, neutron, and positron, most of these subatomic particles exist in free space for no more than a ten billionth of a second. Certain combinations of them, "resonances," have an even shorter life span of no longer than a hundred thousandth of a billion billionth of a second. Almost instantly these particles *diverged*, gropingly exploring all the possible forms energy-matter could assume on the subatomic level. But just as quickly as energy diverges on this level, it *converges*. Drawn together by electromagnetic and other forces, these subatomic particles are brought into contact and union. Thus a differentiated union which preserves the integrity of the component elements leads to the *emergence* of the atom.

On the atomic level, the dialectics is again repeated as matter-energy undergoes a stage of *divergence*, producing the ninety-two natural elements, those stable and somewhat unstable unions of subatomic particles which comprise the building-blocks of our universe and earth. Divergence on the atomic level also included several hundred natural (and now artificially produced) isotopes of the elements. Once all the possibilities had been explored on the atomic level, a new phase of *convergence* set in during which individual atoms were drawn together to form chemical bonds. Thus *emerged* the molecular stage of evolution.

The possibilities of chemical compounds are limited because the most common elements in our universe have low valences, those "openings" which permit chemical bonding of two different atoms. Yet there is one common atom which has a valence of four. It is possible for a single carbon atom to bind four atoms. More important for evolution is the fact that carbon atoms can link up in chains, thus multiplying the possible combinations fantastically. *Convergence* around the carbon atom leads to the *emergence* of the mega-molecules, the organic compounds and especially the twenty forms of amino acids which act as the building-blocks of all life on our earth.

Any college student who has waded through a course in organic chemistry is well aware of *divergence* among the organic compounds. The number of such compounds is almost infinite. Yet certain organic compounds are drawn together, either by mere physical lack of space on our round globe or by chemical affinities. And slowly, tediously, gropingly, from this *convergence emerges* the world of life, at first represented by the simplest and most elementary form of one-celled living being.

With the emergence of life and the one-celled animals, evolution entered an entirely new world, rooted in the old and yet transcending it. Some twenty thousand species of protozoans (one-celled animals) have been classified by the biologist today. Most of these are very ancient and testify to the *divergence* of primitive life early in the history of our earth. Evolutionary instability at this stage rested in the flagellated protozoa and thus when *convergence* began, it was most active in this group. Today we have examples of such convergence in the colonial flagellates such as Volvox and Eudorina. From such colonies gradually *emerged* the metazoa, the animals and plants composed of more than one cell.

Evolutionary dialectics on the level of the higher plants and animals is very complicated, since it involves constant repetition of divergence of forms following the birth of a new species, the chance evolution of varieties by gene mutations and natural selection. Each new species undergoes this explorative phase before one branch responds to the forces of natural selection and begins to concentrate its creative instability, its lack of adaptation, to meet the challenge of a new environment and evolve ever so slowly into a new species.

As the animals evolve, Teilhard de Chardin sees a gradual shift in emphasis from the Without of things to the Within, a growing emergence of Spirit out of the material. As the animals become more complex they also become more conscious, more responsive to their surroundings, and freer of the limitations of that milieu in which they live. Organic, biological evolution is continued now more and more on the psychological and social level. Evolution shifts its emphasis from the biological to the psychological. As Henri Bergson so well summarized it in his *Creative Evolution:*

> . . . the consciousness of a living being may be defined as an arithmetical difference between potential and real activity. Throughout the whole extent of the animal kingdom . . . consciousness seems proportionate to the living being's power of choice. . . . Bewteen mobility and consciousness there is an obvious relationship. No doubt, the consciousness of the higher organisms seems bound up with certain cerebral arrangements. The more the nervous system develops, the more numerous and more precise the movements among which it can choose: the clearer, also, is the consciousness

that accompanies them . . . While consciousness sleeps in the animal which has degenerated into a motionless parasite, it probably awakens in just the degree to which the vegetable has reconquered this liberty. Nevertheless, consciousness and unconsciousness mark the directions in which the two kingdoms have developed, in this sense, that to find the best specimens of consciousness in the animal we must ascend to the highest representatives of the series, whereas, we must descend as low as possible in the scale of the plants—down to the zoospores of the algae, for instance, and more generally, to those unicellular organisms which may be said to hesitate between the plant form and animality. From this standpoint, and in this measure, we should define the animal by sensibility and awakened consciousness [i.e., liberty or freedom], the plant by consciousness asleep and by insensibility.[12]

Though some of Pierre Lecomte du Nouy's ideas about the origin of life are debatable in the light of modern theories of probability applied to the evolution of organic systems, this qualification should not disqualify his whole work. His comments on the evolution of the animals are useful in the context of the present discussion. Working quite independently of Teilhard de Chardin, though to some extent indebted to Bergson as a pioneer, Lecomte du Nouy pointed out that:

The fish is freer than the coral or starfish; the mammal is freer than the reptile. But from top to the bottom of the scale, all animals, without exception, are slaves of their physiological functions, and of their hormonal, endocrine secretions. In no case can they liberate themselves from these any more than [they can] from their hereditary instincts, because physiological functions, endocrine secretions, and instincts are the direct and inevitable consequence of their very structure. . . . [At the same time, there is a difference in consciousness seen as freedom or choice.] The increasing freedom of living beings is evident if one starts from the monocellular being and the mollusks; freedom of movement, liberation from the chains imposed by a strict dependence on the environment

12. Henri Bergson, *Creative Evolution* (Modern Library), pp. 122, 124, 160, and 197.

(concentration of the saline medium, temperature, food, etc.), liberation from the necessity of using the hands for walking or digging, liberation from the time-consuming method of transmitting acquired characters and experience (through speech and tradition) ...[13]

Other modern thinkers have taken a position quite similar to this, but once again working from a totally separate and often in a quite disparate discipline. Theodosius Dobzhansky's views on the *Biological Basis of Human Freedom*[14] offers some interesting insights into the question as does Edmund Sinnott (from a different philosophical basis) in his works on *The Biology of the Spirit* and *Cell and Psyche*.[15] One of the greatest of the process philosophers, Alfred North Whitehead, speaks of a "decisional essence," in all things[16] while Charles Sanders Peirce has suggested certain fruitful ideas on the spontaneity possessed by all beings.[17] Psychologist David Reisman has written extensively on what he calls the "inner-directedness and other-directedness" of all beings in our universe.[18] Inner-directedness, similar if not identical with Teilhard's Within (psychic energy), comes from within the individual and drives it towards a center, while the other-directedness, or as Teilhard said, the Without or physical (tangential)

13. Pierre Lecomte du Nouy, *Human Destiny* (Longmans, 1947; New American Library, 1965), pp. 93, 112-13. (Citation from the first edition.)

14. Theodosius Dobzhansky, *The Biological Basis of Human Freedom* (Columbia University, 1956).

15. Edmund Sinnott, *Biology of the Spirit* (Compass, Viking, 1955); *Cell and Psyche* (Harper Torchbook, 1961); and *Matter, Mind and Man* (Atheneum, 1962).

16. Alfred North Whitehead, *Process and Reality* (Harper & Row Torchbook, 1963); *Modes of Thought* (Capricorn & Putnam, 1959); *Adventures of Ideas* (Mentor, New American Library, 1933). See also *Alfred North Whitehead: His reflections on man and nature,* ed. Ruth Nanda Anshen (Harper & Row, 1961).

17. Charles S. Peirce, *Collected Papers* in eight volumes (Harvard University Press), and *Essays in the Philosophy of Science* (Bobbs, 1957).

18. David Riesman, *The Lonely Crowd* (Yale, 1950); *Individualism Reconsidered* (Free Press, 1954); and *Faces in the Crowd* (Yale, 1952).

energy, affects all objects within a group, passing externally from one to another. On the human level, there is much discussion today of a psychobiology, or of a psycho-social biology. Cultural anthropologists, like Leslie White and Carlton Coon, now speak of man's cultural achievements as an expression of a growing energy potential, stressing the shift in mankind from the muscle to the brain, from pure brute force to thought, from physical to psychic energy.[19] Dobzhansky has noted that such an insight offers a "very reasonable objective approach to an otherwise highly complicated history."

It should be noted here that these scholars have situated themselves in a world perspective that is totally dynamic and evolutionary. They are not talking in the same terms or with the same premises as the pre-Darwinian thinkers, even when they revert to the more classical terminology of body and soul, matter and spirit, or physical and psychic energies. If we insist on ignoring the premise on which these thinkers base their thought, then the charge of panpsychism can easily be leveled against them. It is only when we read carefully their precise expressions and note particularly the *verbs* they use, verbs indicating very clearly an evolutionary perspective and world vision: "emerging," "developing from," "the growing dominance of spirit over matter," etc. Once we realize that the thought of men like Teilhard, Dobzhansky, Coon, Peirce, Reisman, and especially Whitehead, is rooted in a four-dimensional evolving world vision, and once we take this dimension seriously, it is necessary to call a halt to all attempts to condemn their views of matter and spirit in terms of a world vision which they reject as out-dated and totally alien to the post-Darwinian world of modern science. Their views

19. Carleton S. Coon, *The Origin of Races* (Knopf, 1962) and *The Story of Man* (Knopf, 1962); Leslie A. White, *Evolution of Culture* (McGraw Hill, 1959); *Science of Culture* (Farrar Straus, 1949); and *Science of Culture: A Study of Man and Civilization* (Evergreen and Grove, 1958).

must be examined, studied and above all criticized in the context and world vision in which they are rooted. To try to force them back into the static philosophy of nature prevalent before the emergence of scientific evolution is to prostitute man's intellectual faculty and deny all the laws of logic, fairness and truth. But we will have to return to this question again towards the end of Chapter Five of Part Two, when we discuss creation and man's nature.

In the animal world certain phenomena prepare for and even prefigure the evolution of man: mating, the development of family and tribal instincts among the animals, etc. Awareness of the surrounding world also underwent a deepening. Up to this point, *on the general plane,* evolution is divergent. On the individual subplanes of the subatomic, atomic, molecular, cellular and animal, the dialectics of the evolutionary process have been repeated: an initial *divergence* after the birth of a new species or form, exploring all the possibilities for expansion; then *convergence,* to consolidate what has been gained and to concentrate and reinforce the creative instability of a particular group, and thus prepare for the *emergence* of a new and higher level of existence in a differentiated union. As the irrational primate stems converged some twenty million years ago, a new critical threshold was reached, a "boiling point," and man emerged.

In its earliest stages, Teilhard maintains, mankind followed the dialectics of divergence on the biological level: races, subraces appeared as man spread across the face of the earth. But as soon as man appeared in the process of evolution the emphasis, *on the general plane,* shifted from physical and biological complexity to the psychological and psychic. Evolution, *on the general plane,* also shifted from divergence, the production of new species, to convergence. Biologically, mankind in its early days still tended to diverge by producing new and distinct races, etc. But from its earliest days mankind also experienced a growing convergence on the psychological level. He did not split up into new and distinct species. Very early in his history, the tribal and familial instincts overcame his tendency to diverge. Ever so slowly, mankind converged on the psychic plane; families, tribes, small unions of tribes, the small city states, until in the Neolithic Age the whole current of human evolution began to assume a convergent character. Family groups were replaced by the larger and stronger tribal groupings, which in turn matured into urban and national unions. Human convergence through national groupings continued up to the 1900's when even wider unions, continental and intercontinental, began to free mankind from the imprisoning and adolescent walls of nationalisms. Today the convergence of mankind continues at a ever-increasing pace.

Where does the future of man lie in this accelerating convergence? For neo-humanists like Julian Huxley and Hermann J. Muller mankind is headed towards a union of all men in a sort of cosmic society. But other interpreters of the evolutionary process have taken a different tack. As the author has pointed out in a previously published summary of Teilhard's thought,

> . . . on the natural level mankind converges and consciousness increases. But a convergent mankind requires a focal point. [Every union, through which the components can emerge into a new and higher existence, is achieved only by centering on some point of focus in which the union is structured dynamically.] Extrapolating from the lower stages of evolution, Teilhard isolates the characteristics of a scientific focal point for man's convergence. In order to realize a differentiated union which will preserve what has already been achieved, namely, man's personality, spirituality, and individuality, while lifting him to a higher level of union, the new center of focus must be *personal* since mankind cannot [and will not] unite around an impersonal point. To attract spiritual beings, the focal point must be *spiritual,* and to attract men, who have an indestructible will to live, the point must be *eternal.* The focal point must function within man; it must be *immanent.* At the same time, it must be supra-

personal and extra-personal; therefore, it must be *transcendent*. The only element which fits all these requirements is a personal, eternal, spiritual, immanent, transcendent *love*. [Love is the only force capable of uniting men in an enduring union capable of perfecting their incomplete personalities while preserving what is incommunicable in those personalities.] Teilhard gives this scientific focus the name "Omega Point," with obvious reference to Christ, the Alpha and Omega of the Apocalypse.[20]

This interpretation of the Law of Recurrence, of Increasing Complexity/Consciousness, with its dialectic of evolution applied on the various levels of the evolutionary process, offers a unique and enlightening possibility of transcending the old categories and problems. By reaffirming the basic validity of a limited cyclism and incorporating this cyclic pattern within a broader and directional process, we can now picture our universe as an ascending spiral. Cycles are present, instructive and informative, but they are only sub-themes within a directional growth. "All that rises [towards the Spirit] must converge," was one of Teilhard's favorite expressions. In the ascending spiral of evolution we resolve many problems by reforming our imagination and restating the questions in the light of a new dimension of thought, a new world vision.

As we integrate the cyclic and linear in our new vision of the world as *an ascending and converging spiral,* dynamic and directional, old questions and old problems can be seen in a new light. We can now turn to some of those questions, particularly related to man's evolution, and explore them within the context of what we have set out thus far as an underlying structure and foundation.

20. R. T. Francoeur, "The Phenomenon of Man," in *Masterpieces of Catholic Literature,* ed. by Frank N. Magill, (Salem Press and Harper & Row, 1965), II, p. 1020.

PART II

Four-Dimensional Theology

CHAPTER I

The Evolutionary Dimension in the Theology of Man's Origins

Once when Teilhard was asked whether he considered evolution to be a fact, a theory, or a system—the favorite question of some philosophers and theologians who enjoy that television pastime, "What's my name?"—he replied that evolution is all of these. As we have seen, scientists may get into some very heated discussions and arguments about the age of the earth's crust, the primordial stock from which the vertebrates evolved or the exact origin of man. Yet these same scientists, in every specialty, are unanimous in accepting the evolutionary birth of our universe and of everything in it as an undeniable reality. For this reason Teilhard added an important qualification to his answer. For Teilhard, as for practically every scientist, evolution is much more than a simple fact among many other facts, one system of thought among many others just as valid and true, or a scientific hypothesis. . . .

> It is a general condition to which all theories, all hypotheses, all systems [of philosophy, theology and science] must bow and which they must satisfy henceforth if they are to be thinkable and true. Evolution is a light illuminating all facts, a curve that all lines must follow.[1]

Just as the dimension of length or breadth is an integral part

1. P. Teilhard de Chardin, *The Phenomenon of Man* (Harper & Row, 1959), pp. 217-18. On evolution as a fact, see Philip G. Fothergill, *Evolution and Christians* (Longmans, London, 1961), p. 242.

of everything we know, so too evolution affects our view of everything in this world. Everything we know is engulfed in a process of becoming, of growing and developing. Naturally as we come to learn more about our world, the details of this growth and development will become more evident. We will fill in gaps and perhaps even rearrange a few details here and there. We might even come to reject some details we now accept as established. Such is the nature of scientific inquiry and our limited knowledge. Even so, it should be more than evident that the evolving character of our world is an indisputable reality, a dimension of thought.

We began our excursion into the evolutionary dimension with a remark of Thomas Aquinas in mind: since the divinely revealed Scriptures can be set forth in many ways, no one should cling to any one explanation, particularly if that explanation should be proven false.[2] This leads to a simple but very important question: where will we find proof that a particular explanation is false? Obviously such proof might come from the teaching authority of the Church which declares some explanation heretical because it is not faithful to the essentials of the revealed doctrine it seeks to explain. But the proof might also come from another source, philosophy, for instance, or from some branch of science. If a theological explanation has been based on a certain philosophical or scientific presupposition, as many of them have been, this explanation will have to be modified when philosophy or science rejects that presupposition. And here lies our problem: to determine just what scientific and philosophical presuppositions underlying our theological explanations of man's origins have been so radically modified or rejected by science and philosophy as to render those theological explanations dated and at least partially false.

No matter how we view the disputes of the past, we can be

2. Thomas Aquinas, *Summa Theologiae*, I, art. 68, q. 1.

more optimistic today, because we are in a much better position to appreciate the complementarity of science and theology.

To obtain some idea of the role the evolutionary dimension can play in our theological explanations of mankind's origins we might glance back into history a moment. In the earliest days of mankind, some million or so years ago, men lived very short lives. What with the problems of rheumatism from damp unheated caves, parasites from uncooked meat, the thrashing feet of mammoths and the threat of his not-too-friendly neighbors, it was very unusual for Peking or Java man to live beyond thirty years. So far as we know, these early men had no written language, tradition or history. Their possibilities for acquiring a broad picture of their world were limited by many other factors, including the lack of extended travel and communications. All in all the Java and Peking men lived in a very circumscribed world, with very little if any appreciation of a world picture in which depth and history, the past and future, could play any role. The family or even the tribe can be a very limiting factor in a man's view of the world around him. Hence in this very early stage of mankind we might almost compare man's world vision to a two-dimensional black and white photograph.

As mankind progressed, he invented writing; he gathered both oral and written histories of his past; he traveled to new lands; he met new and strange peoples who had till then been isolated from him on the other side of the mountain. He listened to their folklore. And slowly a new reality, a new dimension, was imperceptibly added to his world picture. The two-dimensional photograph began to take on perspective and depth. Men slowly began to see their world as a historical reality embedded in time. We might say that the three-dimensional stereoscopic color slide was replacing the black and white print, and adding at least a hint of depth.

About four hundred years ago the world view began to undergo a new change. The natural philosophers and scientists began to shift their studies from a basis in beings and abstract essences to the more meaningful context of becoming. Through Leibnitz and Goethe the evolutionary perspective matured till it could explode in the Darwinian revolution of 1859. Darwin's prime contribution to the world of thought was his exposition and defense of a fourth dimension in man's *Weltanschauung*. With Darwin, man's static three-dimensional world began to move. No longer was it simply a world of length, breadth and depth; it was now a world where the past is organically and integrally linked to the present and future in a continuous process. No longer just a world with a history in which the past has nothing to do with the present, where the future in no way depends on the present or past, it is now a world where everything participates in a universal growth and organic process. Darwinian evolution added the dimension of movement by exposing the deepst implications of time. Cyclic time was no longer tenable, except perhaps as incorporated into an ascending spiral where there are cycles woven into an ascending process which adds something essentially new with each "recurrence" of the cycle.

First a flat photographic print of our world, then a stereoscopic view with at least the illusion of historical depth, and finally, if I may continue the comparison, a Cineramic production in which the contents of our stereoscopic slide begin to move. If we were to ask which of these three representations of the world comes closest to the world we know, we would undoubtedly choose the Cineramic portrayal. And yet there is an element of truth in each. For the man who lived before the invention of motion pictures, the stereoscopic color slide and the black and white photograph were meaningful. They may remain meaningful even today, though perhaps our satisfaction with them is more a matter of financial limitations than a question of actual choice. It might help to apply our little comparison to the present discussion of man's attempts to portray his world and explain his religious beliefs within the context of a particular world vision. The man of the pre-Darwinian world of thought, for instance, cannot comprehend or understand any philosophical or theological explanation based on a four-dimensional evolving world vision. His world vision, his theological explanations, are *valid and true* for his culture simply because this is the closest he can approach reality given the limitations of his scientific and philosophical knowledge. This does not, however, solve for us the problem of people in a post-Darwinian world who insist on living as if Darwin had never been born.

This problem of two different world visions coexisting today is exactly the problem we would like to throw a little light on here. Most, if not all, the conflicts that have arisen in the past four hundred years between science and theology have stemmed from the theologians' insistence on remaining within a three-dimensional framework while science and modern men have moved into a four-dimensional world vision.[3]

There are a number of problems which have troubled the

3. "Any effort to understand what is now taking place in the human consciousness must of necessity proceed from the fundamental change of view which since the sixteenth century has been steadily exploding and rendering fluid what had seemed to be the ultimate stability—our concept of the world itself. To our clearer vision the universe is no longer a State but a Process. The cosmos has become a Cosmogenesis. And we might say without any exaggeration that, directly or indirectly, all the intellectual crises through which civilization has passed in the last four centuries arise out of the successive stages whereby a static *Weltanschauung* has been and is being transformed, in our minds and hearts, into a *Weltanschauung* of movement." Teilhard de Chardin, "The heart of the problem," Sept. 8, 1949, in, *The Future of Man* (Harper & Row, 1964), pp. 261-62. See Ernst Mayr's comment on the typological/populational divergence which fits in this same area.

philosopher and theologian over the years without ever being solved with any satisfaction. Among these would certainly be the question of creation, the relationship of body and soul, matter and spirit, the origin of mankind, original sin and the fall.[4] On these questions, it would seem from some recent studies, the evolutionary perspective can be very enlightening, if only we can muster the courage to accept it in working out some new explanations of eternal truths. This advantage was noticed by Teilhard as far back as the 1920s, and he often mentioned it in his writings. For instance in his 1951 essay, appropriately entitled "Un seuil mental sous nos pas: *Du Cosmos a la Cosmogenese,*" he wrote:

> From this corrected viewpoint, it is surprising to note how a whole series or family of questions, which up till now have been insoluble or obscure, are untangled and clarified when confronted by a mind armed with this added dimension in its effort to grasp the real, questions such as the relationships between matter and spirit, the origin of evil, the place of the individual element in the total picture, the final form of the universe.[5]

More relevant to our excursion here is the comment Teilhard made in his "Esquisse d'un Univers Personnel," which was written in 1936 during his stay in Peking:

> Ever since the birth of thought men have been incessantly wondering about and discussing the co-existence and opposition of matter and spirit. Plurality and unity: the unique problem to which all physics, philosophy and religion, in their essences, can be reduced. It seems that today we are moving towards a solution which consists, as always happens in the case of the most irritating paradoxes, in recognizing that the question has been wrongly stated and that the problem does

4. Robert T. Francoeur, "The dimension of Evolution: Aquinas and Teilhard," *The Dayton Review* (University of Dayton, Summer, 1965).

5. In *L'Activation de l'Energie,* volume 7 of the *Oeuvres de Teilhard de Chardin* (Editions du Seuil, 1963), p. 266.

not exist. There is, in fact, no contradiction between the one and the many, *if one views things as existing in a flux of personalisation*. Both matter and spirit are simply two phases, or more exactly, two senses of the same reality moving around us. Spirit and matter contradict each other if we isolate them or symbolize them in the form of fixed, abstract and, in fact, unrealizable concepts: pure plurality and pure simplicity. In the nature of things, one is inseparable from the other. One does not live without the other and this for the good reason that one seems to appear essentially as the result of the synthesis of the other.[6]

To these comments of Teilhard we might add an obvious common sense reflection which might be passed over because it is so obvious. When we add a new dimension to something, say for instance, the dimension of depth in stereophonic sound, we do not simply change our appreciation of a particular recording. Having been exposed just once to this new insight and experience spontaneously fills us with a slight dissatisfaction with all the old monophonic albums in our collection. We are not satisfied till we have applied our new experience to our whole record collection. The same holds true here in an even more important way when we are discussing the possibility of adding the evolutionary dynamic dimension to our world vision. *If we accept that perspective in a single area, we must be willing to face its implications in every other detail of our Weltanschauung.*

In our discussion here we will be approaching the same problem of the origin of mankind that we dealt with in Part One, only this time our approach will be by way of an entirely different path. Science tries to solve the question of man's origins by studying empirical data and visible phenomena: fossils, population and genetic pressures, mutation rates, phylogenetic relations, and the like. The theologian must be

6. In *L'Energie Humain,* volume 6 of the *Oeuvres de Teilhard de Chardin* (Editions du Seuil, 1962), pp. 73-74.

aware of these essays at truth simply because his approach is far more speculative and theoretical than that of the scientist who observes and measures concrete realities. The theologian who is not aware of the scientific approach to the origin of man runs the risk of erecting a beautiful explanatory structure that has no relation at all to the cultural and social milieu of the very people to whom he wishes to communicate the truths of revelation. The theologian must incorporate the latest findings of the biblical scholar and the scientists into his speculations and explanations if he hopes to make his work relevant and meaningful to contemporary man. Science and theology are two distinct but complementary approaches to the same reality. This should not, however, be construed as any form of concordism, where we bend our scientific facts to fit our theological structure. Such misguided missionary endeavors have no place either in modern science or intelligent theology.

Augustine of Hippo long ago wrote one of the finest commentaries on the problems resulting from Christians who do not heed this distinction. In his *De Genesi ad litteram*, I, 19, he pointed out that when Christians discuss the origin of the earth or other scientific matters they often speak of these things as if they were taught in our biblical writings. This despite the fact that the non-Christian often has knowledge to the contrary derived from the "most certain reasoning or observation." The result is most disgraceful and the cause of untold harm because the unbeliever can hardly refrain from laughing when he hears the Christian uttering pure nonsense on scientific matters. But the real evil is not so much that one man is held up to ridicule as it is that in the unbeliever's eyes the authors of the scriptures are placed in the same ridiculous position.[7]

7. Cf. R. Francoeur, "Intellectual freedom—A question of geography?" in *Generation of the Third Eye*, edited by D. Callahan (Sheed & Ward, 1964), pp. 74-79.

Every man who gets the urge to write is prompted by some motive, conscious or not so conscious. And so there must have been something in the circumstances of the day, or in the psychology of the men themselves, which caused some Jewish sages to put down in writing what we now know as the Bible. Undoubtedly their motives and promptings came from many sources, particularly since these men lived in different countries, ages and cultures, from the nomadic life of Abraham to the urbanity of Solomon's court, from the pagan luxuries of Moses in Egypt to the wilderness voice of the prophets. Even with all these varied human motives which the scholar can trace by studying the writings themselves, one motive seems to underly all, the intangible breath of the Spirit inspiring them, as Augustine put it, to "tell men how to go to heaven" even as the pagan astrologers and wise men puzzled over "how the heavens go." While others mulled over the mysteries of the universe, the sacred authors plumbed the mysteries of man and his relation to the infinite.

Augustine's principle may seem too simple to be true in such a complex question as the motives that brought men scattered over a thousand years to write that multifaceted encyclopedia we call the Bible, but it may well be that here the simplest answer is the truest answer, and that the simplest answer is not so simple when we look below the surface. That deep and underlying impulse which inspired the sacred writers to set down their narratives, the breath of the Spirit, is not subject to analysis or dissection. Divine inspiration can only be seen in its fruits. Whatever may be the meaning we give "divine inspiration," we can observe its effects, ascertain its purpose and note its intent only by studying the biblical writings as a literary testament.[8]

Actually, in the days before Darwin there was little reason

8. Werner Bulst, *Revelation* (Sheed & Ward, 1965). Cf. also Rudolf Schnackenburg, "Biblical Views of Revelation," *Theology Digest*, 13:2 (1965), 129-134.

not to view the Bible as the verbatim word of God. The problems began with the explorations of Marco Polo and Columbus but they became insupportable only during the last century. It was then that we began to put into practice the theoretical distinction held over the ages. At the same time we began to realize that putting this distinction into practice means studying the Bible as any other piece of literature. The breath of the Spirit, which is the root of our distinction, cannot be analyzed, but we can study the purpose, intention and history behind the writing of various sections of the Bible in order to interpret it better and more accurately. To understand what makes the Bible so different from other literature, namely its divine inspiration, we must first study it like any other piece of literature. To appreciate the difference we must understand the results of the difference through a detailed study using those very principles and techniques commonly used in our study of other literature.

One of the primary facts to be ascertained in the study of any document is the authorship. To some the question of just who wrote the Genesis account of creation, and the time or circumstances of its composition, may seem unimportant as long as we accept the biblical narrative as the inspired word of God. But it is always important to know when and by whom a book is written if we are going to understand just what it is all about. If we know who the author was and when he wrote we can better understand just what it is he is trying to say. In the past, Moses was thought to have written the whole of the Pentateuch, the first five books of the Bible, just as God dictated it to him. Today we know that very little of these books was actually written by Moses. Substantially they take their origin from him in an oral tradition which was passed on by word of mouth for several centuries before it was finally put down in written form. The first chapters of Genesis are the result of a long tedious evolution in which a great many oral traditions, which can be traced back to their Mosaic roots, were woven into a harmonious pattern by a number of anonymous editors and writers who lived over several centuries. What started with Moses as a germinal seed matured and grew through many minds and hands till finally it bore fruit in the fifth century before Christ in its final form.

Today our knowledge of the editing and authorship of Genesis is much more detailed than in the days of Augustine, Jerome or Aquinas. Tomorrow we may hope it will be even better. But our hopes for tomorrow's clarity should not discourage us in presenting a summary of today's knowledge. It should only warn us of the tentative nature of all human knowledge. The history of Genesis and the Pentateuch as we know it now begins with an attempt to interpret cosmic and human history prior to the election of the chosen people. This cosmic and protohistory is given as the background and setting for the history of the Israelites from their origins with Abraham around 1850 B.C. down to the conquest of the promised land after Moses led the chosen people out of Egypt sometime in the thirteenth century B.C. The history given in the Pentateuch is not ordinary history, just as the chosen people were not ordinary people. All the details and facts of this cosmic and human history are viewed in the perspective of salvation history, God's providential care and love for his own people whom he chose to be his witnesses until the rod of Jesse could blossom in the fullness of time.

The history not only of Genesis and the Pentateuch but also of the whole of the two covenants is this special type of history known to the biblical scholars as salvation history, the account of God's dealings with his creatures. The whole purpose of the historical record given in the old covenant is to tell the Israelites who they were, how their election came about and why as well as what God expected of his chosen people in return for all the favors he had worked in their behalf. With this purpose in mind, the sacred writers naturally felt free to manipulate and modify what we would consider the facts, hard and cold, of history. For the Israelites such treatment did not at all lessen the historical nature of the Genesis account. They took it for granted that writers would use history as the backdrop for the drama of salvation. The details interested them only in so far as they formed the background for that drama. By themselves, the details were meaningless. For the Hebrew, secular history as we know it today was senseless, because it carried no religious dimension.

By now it should be clear how interwoven are the differences and similarities between biblical and other literature. The opening chapters of Genesis are the inspired word of God, but they are also an account, written by men, of historical realities they knew nothing of by personal experience and little of even through folklore and legend. Divine inspiration assures us that the Genesis account will contain those essential religious truths which God knows are helpful in our search for salvation and our ultimate goal. But this inspiration assures us that this account is free from error only in those matters directly concerned with the essential religious truths. It is not at all concerned with the accessory facts and details which the author used to present the religious truths in a way intelligible to the man of his day. The human writer was in no way exempt from the ordinary labors of an author. He was not just a secretary taking dictation from the Almighty; he was in every sense an author who had to collect his material, sort it out, and finally select certain elements to be woven into his final draft. Even the "revealed" truths which are guaranteed by divine inspiration are subject to this. Some of them were most likely already contained in the oral and written traditions and folklore the sacred author used. Some of them were undoubtedly so wrapped in pagan legends that their religious meaning was almost smothered. Hence the role of divine inspiration is not so much to reveal or dictate religious truths verbatim as it is to guarantee that these truths will shine through the narrative composed by the human author with a clarity no intelligent man of any age will be able to mistake or miss.

In this sense we can now see more clearly the revealed truths of the Bible. Looking at the introductory chapters of Genesis, we realize that these cannot be called historical in our sense of the word since they deal with events which occurred before any historical records, oral or written, existed. Still we cannot say they are mere fables or myths in the ordinary sense of those terms. These chapters are unique in a way. They are historical because they are presenting religious truths and not fables. They may also be folklore and myth in the sense of Mircea Eliade, who tells us that a myth is a sacred history relating an event which took place in primordial time, the fabled time of the "beginnings." In Eliade's view a myth is always an account of how something came into existence through divine action, it is a religious account of a real happening. Even so, the Genesis accounts cannot be considered as purely mythical in their origins, nor as on the same par with pagan myths of creation. These biblical narratives arose in a tradition and religious setting totally different and even totally opposed to that from which the pagan myths arose.[9]

In setting the stage for their account of God's providential plan and his election of the Israelites to be his chosen people and the source of the Messiah, the biblical editors were very careful in their selection of material. They did not care to write a complete history of the universe and mankind. The scientific facts of our earth's creation, such as they knew them, were of no concern to the Israelite. He was only interested in

9. Mircea Eliade, *Myth and Reality* (Harper & Row, 1963), pp. 5-6. The summary given by André-Marie Dubarle, *The Biblical Doctrine of Original Sin* (Herder & Herder, 1964), pp. 52-70, is the finest available in English.

them as a backdrop for certain religious truths and as the stage setting for the salvation history of the chosen people. One could almost say these first eleven chapters of Genesis are the prologue or preface to the great drama of mankind's redemption. The essentials in this prologue are not the stage props but the outlines of the main thoughts that will run through the whole play. These religious themes are very evident to us today as we look at the opening pages of Genesis: in the beginning of time God created all things, he made man different from all the other animals and chose him as the special object of his love; all men, male and female, share in this predilection which mankind rejected; and finally, despite this rejection, God's love would prevail in the end.

These and other religious facts, some of them coming from direct divine revelation, are woven into a delightfully human narrative of perennial interest. With a wealth of imagery and figures of speech, the sacred authors carefully selected suitable elements from pagan myths, folklore and legends to act as carrier for these truths. With poetic genius they freely moved from one literary genre to another, weaving together a multitude of diverse elements into a harmonious and flowing prologue to man's redemption. Of course there were no living witnesses to the origin of man living in the days of Moses and Abraham; there never had been any human witness to those events which took place before the appearance of man. With no knowledge of the times before Moses, the authors of Genesis resorted to a psychological device, a literary tool known to the biblical scholars as "historical etiology." To explain the present situation of mankind they looked to the past. The election of the Israelites had to be traced back to the past, to the first moment of creation, in order to stress for the Jews their prime role in God's plan. The present is then projected into the past to show the consistency of God's plan and to explain the present situation. A typical instance of this is found in the account of Adam and Eve. The sacred author had no idea of evolution or the origin of the world. He knew nothing of the heliocentric theory or Peking man. As a result the picture he drew of man's original state was simply a retouched portrait of the typical Palestinian shepherd who saw in his home, his progeny and the fruits of the earth a mark of divine favor and blessing.[10]

In recent years and particularly since the discovery of the Dead Sea Scrolls, we have been able to study some of the ancient documents written by Israelites and gentiles during the very time the biblical traditions were being put down in their final form. In a number of cases we have found non-biblical stories which are so close to those in the Bible that they could not be the result of a coincidental and chance

---

10. André-Marie Dubarle, *op. cit.*, p. 234. For more details on historical etiology, see Rudolf Fattinger, *War der Adam des Paradiese der Urmensch? Lösungsversuch der paläontologisch, biblisch chronologischen Schwierigkeiten* (Veritas, Linz, 1961); H. Renckens, *Israel's Concept of the Beginning* (Herder and Herder, 1964); Paul Overhage and Karl Rahner, *Das Problem der Hominisation: Uber den biologischen ursprung des Menschen* (Herder, 1961), pp. 35-42. Rahner, *Schriften zur Theologie, VI* (Benzinger, Einsiedeln, 1960), pp. 401-28. Particularly helpful is the article on "Aetiologie" in *Lexicon für Theologie und Kirche*, vol. 1, 1011ff.

Rahner's description of etiology begins from a very broad base where the term refers to an attempt to give a reason or cause for another reality. This he immediately restricts so that he then uses etiology to mean the presentation of an earlier event as a reason for an experienced situation or event in human affairs in which the present situation is the source of our knowledge of the cause. In this limited form, etiology deals with an experience known to the writer which gives him a clue to an earlier historical cause about which the author has no personal or historical accounts. Rahner then goes on to distinguish a mythological and a historical etiology. However since he is working primarily as a dogmatic theologian there are some problems raised by his approach to historical etiology as a literary genre and his claim that truth is the distinguishing mark between historical and mythological etiologies. See Norbert Lohfink, "Genesis 2-3 as 'historical etiology'," *Theology Digest,* 13 (1965), 11-17. (Translated from: "Genesis 2f. als 'geschichtliche Atiologie'," *Scholastik,* 21 [1963], 321-34.)

parallel. Written about the same time as the biblical stories, these pagan myths have come down from a more ancient source which they share in common with the biblical stories. Such parallel narratives help us to demonstrate and analyze the complex nature of Genesis.

Another source of information about the material used by the sacred writers can be found in the repetition of basic stories such as the creation and flood accounts, where the same basic fact is told against backgrounds which are different in certain details. The two versions of creation, for instance, locate the action of the Creator within a seven-day period in one story and in a single day in the other. Such a seemingly minor detail may appear insignificant but it is just such minor divergences which help us to trace the sources used by the biblical writers and thus learn more about just what the author intended to teach. If details in two accounts of the same fact differ radically, then they must not have been very important to the author. They could not have been a very important element in the teaching intended by the author.

All of this has a very important bearing on our interpretation of Genesis and the Bible. By examining these details we have come to realize that the sacred authors often quoted folklore and legends from different sources, whereas in ages past Christians thought that they were only putting down in writing information which was revealed to them directly by God. If this be true then what is important for us is not so much what the story may have meant in its original form as what the biblical author intended when he adapted it to his purpose.

Unfortunately the biblical writers did not always make it a policy to tell us when they were quoting and adapting material from their pagan neighbors. As time passed, cultural conditions changed, and the pagan cultures passed into the forgotten shadows, it became harder and harder to recognize the different sources of the biblical writers. The confusion resulting from a failure to recognize the different sources used by the biblical authors reached its peak in the years between Galileo and Darwin. By force of circumstance, particularly the explosion of critical biblical scholarship among the Protestants at the turn of the twentieth century, Catholics finally and often reluctantly (after the Modernist affair) began to explore non-biblical literature and draw some very informative comparisons. As a result we can today understand much better just what was the message and teaching intended by the author of Genesis.

To say today "The Bible says so" is no answer. To quote passage after passage from the Bible is useless and often misleading. What we have to do, and what the scholars have been trying to do even before the days of Lagrange, is to find out what the author was trying to tell us when he wrote a certain passage. Certain passages obviously cannot be taken as literally true. When Christ spoke in parables he said very plainly, "the kingdom of heaven is *like* . . . " But sometimes that conjunction "like" is implied and we have to resort to more subtle tools to find out the meaning intended by the writer.

Here is where we meet a very old and yet quite new concept, that of the literary genre or literary style. Everyone knows that the historical lesson taught by the history book, the epic poem, and the historical novel may be the same even as the media necessarily are very different. In reading the epic poem we must recognize the literary style of the author and make certain allowances for poetic license. The same holds for the historical novel. We can and must apply the same principle to the Genesis account if we are to read it intelligently. It is only if we recognize the literary form of a particular text that we will be able to determine exactly what the author meant to teach us. Unless we acknowledge that the biblical writer had a very definite religious purpose in his narrative and adapted his facts and scientific impressions to suit that religious purpose, we will be in serious danger of misinterpreting his message. The author of Genesis did not give a second thought (perhaps not even a first thought) to the scientific details of the origin and structure of our universe. The details he needed for his story along those lines he simply borrowed from the pagans who had spent much time studying these matters. Neither Genesis nor any other part of the Bible was written by scientists. None of it was written primarily for the university man. The biblical approach is very non-scientific and popular. This we must recognize as we read the accounts of man's origins.

For some this distinction may seem dangerous. It may seem to lessen or even destroy the truth of the Bible. Dissecting the Genesis story with all sorts of scientific and analytical tools may seem to reduce it to the level of just another book. It may seem to destroy its inspired nature or at least cast a shadow on the word of God. It may seem to put us in the same category as skeptics and rationalists.

Actually, making this distinction has just the opposite effect. When we apply the tools of scientific literary interpretation to the biblical stories we are showing them much more reverence than if we were to accept them word for word as the inspired and dictated word of God. We can only find out what the author intended to teach us by understanding what, how and why he said what he said. If we neglect these principles of literary interpretation we are doing no service to the truth, to the word of God or to God himself. We can only treat the Bible with the respect due it if we understand its true meaning. Should we ignore these principles of interpretation we end up lazily offering men not the inspired word of God in its pristine clarity but rather the penchant prejudices of our own blind imaginations of what the sacred writer said. If we accept the fundamentalist or literal interpretation of the Bible we do not respect it as the word of God. In fact just the opposite, we show our contempt for it.

It is a complicated question no doubt, but we have made tremendous progress in recent years. Thanks to the work of biblical scholars everywhere we can today determine more clearly than ever before the exact doctrinal content and message of the Bible, and particularly of the early chapters of Genesis. By placing many of the details of the Eden narrative in their proper perspective, the recognition of the etiological style and other literary forms has allowed the scholar to highlight the doctrinal content in a much more meaningful way by de-emphasizing our concern with the figures, symbols and presuppositions which the sacred writer used merely as incidental supports for his main lessons.

Our task should now be clear: we must look carefully at the Genesis account in all its details. We must study it reverently and yet scientifically. It is only with this attitude, and using the principles we have mentioned here, that we will be able to approach intelligently some of the critical problems and questions posed for the theologian by our scientific and evolutionary world vision.

Our purpose now is to deal with the main elements in the Genesis account of creation and to attempt to see these in the light of our modern scientific knowledge. We will be concerned with the accounts of Adam and Eve, their original state and their fall. We will have to speak of man's nature as a complex creature with a material and a spiritual aspect. Even more fundamentally, we will have to deal with the concept of creation.

CHAPTER 2

The Origin of Man

When we approach the question of man's origins we have to keep in mind our all important distinction between the theological and scientific approaches. This is particularly important when it comes to a matter of terminology, for the scientist uses certain terms with a special meaning. The theologian, for his part, has his own vocabulary too. Much of the fury and confusion in the past has come because the theologians have failed to understand just what the scientists meant when they spoke of a scientific fact or theory. On the other hand, the scientists have often found it almost impossible to comprehend the three-dimensional scholastic vocabulary so common in theological texts. Before we move deeper into the question of man's origins, we ought to clarify some important terms.

Following their own methodology, theologians commonly speak of *monogenism* and *polygenism* when they discuss the origin of mankind. When the theologian speaks of monogenism, he is working within a certain religious context in which he attempts to account for the universality of sin and pride today by tracing man's propensity for rebellion back through physical generation to a single, unique couple, Adam and Eve. Polygenism, for the theologian, refers to any and all other theories which would trace the origin of mankind not from a single unique couple but rather from a more or less broader base.

The scientist looks at the problem of man's origin from another vantage point so that his terminology is necessarily different. The scientist works not with individuals as such but only with individuals as members of populations. For this reason monogenism has no meaning for the modern scientist. In discussing the origin of mankind the scientist speaks only of what the theologian would call polygenism. For the sake of accuracy he distinguishes two types of polygenistic origins: the monophyletic and the polyphyletic theories. *Monophylism*, for the scientist, indicates the working hypothesis that all mankind arose from a single evolutionary group or phylum centered in one locality at one particular time. Note that monophylism is not monogenism! *Polyphylism* would trace mankind back to several groups or phyla scattered through time and space on the earth's surface. Obviously both monophylism and polyphylism fall into the theological category of polygenism. As *scientific* theories of man's origins they are both *modifications* of theological polygenism.

Among the scientists polyphylism is almost a forgotten explanation of man's evolution. It has a certain historical interest, and has been proposed even recently by certain scientists, though perhaps more as a devil's advocate would throw out a patently ridiculous claim to get his opponent to clarify his arguments and evidence.[1] While the scientists may

1. Carleton S. Coon, *The Origin of Races* (Knopf, 1962). Dr. Coon maintains that the races of mankind differentiated and separated from each other at different times before the modern type of man, *Homo sapiens*, evolved. The Negro race of Africa, he claims, began its evolutionary ascent some 40,000 years ago while the white race split from the common ancestral group some 200,000 years ago. The common ancestral group being *Homo erectus*.

In "Race as an evolutionary episode," *American Anthropologist*, 64 (October, 1962), 929-945, Frederick S. Hulse labelled Coon's polyphyletic theory an "extreme opinion" which "has no evidence of any nature to support it." See also Theodosius Dobzhansky, *Mankind evolving: The evolution of the human species* (Yale, 1962), pp. 188-91.

find polyphylism unacceptable as a scientific explanation, this should not imply that they are thereby inclined to accept theological monogenism. For the biologist the basic unit of thought, the evolving biological unit, is not the individual but a natural group of individuals, the population. Evolution, for the biologist, occurs through the appearance of mutations which accumulate and are handed on to descendants within a population. New hereditary characteristics appear here and there by chance in a population and if the circumstances are favorable they might end up being realized in all the individuals within a biological group but only after a fairly large number of generations. Thus a new species might emerge, but this is always worked out within a *natural group*.[2] Teilhard de Chardin courageously made the same point in 1930 when it certainly was not very popular to question the theologian's monogenism. "Science," he wrote, "would never think of attributing to such a small basis as one couple the enormous structure of the human race."[3] In 1950 when Pius XII dealt with the evolution of man in his encyclical *Humani generis,* Teilhard responded with a short comment from the scientific point of view. He noted that the scientist can only speak in terms of phyla and populations and that thus the theologian preserves a certain freedom "to suppose something, namely monogenism, which appears to him as dogmatically necessary within that indeterminate zone created by the imperfection of our scientific view of the past."[4] The scientist cannot and never will be able to prove that the hypothesis of an individual Adam is scientifically untenable for the simple reason that we

2. Edouard Boné, "Polygenisme et Polyphyletisme," *Archives de Philosophie,* 23 (1960), 133.

3. "Que faut-il penser du Transformisme?" in *La Vision du Passé,* volume 3 of the *Oeuvres de Teilhard de Chardin* (Editions du Seuil, 1957), p. 219.

4. Teilhard de Chardin, "Monogénisme et Monophylétisme," an unpublished essay dated 1950.

will never be able to find and identify all the members of that original human group from which mankind has descended. Still the scientist can point out many scientific facts which by implication would make the origin of mankind from a single unique couple untenable for him.

Much of this indirect evidence comes from the science of genetics where our knowledge of speciation—the genesis of a biological group or species—indicates that the simultaneous appearance of a mutation in a unique couple, male and female, is "infinitely improbable." Even if such a double mutation should occur, we must face the high improbability that such a limited mutation could be propagated and result in the enormous structure we know as the human race today.[5] For the scientist monogenism is very highly improbable and contrary to all the laws of nature as we know them today. Yet we can always claim that God overrode the biological tendencies of nature and allowed an exception to the ordinary course of nature. Such extraneous interventions cannot be ruled out on the basis of scientific evidence, but they do seem unnecessary in the light of our knowledge of the created universe today. In a very real way they weaken our image of the transcendent Creator by reducing him to our human level where the carpenter must occasionally make adjustments in his plans because of his own inaccurate measuring or inadequate planning.[6]

5. *Loc. cit.*
6. Robert North, "Teilhard and the many Adams," *Continuum,* 1:3 (1963), 329-42; J. Carles, "Polygenisme et monogenisme: l'unité de l'espèce humaine," *Archives de Philosophie,* 17:2 (1948), 90; D. Rosa, *L'Ologenese* (Alcan, Paris, 1931); G. Montandon, *L'Ologenese Humaine* (Alcan, 1928), p. 72; G. Picard, "La science experimentale est-elle favorable au polygenisme?" *Science Ecclesiastiques,* 4 (1951), 81; M. M. Labourdette, *Le Péché Originel et les Origines de l'Homme* (Alsatia, Paris, 1953), p. 165; and André-Marie Dubarle, "Evolution et evolutionnisme," *Lumière et Vie,* 34 (1957), 88.

Both North and Labourdette suggest that there is no reason for science to hesitate in positing a simple intervention on God's part with the appearance of man. They admit that science clearly shows the tendency of new species to arise as populations rather than as single individuals, but they both feel—as undoubtedly do many other theologians—that God could and did intervene to supersede this awaited emergence of mankind through an evolving population, and thus achieved the transition from animal to rational animal through a single unique couple. While such a solution may be incongruous with our present scientific knowledge and understanding of the natural laws, it might be better to withhold our judgment on the monogenetic-monophyletic origin of mankind until we have a few more pieces in our puzzle, particularly those which will appear in our discussions of original sin, the body-soul relation and creation.

For the moment we might more profitably concentrate our attention on the Genesis account of man's origins. The story of Adam and Eve is known well enough to allow us to presume the reader is acquainted with its essential lines. Prior to Darwin most theologians accepted the literal reality of Adam and Eve as the parents of all mankind. There was not even the slightest hint from the scientific world that man had arisen from an animal ancestor or that in this evolution a group rather than a unique couple might have been involved. There was no reason why the biblical scholars should ever question the reality of Adam and Eve as the unique parents of all men. Historical etiology, genetics, paleontology, comparative Eastern literatures, all these and many other pieces of evidence we enjoy today were unthought of years ago. But let us look at the biblical picture as we see it today.

The rabbis and priests who lived around the temple in Jerusalem in the seventh and sixth centuries before Christ spent most of their time teaching the people and preserving the revelation of Yahweh. Like any group of men pursuing the same general purpose they developed a style of teaching and a tradition all their own. Being priests for the most part, they had certain preoccupations which naturally showed up in their teachings. The observance of the Sabbath was of prime importance, but another point which concerned them very much was the hierarchical order of the universe in which everything had its own proper place and dignity, somewhat reminiscent of the "Great Chain of Being" so popular in Christian thought just prior to Darwin. At first this *priestly tradition* was handed on by word of mouth, particularly during its formative period. Some time after 538 B.C., when the Israelites had returned from the Babylonian captivity, this tradition was put into its final and written form.

The whole of Genesis Chapter 1 and the first three and a half verses of Chapter 2 belong to this priestly tradition.

Surrounded as they were and occasionally conquered by the Chaldeans and Persians, Greeks and Egyptians, the Hebrews were often tempted to imitate their pagan neighbors in worshipping the moon and stars, earth and animals. The priests were very much concerned with this constant temptation and so they focused their account on the one supreme God who creates the earth and fire, the stars and animals not by conquering the primeval chaos but in a simple effortless gesture. In the priestly tradition the same supreme God creates man on the last day as the culmination of his labors, as lord and master of all God's creation, formed in the image of God.

While the Babylonian and pagan myths of creation showed the gods wrestling with a pre-existing chaos in a struggle to form the earth and its firmament, the priestly account shows the Creator effortlessly commanding into existence all things. Once this initial command brought order out of chaos, the priestly account sets up a very artificial work schedule for the Creator. By projecting the present situation into the past in etiological style, the priests could reinforce the custom of six days of work and one day of rest and worship, since their account clearly implies that even the Lord God approved such a practice in the beginning. It is not improbable that the priestly account was also influenced indirectly by the Babylonian story of creation which was told on six stone tablets, though this pagan myth is very polytheistic in character. Modeled on the seven-day week of the Hebrews, this artificial framework would serve another purpose besides reminding the people that the seventh day belonged to the Lord God. It was also a helpful memory device for a people who in general could neither read nor write.[7]

The chosen people were very practical. Spending much of their time in the fields with their flocks, most of their worldly interests came by way of imitation of their pagan neighbors. Their dissatisfaction with being ruled by a prophet and their envy of the pagan kings is only one example of this. As a people they lacked any interest in science, mathematics, astronomy and medicine. They were not concerned with how the world came into being or how it continued in its course. The Lord God took care of all that! In the biblical narratives, natural causes are completely ignored and the jump is made immediately to the ultimate cause of all, God. In a sense the chosen people often exhibited the extreme of an eschatological preoccupation. They were so concerned with the coming of the Kingdom and the Messiah that more "worldly" interests were ignored. The *how* of creation meant nothing to them, it was only the *why* that absorbed their interest. Thus the priestly account of creation revolves around a special type of history known as salvation history. This approach to human and cosmic history is unique because it is not concerned with names and dates or even relationships, causes and effects, as the ordi-

7. Charles Hauret, *Beginnings: Genesis and Modern Science* (Priory Press, 1955), pp. 70-71. The 1964 edition omits some material.

nary historian would be. What would ordinarily absorb the whole attention of the historian is of interest to the writer of salvation history only as the setting for his account of the covenant which existed between creature and Creator from the first moment of creation. Promulgated to the first man, this alliance was confirmed and strengthened at the time of the great flood despite the infidelity of mankind. Renewed and ratified with Abraham, the prophets and kings of Israel, this covenant culminated in "He who is to come," the Messiah. The history of this alliance is the sole concern of the biblical writers. This was all they intended to teach in their accounts. Hence there is no need to be disturbed by such unscientific ideas in the creation narrative as light being created before the sun or wild fowl taking their spontaneous origin from the sea.

The division of the Old Testament into chapters and verses is a relatively recent innovation, an artificial dissection made at a time when the oral traditions were not recognized as such. For this reason the priestly account stops in the middle of the fourth verse of Chapter 2. Perhaps suspecting that his point might not be fully appreciated by the Hebrews, the sacred writer chose to repeat the whole story of cosmic and human origins as viewed by another tradition, that known as the *Yahwist tradition*. Much more ancient than that of the priests, this tradition can be traced back in its written form to about the tenth century B.C., most likely to the reign of Solomon. The Yahwist account always refers to the Lord God as Yahweh, so that we can easily recognize the sections of Genesis which come from this tradition. While the priestly account revolves around the transcendent God and the Sabbath observance, the Yahwist tradition centers its attention on man, on our origins, on the duality of man and woman, on the relationship of man with his God, the origin of evil and our hopes for the future. Yet even with all these differences, the two traditions betray their common source in a much older oral tradition which arose sometime in the twelfth century B.C. in the shadow of Moses. In many respects the two traditions do not really overlap as much as they complement each other in their religious message. As for the "scientific" or non-religious details, these are not really important. That some of these details are contradictory should upset no one, as they are beyond the scope of the author's intended teaching. That some of these facts and details betray a very naive concept of the world long ago rejected by science should also upset no one.

Completely unaware of the Peking and Java men, of prehistory and anthropology, the sacred writers faced a real problem when they set out to explain the origins of mankind to their contemporaries. Their pagan neighbors had soothed their curiosity about the past with myths which clearly mirrored their own petty human foibles. The gods fought and squabbled just like men. For the true Israelite such a human approach was tempting, though in the end the sacred authors solved the temptation in an interesting way. They adopted these pagan myths which were so familiar to their fellow Israelites, and completely reworked and recast them in a monotheistic pattern which totally transformed these accounts.

The pagan myths, it seems, were constructed slowly over the ages and their history is lost forever. Even so, it seems fair to say that both the myths and the biblical accounts of creation were worked out in a very anthropomorphic way with a strong etiological flavor which projected many present conditions back into the past in an attempt to explain or answer certain questions. Typical in the attempt to answer the question of how man became so filled with hatred, rebellion and sin in Mosaic times is the episode of Cain and Abel.

The original story of Cain and Abel probably took place sometime in the tenth century when the Israelites were still nomads and primarily engaged in herding sheep. They were in constant conflict with their more civilized pagan neighbors, who as farmers were very attached to their land. The spiritual contrast of the faithful Jew who viewed this earth as a place of pilgrimage and the pagan farmer who made this earth his home is quite evident. The conflict between the two was well known to the Jew of Moses' time and probably found many parallels in pagan literature. The fight between the farmers and cattlemen of our own West in the days of the pioneers is nothing new to man. In this original setting, which supposed a well developed civilization and a fairly well populated earth, there was no problem about where Cain would get his wife after he slew Abel. Nor was there any problem about who the men were whom Cain feared would kill him. But the biblical editor wanted to make a much clearer connection between the strife and hatred he knew and the original rebellion of man against his God, so he simply transposed the present into the past and made Cain and Abel the direct sons of Adam and Eve. Questions of marriage and genealogy did not matter to the biblical author. Such is the historical optical illusion of Cain and Abel, a typical example of historical etiology which plays such an important role in this portion of Genesis. "Cain and Abel are the sons of the first Man and Woman in about the same sense that we are" also the sons of the first humans.[8]

The etiological nature of Cain and Abel is well established today and almost universally accepted by biblical scholars. The question of Adam and Eve is not so clearly decided, mainly because there is much more at stake in this latter narrative. However, many scholars now suggest that Adam and Eve are also suppositions or figures of speech underlying an etiological narrative. These supporting details they suggest are not truly essential to the doctrinal elements of the narra-

8. Ignatius Hunt, *The Book of Genesis, I* (Paulist Press, 1960), p. 17; see B. Vawter, *God's Story of Creation* (Knights of Columbus Press), pp. 36-37.

tive. Jean Defraine, for one, views Adam and Eve as symbols of all mankind, of you and me, of the whole human race. He sees Adam as a sort of "corporate personality." Adam is seen not only as the first human but also as the real representative or embodiment of all men taken in their totality. The "corporate personality" contains the past, present and future. An instance of this is clear in God's threat to "destroy Achab," which really means that God will "strike Achab's descendants." The corporate person is a real individual even though he is often portrayed as the whole group he represents. In fact, a nation or tribe may often be represented by an individual.[9]

More recently Ignatius Hunt has noted that the Man and Woman whom the author of Genesis presents to us should not be regarded as individuals in the usual and exclusive meaning of that word. The very names chosen for these first humans, Man and Woman, indicate they have a special meaning. While we might, for the moment, concede that there was a first human being who personally committed the original sin, this is not at all certain even from the Genesis account. Yet since the sacred authors really knew so little about them, they presented the first human almost as the medieval playwright spoke of Everyman and Everywoman. It is easy to see ourselves in these first humans and their actions.[10]

There is a danger in this idea of a corporate personality in that we might fall into past patterns of thought and see in the statement of the real existence of the corporate person as an individual an affirmation that all men have descended from

9. Jean Defraine, *The Bible and the Origin of Man* (Desclee, New York, 1962), pp. 55-60. The original Dutch version appeared in 1956, hence his reservation on monophylism should be read in the light of more recent thought. See also Defraine's *Adam et son Lignage* (Desclee, Brouwer, 1959), and A.-M. Dubarle, *op. cit.*, pp. 223-24, and W. Wheeler Robinson, *Corporate Personality in Ancient Israel* (Philadelphia: Fortress Press, Facet Paperback, 1964).

10. I. Hunt, *op. cit.*, p. 11.

that first man by way of physical descent. Paul admits that one can be an Israelite without being a true son of Israel or a child of Abraham without having him for a physical father, and this in the very epistle where Paul delves into the question of original sin and the necessity for redemption. There are many cases in the Bible where the solidarity between an individual and the group he represents is not derived from physical descent. Considering this, Defraine has raised the possibility that perhaps we have understood the connection between Adam and all men in a too one-sided biological sense. He asks if perhaps there are other ways we can explain the inclusion of all human beings in Adam, as Paul clearly teaches, and then suggests some possibilities. Among these he mentions the influence that is exercised by a person who is the first in a temporal series without at the same time being the physical parent of the later members of the chain and the possibility of a juridical transference. His final suggestion, and the one he seems to favor, is the idea of real participation which is proper to the whole corporate personality.[11] In keeping with this line of thought is the comment of Mary Charles Bryce, O.S.B., in a catechism for first Communion, "When man (Adam) rejected God's love he did so for all his descendants *for Adam* WAS *the whole human race.*"[12]

With this in mind, it may be a little easier to appreciate the explanation of Adam proposed by Defraine and Renckens. Both these scholars agree that the story of Adam is strictly monogenistic in its pattern. At the same time they propose that we re-interpret the concept of monogenism. As they point out, the doctrine which the biblical writers stress by using the image of a unique couple is quite clear: all men

11. J. Defraine, *Origin of Man,* pp. 57-59.

12. Mary Charles Bryce, *Come Let Us Eat: Preparing for First Communion,* and *First Communion: A Parent-Teacher Manual for "Come Let Us Eat,"* (Herder & Herder, 1964), p. 53 of the parent-teacher manual.

belong to the same human family, all men owe their existence to the same God who not only created them but also sustains them, all men share in the historic and on-going drama of divine election and salvation, and finally, all men share in a proud and sinful resistance to this divine vocation. In the image of Adam and Eve, the Man and Woman, we have the revealed doctrine of our solidarity in creation, election, rebellion and redemption. For the Israelites, with their horror of philosophy, a concrete symbol was necessary to express this solidarity and unity of the human race. Today, with our knowledge of anthropology, paleontology and genetics with its cumulative evidence for monophylism, such a concrete symbol of human unity may still be useful for some, but it is no longer essential or even necessary.

Our biblical knowledge of the origins of mankind is concentrated in the first chapters of Genesis, but we do find a few references to Eden scattered through the Wisdom of Solomon and Sirach. In the gospel of John and decidedly in the letters of Paul we have more distinct mention of that original state. In most cases the person of the first man is not mentioned and the reference is only to the general and universal sinfulness of mankind. After examining all the texts very carefully, a number of biblical scholars have come to the conclusion that we cannot invoke any biblical text of the Old Testament as a final authoritative proof that mankind has descended from an original unique couple by way of generation. Even in the New Testament there would seem to be no text which would definitively hold us to a belief in the physical descent of all mankind from one unique couple.[13]

13. J. Defraine, *Origin of Man,* pp. 18-64; A.-M. Dubarle, *Biblical Doctrine,* pp. 45-200.

Karl Rahner has attempted a philosophical proof for monogenism on the basis of two arguments, one from what he terms a "metaphysics of procreation" and the other from God's mode of operation. (*Theological Inves-*

There is, however, a problem with one text in Paul's letter to the Romans, Chapter 5, verses 12 and 18. (We will return to this passage in more detail in an appendix where we take up the question of the preternatural gift of immortality which has traditionally been attributed to the first Man and Woman.) For the present let it suffice to note that this passage has commonly been translated from the Vulgate version of the Bible, the Latin translation made by Jerome. Most if not all Catholic translations and interpretations of this passage have been based on Jerome's version whose accuracy has recently been questioned in the light of new scholarship and evidence. Traditionally this comment by Paul has been rendered somewhat along the lines followed by Monsignor Knox:

> It was through one man that guilt came into the world: and, since death came owing to guilt, death was handed on to all mankind by one man. . . . Well, then, one man commits a fault, and it brings condemnation upon all; one man makes amends, and it brings to all justification, that is, life.

For a long time this key phrase which refers to one man in whom all have sinned was a real stumbling block in the path of biblical scholars trying to work out a solution to the mono-phyletic-monogenistic problem. Thanks however to papal encouragement of a return to critical study of the original texts rather than allowing our biblical studies to remain limited to the Vulgate, scholars have recently shed some new light on this important phrase of Paul's. Already in 1956

---

tigations. Vol. I. God, Christ, Mary and Grace [Helicon, 1961], pp. 229-296.) We would be inclined to agree with the appraisal given by Schoonenberg in God's World in the Making, pp. 57-59, where he rejects Rahner's proof: "We believe provisionally that Rahner has given us a description of the ideal origin of every man, rather than of his metaphysically necessary origin. We believe therefore that the question of a monogenetic or polygenetic origin of man remains as obscure for the philosopher as for the paleontologist." Smulders also disagrees with Rahner's defense of monogenism (La Vision, p. 204, note 10).

Defraine suggested that Adam, the Man referred to in this Pauline text, can be viewed in the same context and light apparent in Genesis, namely, Adam is Everyman. He emphasized that like the authors of Genesis, Paul is concerned with a religious truth, the unity and solidarity of mankind in sin right from the first moment of mankind's existence. However, Defraine proposes that Paul is just as little concerned with the specific source or cause of this unity in sin as was the author of Genesis. They both use the figure of the Man but make no attempt to specify that an individual man is the source of man's sinfulness which is handed on to us by physical generation. By thus clarifying the symbolic character of Adam and Eve, Defraine is not in any way denying our solidarity in sin nor the origin of that sin. He is simply proposing that this unity and solidarity in sin does not necessarily entail as a religious doctrine a single ancestor from whom all men have physically descended and from whom we have all received a share in the first rebellion.

But if revelation in the biblical writings does not directly require our acceptance of a single unique couple as an infallible and certain doctrine, what can be said of official teachings and definitions of the Church? The descent of all men through generation from an original couple is very rarely mentioned in the liturgy. There are a few allusions in the Divine Office, the official prayer of the Church, but these are far too indistinct to form a solid foundation for such a doctrine. The situation with our official catechisms is about the same, for our biological union with the first parents is assumed without ever being clearly imposed as a revealed doctrine.[14]

There is however a very pointed statement by Pius XII on theological polygenism, which would touch our discussion here of scientific monophylism. This statement came in 1950 at a time when apparently many in the Church were troubled

14. J. Defraine, *Origin of Man,* p. 76.

by certain scientific, theological and biblical trends. The encyclical *Humani generis,* "On the human race," deals with a number of these troubling questions. Its treatment of polygenism is very precise and carefully worded as befits the tenuous state of the question.

> When, however, there is a question of another conjectural opinion, namely polygenism, the children of the Church by no means enjoy such freedom [as they do in the matter of evolution in general]. For the faithful cannot embrace that opinion which maintains either that after Adam there existed on this earth true men who did not take their origin through generation from him as from the first parent of all, or that Adam represents a certain number of first parents. *Now it is in no way apparent how such an opinion can be reconciled with that which the sources of revealed truth and the documents of the teaching authority of the Church propose with regard to original sin,* which proceeds from a sin actually committed by an individual Adam and which is passed on to all through generation and hence is in each of us as our very own.[15]

The articulation of this position on polygenism, certainly very weighty though certainly not infallible, should be noted well. First of all, in taking a position against polygenism in any form, Pius XII makes no reference at all to scripture as support for his position. Secondly, theologians who have studied the statement indicate that the explanatory clauses at the end which deal with the transmission of original sin and its effects through physical generation of all men from one original couple are in all probability not an explicit element of faith. And finally, the fact that in 1950 we could not see how we could reconcile polygenism with the revealed doctrine of original sin does not mean that we find this reconciliation impossible today.[16]

That little adverb "now" is a very important qualification

15. Pius XII, *Humani genris,* #66.
16. J. Defraine, *Origin of Man,* p. 81.

as is the verb used, "it is in no way apparent." In 1950 our knowledge of this topic was very much limited. Only nine years later, during the hundredth anniversary of Darwin's *Origin of Species,* on February 28, 1959, a public lecture was delivered at the University of Rome with Eugene Cardinal Tisserant attending. The account given in the New York *Times* and cited by Cyril Vollert during the Darwin Symposium at Duquesne University that same year indicates that the Vatican's appraisal of the evolutionary theory had already, in nine years, gone far beyond the positions laid down in the encyclical *Humani generis.* As Vollert notes this is only a newspaper account and no names are given of the person or persons giving the talks, yet "there seems to be little reason to quarrel with their credibility."[17] Recent developments certainly would bear out the suggested advance beyond the position of 1950 as we will see shortly.

There is another question, though, with which we must deal here, the ever puzzling question of woman. That question is just about as puzzling today as it ever was. But perhaps it is not quite as annoying today for the person who accepts the evolutionary perspective and has kept abreast of recent biblical trends. When the evolutionary theory first came into vogue there were many bizarre explanations suggested to explain the origin of Woman from Man.[18] Today we have pared away

17. Cyril Vollert, S.J., "Evolution and the Bible," in *Symposium on Evolution* (Duquesne University Press, 1959), p. 117.

18. Theologians of forty years ago who first accepted the concept of man's biological evolution shied away from any discussion of the origin of Eve. Some pointed out an important phrase in the Church's definition on the origin of Eve which maintained the "formation of the first woman from the first man *in aliquo modo,*"—in some way or manner. The details of woman's origin were left open for discussion as long as woman was derived from man in some manner that safeguarded her position of subordinance to man in the family and society.

Actually discussions of woman's origin are age-old. The scientific question of man's biological evolution may be new, but wonderment at how woman got into the picture is not. The Jerusalem Talmud, Moses Maimon-

the non-essentials to disclose the essential core of this point of revelation. The theological definition, as it stands today, holds that the Woman came *in some way* from the body of the first Man. This, of course, was formulated before the present discussion about monophylism, though it can be adapted quite easily to fit the newer suggestions. Although the obvious explanation of this formulation would be that the first woman was formed by divine action directly from the body of the first man, the doctrine is not necessarily that clear or limited. Many modern exegetes tend to favor an interpretation of the formula in such a way that symbolism plays a very important role. They suggest that this new creature known as woman is so identical to man in nature and suited to fulfill all that he lacks, that it seems almost as if God had modeled her on the unconscious or unspoken desires of his very heart. Another suggestion proposed by the biblical interpreters is that the body of Man served as an exemplary cause in the sense that woman evolved (was fashioned by God indirectly) in the same pattern as man. In these interpretations there is no mention of any physical connection between the first Man and

---

ides, Geoffrey Saint-Hilaire, and other more modern writers have suggested that the first human was a "lateral hermaphrodite," half male and half female. This androgynous human then rebelled against his creator and, as punishment, was condemned to live as two half humans, male and female—each half being incomplete and imperfect without the other. In such an explanation, quite common among primitive peoples, the origin of human sexuality is involved in the "original sin." Both Augustine and Aquinas held that, even admitting the existence of human sexuality prior to the fall, there must have been an essential difference between that first state and the existence we know today. According to Augustine and Aquinas, as well as many other theologians, if man had not sinned, he would have reproduced sexually but without any contamination by the emotions and "filthy animal-like" passions which escape all control of man's higher faculties, his intellect and will. Some theologians went so far as to suggest, in a beautiful example of Platonic-Manichean dualism, that in Eden man might have reproduced by some sort of "chaste kiss" rather than as he does now.

More recently some have suggested that the first man and woman were "twins, formed by the division of a double cell in the womb of a subhuman

Woman. In fact, the derivation of woman from man is more in the realm of the ideological, much as a portrait or statue is related to an artist's model.

Such interpretations of the biblical account see in the detail of the rib a very appropriate symbol for the love and respect a man ought to have for his wife, since God has so delicately and carefully proportioned her to the deepest desires of his heart. The rib also touches on other aspects of the relationship between man and woman, the intimacy and closeness of the union between a husband and wife and their mutual need for each other.[19]

From what has been seen thus far, and particularly from the statement of Pius XII, it should be clear that the answer to our question of the how of mankind's origin hinges on our explanation of the original sin and fall of man. Scientifically, we may be inclined toward a monophyletic origin of man. It

---

parent, or that a few cells were miraculously extracted from Adam's body, and later developed into a woman, or again that Adam, before receiving a rational soul, married a sub-human wife." Perhaps Augustine's suggestion is not so disturbing after these grotesque explanations of woman's origin. Following out his concept of seminal potencies, Augustine had suggested that Eve might have been in the rib of Adam as a seminal potency.

Another interesting explanation of Eve's origin was suggested by a scriptural professor at the Gregorian University in Rome (and a Consultor of the Biblical Commission), Fr. Mechineau, as early as 1910. Despite the fact that Mechineau was well known as a very conservative biblical scholar, he proposed that the idea of the six days of creation were actually six days during which the Creator revealed to Adam six visions portraying the formation of the universe. In this context, the Genesis narrative of Eve's formation from the rib of Adam was simply an account of that vision, a vision whose details did not necessarily have to correspond, point for point, with the reality of woman's creation. Adam's deep sleep, mentioned in Genesis, was only an indication of the sleep during which God communicated these six visions to Adam.

The essential religious truth contained in the definitions and Scriptures is simply that woman possesses the same human nature as man and is subject to him "in aliquo modo." See Ernest C. Messenger, *Two in One Flesh,* I (Newman, 1956), pp. 24ff.

19. Cyril Vollert, S.J., *op. cit.,* pp. 98-99.

may well be that nothing in the Bible contradicts a mono-phyletic origin as such. But, as Pius XII so wisely pointed out, there is the question raised by our understanding of original sin and its transmission to all men. This is the point we must now take up.

CHAPTER 3

The Original Sin

At this point let us survey the Eden from which man arose. Like Noah's Ark and many other elements in this section of Genesis, the Garden of Eden has long intrigued the minds of men.

"The Lord God planted a garden in Eden, in the east, and there he put the man whom he had formed." In the mysterious east, somewhere out on the steppes of Asia where endless stretches of sand and gravel would make an oasis a true utopia, the Creator put the man he had formed. The garden of Eden, symbol or reality? Certainly its description is filled with symbolisms drawn from Babylonian and other sources: the cherubim, the serpent, the tree of life, etc. The four rivers which took their origin in the center of the Eden are certainly to be included among these symbolic elements. Men have often tried to use these four landmarks as a key to the location of Eden. Such attempts are fruitless for the simple fact that here again we must recognize the religious preoccupation of the author. The account of the four rivers was inserted into the narrative years after the original account was written, to strengthen the image of a utopian paradise. It mattered little to the editor that two of the rivers were the Tigris and Euphrates in present-day Iraq, that the third one was in northern Arabia, and the fourth not even in the east but rather far to the west in northern Egypt.

185

Obviously the garden of Eden is symbolic, but of what? Beyond the utopian symbolism of the garden in the east with its rivers, which is too general to give us an answer, we have a key in the two elements borrowed from the pagan myths of creation, the two trees. Traditionally the tree of life is symbolic of access to immortality and divine grace, while the tree of the knowledge of good and evil is closely related to that access in a negative way. If man were to eat the fruit of the tree of life he would live forever in the friendship of God, but it was the fruit of the other tree he chose. "You shall be like God, knowing good and evil." When man proudly tries to play God, a judge of what is right and wrong, the access to divine grace and immortality is closed to him. Here is the key to the symbolism of Eden.

It is precisely this closing of the access to immortality and divine grace that caused Pius XII to caution Catholics against the monophyletic theory of man's origins. "It is in no way apparent today how such an opinion can be reconciled with what the Church proposes in regard to original sin." The score of years that have passed since Pius XII wrote *Humani generis* has been the scene of a thorough re-examination of the whole question of the original sin and fall of man.

The theologians and biblical scholars who have explored this new field are scattered all over Europe and represent a wide variety of backgrounds, interests, and areas of competence. Theologians from the Lowlands have been the most active in the question of original sin, with such eminent scholars as Schillebeeckx, Brentjens, Schoonenberg and Smulders. France has been almost as productive, though perhaps not quite as creative, in the thought of Labourdette, Troisfontaines, Piault and Teilhard de Chardin. Karl Rahner, Ladislaus Boros, Feiner and Pas, Freundorfer and others have also added details to our new appreciation of man's origins. Yet we must frankly admit that our picture is far from complete. The adaptation of an eternal truth from a three-dimensional world vision into a four-dimensional existence is not an easy task. Care and caution are very necessary even as much as are a strong heart and creative courage. Despite the library of material already published, there are still many unanswered and undeveloped questions. Many of the ideas to be suggested here have not even reached the stage of final publication and have thus far been presented only in lectures and discussions. All of this is simply a word of caution and apology: a word of caution lest the reader forget the tentative nature of this summary, and a word of apology for the unanswered questions and incomplete details in certain phases of our discussion. Our task here is not easy, considering all these factors. Any attempt to expose the pregnant thoughts of the modern theologians without distorting in summarizing, without eviscerating their true beauty, and without diminishing at the same time their tentative nature, is a somewhat terrifying if necessary task.

A door has been opened. The evolutionary dimension sheds a very revealing light on old truths, but this new light requires of us serious and scrutinizing study of the new insights. What is presented here is a survey of this serious and scrutinizing study as it is now being carried on by theologians and biblical scholars everywhere. But the study has only begun.

The suggestions offered here are exploratory attempts to penetrate deeper into the mysteries of man's origin and nature, explanations proposed for further study and—above all—explanations which, like every human explanation, will always escape the definitive and beg for constant revision and deepening. Some of the suggestions may even be contradictory, some may be modified greatly in the years to come, some may finally be accepted—while others will be accepted almost as they stand today. Yet each one is a step forward in our search for the ultimate truth that will be revealed only at the end of time. Each of these explanations or insights is true and useful to the extent that it remains faithful to the essence of our revealed doctrines. No matter how unsatisfactory and incomplete they may seem, if they are faithful to that essence, they will inevitably aid us to a deeper vision either by highlighting some aspect or by sharpening the contrast with a shadow or negative. The scholars themselves would be the first to agree with these words of caution.

At the very root of all discussions about original sin is the fact, stressed by Paul in his second letter to the people of Corinth, that God reconciles the world to himself through and in Christ. Life and salvation come only through the Christ, and no man knows the Father or possesses life everlasting except him to whom the Christ has revealed the Father. The essence of salvation history is man's universal need for salvation. Implicit in this universal need for salvation is the underlying cause for that need, the sinful rebellion of every man against his God-given vocation: to love the Creator and our neighbor. Redemption implies sin.

The consciousness of the universality of a willful rejection of divine love is evident in the early Christian community where the sacrament of penance was taken very seriously as a personal encounter with the redeeming Christ which restored the gift of life and light. The baptism of an adult was seen to have a two-fold effect, the first parallel to that of penance, namely, the forgiveness of personal sins, and the second touching a reality beyond our own personal guilt from which we must be liberated through a meeting with Christ. That reality is the domain of darkness and evil, the influence of the world and the flesh which wars against the spirit. Man needs redemption not only because of his own personal sins, his refusal to love others, but perhaps even more radically because of his situation within a sinful mankind. It is our situation or state within a sinful mankind, in the domain of darkness, that has been traditionally known as original sin.

The theologians have formulated a distinction in their discussions of original sin which it would be well for us to keep in mind, for it will form the base of all our thought even as we move beyond the classical interpretation of that basic distinction. The sinful state or situation in which every man finds himself by the very fact of his birth has been called the *passive element* in original sin in order to distinguish this aspect from the *active element* in original sin, that action of the first man which traditionally was said to have introduced this sinful state into our world. This active element has also been referred to as the original fall or the fall of man.

The tendency in much of the modern thought on original sin is to deepen our appreciation of the essence of original sin by de-emphasizing the active element or contribution by Adam. In this way the attention of the theologians has concentrated on certain aspects of the sinful state of mankind, the passive element, which have been neglected until now. In the past, when human knowledge of psychology and anthropology was pretty much limited, a real appreciation of the passive aspect of original sin was not possible. The seeds of these new insights are contained within the more traditional presentations, and in fact one of the tasks of the theologians is to trace the development of these new insights from their germinal roots in the Bible and tradition. As the theologians shift away from viewing original sin almost exclusively as the single and unique action of one couple far back in mankind's shadowy history, and as we begin to explore some hidden aspects of the "passive" original sin, it is very important to keep in mind that the modern explanations truly emerge from biblical roots. They are a flowering or (if you prefer) a resourcing, but certainly not revolution or heresy.

It is interesting to note in the history of human thought certain patterns or parallel developments. A new insight is uncovered in one field and either soon finds its way into other fields or is discovered quite independently in a quite unrelated field. This shift in emphasis away from the concept of Adam as the archetype of sinful man has a striking parallel in biology. Since this is so, it might be helpful to use the development of populational thought among the biologists as an introduction to the recent interpretations of original sin.

In the biological sciences a new approach to phenomena began to dominate our thinking about 1930 when the synthetic theory of evolution was proposed by Fisher, Haldane and Wright. It was at this broad point that the biologists began to explore a fundamental shift in thought patterns which has become essential to the evolutionist, the shift from a typological to a populational thought pattern. As Ernst Mayr has noted: "The replacement of typological thinking by population thinking is perhaps the greatest revolution that has taken place in biology."[1]

The scientist who thinks in typological patterns is the classical biologist of pre-Darwinian times. Working from those subconscious philosophical suppositions which so often underly our conscious approach to nature, the typologist maintains that all individuals are but illusions. The individual is really only an accidental incarnation, or better, only a shadow of the one real, eternal and unchangeable archetype. For the typologist science must, then, be concerned with a study of individuals only in the light of the eternal models on which all creation is patterned. The populationist, on the other hand, recognizes the individual as a concrete reality in his own right. For the populationist the individual and not the archetype is the true reality and subject of study. The popula-

1. Ernst Mayr, *Animal Species and Evolution* (Harvard University, 1963), p. 5.

tion is an organic grouping of individuals in which the average man is a statistical abstraction rooted in a recognition of individuals rather than an eternal immutable archetype of which the individuals are only shadows. Within a population individuals differ, and these differences as well as similarities form the basis of the scientific endeavor. The model of the "ideal" or "average" cat or dog may be a useful tool for the population biologist, but it remains just that, a useful tool. It never becomes an archetype model of all cats or dogs. As Ernst Mayr so succinctly put it, "For the typologist, the type *(eidos)* is real and the variation an illusion, while for the population-ist the type (average) is an abstraction and only the variation is real. No two ways of looking at Nature could be more different."[2]

While the science of biology is relatively young, the roots of both typological and population thinking reach far into the past.

Symbolic language was perhaps the first attempt by man to reduce the wild variety of individual experiences and observations to a manageable and communicable structure. Words are basically types or abstractions which can be very useful as long as we recognize their symbolic character. It is much easier to remember a three-letter word than to carry a cat around with us. Even though the existence of individual cats, dogs and people is pretty much undebatable, men have not been too willing, let alone eager, to admit an unstable world of change and diversity, as we have already seen. Parmenides was the first philosopher we know to deny the phenomenon of change some twenty-four hundred years ago, but it was Plato who gave us the classic expression of typological thinking, and also the seed that over the years would germinate every conceivable form of typological thought. In the beginning the Supreme Being formed an eternal, unchangeable,

2. *Loc cit.*

and inconceivably beautiful prototype or pattern of everything in this world, as *the* ideal dog, the perfect archetype of a cat, etc. The things we see around us are only shadows of the true realities, participations or imitations of the great archetypes. Aristotle may have been more realistic and down to earth, but his thought is basically only a variation on the typological theme. There exists but one cosmic idea which manifests itself in different ways in the world of nature. Everything in this world spends its life striving to achieve the ideal form of that one cosmic idea. This typological approach to nature adds to the anti-evolutionary character of both Platonic and Aristotelian thought. Neither can comprehend the reality of evolutionary change.[3]

Many of the ideas so fundamental to the concept of synthetic evolution are patently meaningless to the typological thinker simply because he has never come to grips with the reality of the individual. Even within the scientific field, where the typological approach was almost universal before Darwin and still often holds sway, the two worlds of the typological and populational biologists have faced the same problem of communication experienced by those who hold the fixed three-dimensional world of cycles and those who maintain the linear four-dimensional world view. In a way this is just another aspect of an old problem we have seen before. The result among the biologists has been practically all the evolutionary debates of the past century. "Virtually every major

3. O. L. Reiser, "The concept of evolution in philosophy," in *A Book That Shook the World,* edited by R. Buchsbaum (University of Pittsburgh, 1958), pp. 38-47. Also Theodosius Dobzhansky, "On types, genotypes and the genetic diversity in populations," a paper prepared for the Burg Wartenstein Symposium on the "Behavioral Consequences of Genetic Differences in Man," held at the Wenner-Gren Foundation for Anthropological Research (New York), September 16-28, 1964.

controversy in the field of evolution has been between a typologist and a populationist."[4]

A perfect example of the typological approach in biology, which has a parallel in theological thought, is the concept of a species. All too often philosophers and scientists have viewed the biological species as an eternal type or model which is the pattern for the individuals within a group. A species is a fixed category, a neat pigeon hole. But for the evolutionist, a species is something just the opposite: it is considered as an inclusive Mendelian population, a reproductive community. In no way would the evolutionist or population biologist view a species as a type or grade of static being.[5]

Even during the lifetime of Darwin the typological approach found many strong advocates. Thirty years after the *Origin of Species,* Karl von Baer, a giant in the field of embryology, insisted that we must distinguish between the ideal relationship based on the eternal immutable archetype and the genetic or evolutionary affinity which he denied. The English anatomist and successor of Baron Cuvier, Richard Owen, contributed an impotant piece of evidence in support of evolution with his concept of the homology of organs, yet he was most reluctant to give up his conviction that all organs and organisms were patterned on the perfect and immutable Platonic archetypes. Towards the end of his life, Owen conceded a type of evolution but only as fore-ordained to achieve the perfect type set by the Creator.[6] Even today the typological approach has its defenders among the scientists, though it is more as an unconscious carry-over than a conscious defense of the position.

4. E. Mayr, *op. cit.,* p. 6.
5. E. Mayr, *op. cit.,* "Species concepts and their applications," pp. 12-30. Also T. Dobzhansky, "On types," *loc. cit.*
6. P. Fothergill, *Historical Aspects,* pp. 92-97.

The roots of populational thinking are not quite so easy to trace as are those of the typological school. Dobzhansky has pointed out that the population approach is founded on the recognition of the individual and suggests that this approach to nature can be traced to the Judaeo-Christian recognition of the uniqueness and value of the individual person. In theory—and to a certain extent also in practice—this may be true, but the formal codification of the individual human as an end in itself came only with Descartes in 1645. Implicit in the Age of Enlightenment, this recognition of the individual person played a major role in the development of the democratic idea and societies. This has an interesting consequence in the field of politics where the typological view of man is most appealing to those of conservative persuasion whereas the recognition of the inalienable rights of the individual, a population mentality, is more acceptable to those of liberal persuasion.

Dobzhansky, whose happy combination of impeccable scientific stature with a broad humanistic interest in all phases of human activity and thought is seldom matched among scientists or philosophers, has touched on one point in this population-typology question which is very apropos here. After tracing the history of population thinking to its roots in the Judaeo-Christian culture, he exposes another of those strange juxtapositions in human thought where two contradictory ideas seem to coexist simultaneously. While we could term the Judaeo-Christian culture as a population approach to man which truly recognizes the individual, our traditional explanation of original sin has been couched in typological terms.

Just how this typological explanation of original sin arose in a religious pattern so thoroughly dedicated to the defense of the individual person poses an interesting puzzle. Certainly the almost universal influence of Platonic-Aristotelian thought was an important if not the prime factor.

Keeping in mind the shift in theological emphasis from the active to the passive element in original sin and the parallel shift from typological to populational thinking in the biological sciences, we can now lead into our main topic of original sin with a quick sketch of the historical development behind our common explanation. In this way the organic growth of the doctrine will be seen and the fact that it is a true development rather than a revolution.

Throughout the centuries the Church has used certain scriptural references to explain the doctrine of original sin. Only a few of these texts are precise and clear enough to appeal to the mind and memory of the ordinary layman or cleric. By chance these more precise statements also contain references to the first man, and so at least for the ordinary person who has not specialized in biblical studies, Adam has become inseparable from any explanation of original sin. The second and third chapters of Genesis and the fifth chapter of Paul's letter to the Romans are the most frequently cited biblical texts. They have appeared, particularly the Pauline text, in the statements on original sin of a number of the Councils and will play a major role in our discussion here. Yet there are other biblical references which cannot be ignored. John the Evangelist has a good bit to say about the passive element in the original sin. In fact, if we examine closely all the biblical references to original sin we find that the typological approach with its concentration on Adam is pretty much limited to the two texts of Genesis and Romans, texts which in the overall picture play a role second to the more frequent references to original sin in a populational context of the sins of all mankind.

Some scholars and a good many non-professionals would urge an unqualified literal interpretation of Paul's comment to the people of Rome as Jerome has translated it in the Vulgate. Even if we should accept such an unqualified literal interpretation of this text and of the references to Adam in Genesis, we should also be aware that there is a more frequent and very strong emphasis on the passive element of the original sin without any reference to Adam as the active source. Paul, for instance, reminded the people of Galatia that "scripture represents us as all under the bondage of sin" (3:22) without any hint of Adam as the cause of that bondage. Throughout the New Testament, we find references to the world and the sin of the world, concepts which John found particularly acceptable and which he frequently used in the context of original sin. When Paul tried to explain to the Romans the need for redemption through Christ, he stressed the sins of the pagan and Jewish worlds and clearly indicated that all mankind is engulfed in a sinful situation where each man must be redeemed by a personal encounter with Christ. It is only after expanding on this theme for four chapters that finally, in the fifth chapter of the letter to the Romans, Paul alludes to Adam as a sort of counter-type of the Savior who triumphs over death. It is almost as if Paul's mention of Adam as the source or cause of the sinful state of mankind was an afterthought, for even in the fifth chapter the emphasis is on the role our personal sins play in bringing death into the world and contributing to the sinful situation of mankind. It is not without reason that Smulders reminds us not to forget that Paul developed his explanation of original sin, as Moses did, always with reference to the sinful pagan and Jewish worlds which he and his audience knew so well by experience.[7]

These pieces of information, along with many other indications from references to original sin in the Wisdom of Solomon, Sirach, John's Gospel and Revelation as well as Paul's letters to the Romans and Corinthians, lead us to conclude that

---

7. Pierre Smulders, La Vision de Teilhard de Chardin (Desclee, Brouwer, 1964), pp. 187-190. See also A.-M. Dubarle, Biblical Doctrine, pp. 142-200.

the general concept of original sin, the specific sin of the first man, the sinful state of his descendants, and the personal sins of all mankind were not nearly so closely linked together in early Christian thought as they have been in the Western Church since the time of Augustine.

In support of this conclusion there is the fact that the Greek Fathers interpret the crucial statement of Paul to the Romans (5:12) as referring *only* to the personal sins of all men following the unique sin of the first man. In this context they make no mention of original sin in the new-born baby, just as Paul makes no mention of it. Lyonnet has found this interpretation of Paul by the Greek Fathers quite acceptable and has further pointed out that "death" in Romans 5:12 (in both the Greek and the Latin traditions) indicates more than simple physical death.[8] Freundorfer agrees with Lyonnet's interpretation of the Greek Fathers, but he believes that they really did not understand what Paul was trying to say.[9] When Dubarle summarizes the various interpretations offered for this Pauline text, he suggests that Paul is not at all clear on whether all men die on account of their own sin or on account of Adam's sin. As for the mortal fate of young children, Dubarle points out that this would not worry a man who has studied the Bible for he would be well acquainted with instances where the sins of parents were visited on their children. As he admits, the modern conclusions are rather vague as to just what Paul meant, but if we were to attempt to pin down his thought in more detail it most likely would be at the risk of forcing Paul into our own thought patterns.[10]

While Paul may not have been concerned with original sin

8. Stanislaus Lyonnet, "Le sens de *eph'oi* en Rom. 5:12 et l'exegese des Pères grecs," *Biblica*, 36 (1955), 437-56.

9. J. Freundorfer, *Erbsunde und Erbtod beim Apostel Paulus* (Munster: Aschendorf, 1927). Also A.-M. Dubarle, *Biblical Doctrine*, pp. 152-53.

10. A.-M. Dubarle, *op. cit.*, pp. 183-84.

in young children, there was a general awareness of the state of sin in the newly-born. Early in the history of the Church, baptism was conferred on the very young as a remission of sins even though the child obviously was incapable of personal sins. While the adult died because of his own personal sins, which resulted from an acceptance of the sinful inclinations he received from his first parent, the young child shared the fate of his sinful parents, both immediate and primordial. Yet even in the early Church there was a tendency to connect in the mind the state of sin which burdens the newly-born with the sin of the first man. The theological explanations of the connection between Adam's sin and the original sin of the child became very explicit when Pelagius began teaching that Adam's sin was only a bad example with no concrete effect or influence on mankind as a whole. When Pelagius attacked the practice of infant baptism as at best of questionable value, the forces of orthodoxy rose to the defense.[11]

The great champion of orthodoxy in the fight against Pelagius was Augustine of Hippo. In the battle that ensued between these two, the doctrine of original sin was articulated in great detail but all within the very definite context of Augustine's psychology and background. And it was Augustine who undoubtedly has shaped practically all theological thought on original sin until very recent times.

Before the Pelagian conflict, certain aspects of original sin had been mentioned both in biblical writings and in the writings of the Fathers, but there never was any attempt to systematize these thoughts and aspects into a unified whole. In the Pelagian debate, however, these thoughts were not only systematized, some of them were developed with great precision just as others were left in the dark. The reason is quite simple: Augustine was not so much concerned with creating a theology of original sin as he was in justifying the practice

11. *Ibid.*, pp. 152-53.

of infant baptism as something more than just a questionable ceremony, as Pelagius had suggested. In such a context, Augustine had to clarify the meaning of original sin and explain its relationship or connection with our need for redemption. Thus he emphasized Adam as *the* sinner par excellence. For Augustine Adam's sin was not just a bad example, it reached out to embrace every man, woman, and child through the concupiscence these received from him by physical generation. It is true, to a certain extent, that Augustine's basic ideas on original sin are implicit in certain biblical texts and the Greek Fathers, but as often happens in a battle between two minds, each stresses certain elements out of balance. Thus while Augustine clarified certain aspects of original sin, he overemphasized them to the detriment of other aspects which he ignored.

The text which Augustine used in his debates with Pelagius was the Vulgate, Jerome's translation into Latin of the earliest biblical texts he could find. Jerome's rendition of the original Greek of Paul's letter to the Romans, 5:12, clearly indicated a genetic connection between us and Adam, the first sinner, whose unique sin was responsible for all of us being sinners and subject to death. In the human family, Adam is *the* sinner par excellence, the father of all men who sinned *in him*. He is the head of the human race, and as head made this choice for all of us. That choice was ours because we were all in Adam:

> Wherefore as through one man (Adam) sin entered the world and through sin death; so death passed upon all men, *in whom* (Adam) *all have sinned.*

Jerome translated the Greek *eph'oi* as meaning "in whom." The term is not at all clear, and scholars today find it difficult to translate without reverting to a paraphrase. Some scholars, Defraine among them, would express Paul's thought as indicating a causal relation based on imitation:

> Therefore as through one man sin entered into the world and through sin death, and thus death has come to pass on all men *because all men have sinned.*

Lyonnet takes a different interpretation and reads this verse as saying that death has come to pass on all men *on this condition, that all men have sinned.* Augustine opted for a particular translation which many scholars today find unsatisfactory. But his choice has led to certain interpretations of original sin. As Augustine himself remarked:

> The fall of the first man, in whom free will was absolute and whose sovereignty was unimpaired by a single deficiency, was a sin of such magnitude that human nature, whole and entire, was impaired in this fall.

All men, then, inherit original sin—a sinful, fallen nature—from their first parents from whom they have descended by physical generation.

In keeping with the philosophy, anthropology (or lack of it), and science of his day, Augustine then proposed as the causal link between Adam's guilt and ours, the biological link of physical generation. Adam's guilt is transferred to us through concupiscence, those irrational and rebellious passions and emotions, those sinful tendencies, which are epitomized in and accompany every act of sexual union, even in Christian marriage where a couple exercises their "duty" for the sole purpose of continuing the human race.[12] Since even the Christian husband and wife cannot have relations without being overwhelmed by concupiscence and thereby committing at least a venial sin, all infants are born with original sin, i.e., concupiscence. Thus all men need baptism (just as Christ told Nicodemus) if they are to be saved. For Augustine this state of concupiscence is a sin, a positive guilt, even

---

12. Refer to our discussion of the preternatural gift of immunity from concupiscence, in the Appendix.

in the child who is not morally responsible; it cries out for the punishment of hell fires. Hence Augustine had no hesitation about consigning infants who die without baptism to the fires of hell, though he did concede that these children might not suffer all the pains of hell.[13]

Two provincial councils were called to deal with the dangers of the Pelagian heresy, the first at Carthage in Augustine's own territory in 418 and the second in 529 at Orange in southern France. Both affirmed the universal subjection of mankind to original sin as explained by Augustine. A thousand years later, the Council of Trent used Augustine's explanations to reaffirm the teaching on original sin against the Protestant reformers. It might seem then that the Church has "canonized" Augustine's explanation of original sin and thereby eliminated the possibility of any other explanation. Yet this would be completely contrary to the whole practice and intention of the Church in defining a doctrine. In making a definition, the Church has always been concerned with a very limited article of faith which is then explained and developed in the light of the knowledge of the day. The explanation and development is not an essential part of the definition. It is of course necessary for a full discussion of original sin to go through the definitions of Carthage, Orange, and Trent in order to determine just exactly what is defined, but

13. For a more extensive treatment see A. Gaudel, "Pèche originel," in *Dictionnaire de Théologie Catholique,* vol. XII, and Pierre Schoonenberg, *Het geloof van ons doopsel, IV* (Malmberg, Hertogenbosch, 1962), pp. 126-31. The first three volumes of *Het geloof van ons doopsel* are in the process of an English translation to be published shortly by the University of Notre Dame Press; the fourth volume, to which we will refer frequently, is not scheduled for publication and will be replaced by a revised version based on Schoonenberg's lectures at Duquesne University (Pittsburgh) in 1961-62. The new version, which will appear first in English, will be published by the University of Notre Dame Press under the tentative title of *Man in Sin.* At the time this book was in preparation it was impossible to cite by page; our references will be simply to the book as *Man in Sin.*

this is a task beyond our scope here. It has been studied very extensively by the theologians, so let it suffice for us here to say that in general they have found nothing in the definitions of the Church which is contradictory to the new insights and explanations. None of the Councils imposes the Augustinian explanation as *de fide* and therefore the only explanation possible for Catholics.[14]

For a number of reasons, a simplistic monolithic education prime among them, Catholics all too often have the strong impression and conviction that "original sin" has always been original sin, and that our explanation of it has never changed significantly in two thousand years. This contradicts the facts, for both in the Bible and among the early Fathers of the Church we can find a wide variety of explanations and interpretations. Starting with a somewhat uncertain and confused, or better an unsystematized and undeveloped, basis in the biblical writings, the Church has continually sought for new and better explanations of this revealed truth. Slowly the doctrine became clearer as we achieved better explanations and insights into its meaning. From an isolated belief, "original sin" found its place within the context of a total picture of the Christian life and belief. Admittedly, Augustine marked a high point in this development but he certainly did not mark its terminus. The essentials have remained the same and always will, even as new clarifications are worked out.

Among the developments in the post-Augustinian world, some during the last four centuries are of special interest for us here. A few theologians, for instance, tried to determine more clearly the connection between Adam and us through which original sin has been handed on. While they admitted

14. P. Schoonenberg, *Het geloof van ons doopsel, IV*. Also *DO-C* (Documentatie Centrum Concilie, Documentazione Olandese del Concilio, or Documentation Hollandaise du Concile, Rome, 1962), Number 45. This and the prior paper, No. 44, were drawn up by P. Schoonenberg for *DO-C*.

that we have all sinned in the first man, they pointed out that Adam has also sinned in each of us. Some theologians suggested that perhaps Adam acted on our wills by reason of our biological descent from him—a juridical explanation in which God decreed that Adam should assume the responsibility of all men since he was our father. Anselm made one of the most important contributions when he suggested that original sin is not a personal sin but rather a sin or evil of our nature. Original sin thus came to be seen as the lack of sanctifying grace and of God's friendship rather than as a positive stain on the human soul brought about by concupiscence.

Gradually over the years original sin came to be viewed not as an act or even as an attitude; it was seen as a passive *habitus*. Concupiscence began to drop into the shadows and relinquish its place as the prime consideration in theological explanations. Even the concept of sin and guilt involved in original sin underwent a growth and clarification. Both sin and the guilt attached to a sinful act are rooted in the free action of an individual person, in a man's free will and choice. Over the years there has been a slow shift in the theological discussions so that the scholars now clearly distinguish between the free, voluntary choice of the first man and the involuntary character of original sin in a newly-born infant. The voluntary element in original sin has slowly been de-emphasized and reduced to its essentials, even to the point that some recent scholars have passed it over in silence. The result of all this has been a gradual separation, in theological explanations, of the guilt involved for all men as a consequence of the original sin or fall, the fall itself, and the responsibility each of us must bear for our own personal sins.

It is important to recall here that all these attempts at new and clearer interpretations of the defined doctrine of original sin were proposed with at least the tacit approval of the teaching authority of the Church and were taught by a wide range of Doctors and Fathers of the Church as well as by learned theologians of every age. The different formulations of the doctrine clearly bear testimony to an evolution and development of the dogma and our understanding of it. When we lay aside our illusion of a monolithic doctrinal structure in the Church and realize that there are a variety of explanations possible, it will be much easier for us to see how the present trends are a growth rather than a revolution. If we attempt to maintain a catechism mentality, we will only be horrified at the new ideas. However, the present developments are simply the more recent steps in a long, gradual and continuous growth in understanding and appreciation.

Still it seems that we have witnessed a sudden spurt in activities recently. After such a long period of seeming inactivity and unchanging explanations from Trent onward, suddenly everything is changing. There are many reasons for this. Neither John XXIII nor the Second Vatican Council popped out of the air; they both had a long, often hidden, germination period. On the theological side we can point to the sudden and rapid advance of biblical scholarship following the Modernist scare of the 1900s. In the early 1940s, the encyclical *Divino Afflante Spiritus* of Pius XII did much to rehabilitate and legitimize the new biblical scholarship. Even *Humani generis,* which seemed at first sight to retard both biblical and evolutionary studies, actually gave a new impulse and direction to these. One influence particularly relevant to the new insights into original sin has been the work of the paleontologists and biologists in showing the high improbability of mankind originating as a single couple in a paradise where immortality and perfect order reigned.

In the evolutionary perspective where both the world and the divine salvific action are explained along the lines Teilhard de Chardin hinted at as early as 1920, the Platonic concepts of Adam as the ancestor of all and of original sin as concupiscence have become a source of humor for the modern man. Such an unpleasant situation has prompted serious theologians to accept the challenge of working out new and more meaningful explanations. A possible fourth factor behind recent events might be the current interest in and development of a theology of the Mystical Body of Christ. Until just recently this great Pauline concept has been little studied since its premises were laid down in the Captivity Epistles and the writings of John. Hardly had the theologians begun to look into this mystery when some pioneers, particularly Teilhard de Chardin, began to expose the cosmic implications of the universal salvific will of the Creator and the role of "inert" matter in the spiritual life.[15] As a consequence of this interest in the cosmic, the concepts of original sin and of Christ as head of the universe are now being viewed in a broader context.[16] The "effects" of the original sin are cosmic and Christ,

15. R. T. Francoeur, "The cosmic piety of Teilhard de Chardin," *Catholic Mind,* 62:1188 (1964), 4-15.

16. "One of the startling discoveries of our day is that a number of positions endorsed in papal encyclicals and decrees of the Holy See and consequently taught in all seminaries have, as a matter of fact, been considerably modified by the Second Vatican Council. Several examples could be cited. Here is one: Pope Pius XII in his encyclical *Mystici Corporis,* and again, with more authority, in the encyclical *Humani Generis,* insisted that the mystical body of Jesus on earth was a body social and that it was identical with the Catholic Church. The Pope insisted that his teaching on the matter was to settle the discussion among theologians. A few years later, the episcopal college gathered in council produced a dogmatic constitution on the nature of the Church in which they defended a different point of view. The body of Jesus and the Catholic Church indeed do not refer to two things, but to *one* complex reality; but they refer to different aspects of this complex reality. We are told that the body of Christ 'subsists in' the Catholic Church. The Catholic Church, in other words, is the social manifestation of Christ's body on earth. But according to the language used in the dogmatic constitution, this does not exclude the existence of other social manifestations, institutionally imperfect, of Christ's body on earth. We have here a theology which can appreciate the ecclesial

the Pantocrator, is no longer head of the universe simply by a legal declaration of his Father but by actual organic influence.[17] "All nature groans in travail, awaiting the redemption of the sons of God."

Undoubtedly the reader might suggest other influences just as important, but these will give us an idea of the factors involved. Because of the integral nature of revelation, developments in other fields have had an impact on our theology of original sin. New approaches to the preternatural gifts, the concept of a purely natural human state in the beginning, the nature of man's life after death, the philosophical question of matter-spirit, body and soul, and many others have contributed to the present discussion. And on these we must touch later, even if only briefly.

Along with the gradual shift from the concept of original sin as the unique act of a single couple, far back in the shadows of time, to a broader view of it as the sinful universal state of man in general, has gone an exploration of certain aspects of original sin which are very biblical and traditional but which have been for the most part ignored till just recently.

Three different approaches to the question of original sin are

---

reality of other Christian Churches." See Gregory Baum, "The Christian Adventure: Risk and Renewal," *The Critic*, 23:5 (1965), 42.

Along these same lines, and related to the question of the salvation of unbaptized babies, and adults who do not belong to the Church of Rome or any Christian Church, see R. Troisfontaines, *I do not die . . .*, pp. 172-77. On page 175, he notes that "perhaps [the problem was] not rightly stated in the first place." Cf. also Tresmontant, *Pierre Teilhard de Chardin: His Thought* (Helicon, 1959), pp. 67-77; P. Teilhard de Chardin, *Christ et Science*, volume 9 of the *Oeuvres* (Du Seuil, 1965), especially "Super-humanité, Super-Christ, Super-charité," and "Note sur le Christ universel."

17. P. Teilhard de Chardin, "Le Christique," (1955), unpublished; and "Super-humanité, super-Christ, super-charité," (1943), in *Christ et Science*, volume 9 of the *Oeuvres* (Editions du Seuil, 1965). See also Claude Tresmontant, *Introduction to the Thought of Teilhard*.

discernible today. The designation of "different approaches" is, I think, the best way to look at these trends because it emphasizes the unique contribution each of the three seems to be making quite independently of the others, and at the same time it stresses, in the concept of an approach, the basic incompleteness of each of the three if one is taken alone and without the complementary insights contained in the others. It seems quite evident today that these approaches are complementary, overlapping in certain areas and yet unique. This should become clear as we work through our brief excursion into original sin by way of the metaphysics of a finite being involved in the process of becoming, the emergence of the human personality in an infant, and the existential situation of man in this sinful world.

Our first approach is based on the metaphysics of being, though perhaps it might be more accurate in our evolutionary perspective to speak of the *metaphysics of becoming or of uniting*.

In the late seventeenth century Leibnitz first suggested that we might add a third category to our concept of evil in this world. Up till that time, the philosophers had always looked at evil as being either simply physical evil—pain, suffering, death, decay—or as moral evil, i.e., sin. Leibnitz believed that a third category should be added in order to complete the philosopher's picture of evil as the lack of a required good—the classic definition given by Anselm. This third category was that of metaphysical evil. Man, by his very nature, is finite and as a creature incomplete. For Leibnitz this limitation posed a type of evil previously ignored by the philosophers.

At first sight, such an extension of the concept of evil seems to dissolve into nothing the very meaning we commonly imply by the term evil. This was exactly the reaction of the philosophers, who totally rejected Leibnitz's suggestion. Today it seems that the outright rejection of this suggestion in the past may have been due to an inability on the part of the philosophers to see how such a metaphysical evil could be integrated into a portrait of mankind possessing individual moral freedom without at the same time destroying completely the concept of guilt and responsibility usually implied when we speak of evil or sin. Even physical evil was supposed to have originated with the first sin in Eden. The Leibnitzian metaphysical evil seemed to come dangerously close to the exaggerated Augustinian concept of man's nature being totally depraved and incapable of any good as the result of original sin.

Today our appraisal of Leibnitz's suggestion is much calmer. While generally his proposal is still rejected because such an extension of the idea of evil lacks the very essential content given it by the ordinary person, philosophers are beginning to see in the suggestion something worthwhile. There seems to be a much stronger and more real relationship between the metaphysical evil of Leibnitz and physical-moral evils than many of Leibnitz's opponents cared to admit in the past.

The evil which all men fear, the evil which the Manicheans and other dualists sought to explain in Platonic terms, is not simply the absence of a good. It is the lack of it. When we speak of evil, we are talking of some good which is required and should be present, but instead is missing. This is the way Anselm tried to clarify the concept of evil proposed by Augustine in his fight against the Manicheans and Pelagians when he defined evil as *carentia boni debiti*. Good is always seen in relation to a subject who possesses that good; the same holds for evil. Something is evil only in so far as a subject lacks something he should have. And since man is a social creature by nature, something may be evil for him because it is lacking in other people within his society. Good and evil, on the human level, must be defined from the viewpoint of the human person as divinely constituted, not in the past but in the future.[18] Man is related to the whole cosmos and thus evil takes on a cosmic dimension centered in man, the crown of creation. Evil centers on man because all evil relates to him, is in him, or proceeds from him in some way. It is this man-centered evil which will occupy us in our discussion of original sin seen from the vantage point of a metaphysical evil, as the limitations of the finite created nature.[19]

With this in mind, perhaps we can presume on the necessary and careful delineations of meaning given by Smulders and Schoonenberg in their scholarly works and say briefly that a number of modern theologians tend to identify original sin, at least in part, with the imperfections inherent in the evolutionary process of cosmogenesis and hominization. Brentjens has expressed it about as succinctly as anyone:

> Original sin, considered from what we know at this moment about man and the cosmos, is the consciousness that all men are involved in a world in full evolution. Man feels that he is not a complete being, that he has not reached the point of having arrived, that he is still lacking [something necessary for] his perfection.[20]

By nature, man is finite; he must seek his fulfillment and completion consciously, willingly and lovingly in a communion with others. This is his social character, an expression of his finiteness as a creature. While the epitome of this is found in that terse comment of the Lord God in Eden, "It is not good for a man to be without companionship; I will give him a mate of his own kind," this need to transcend one's self is not limited to the psychological-emotional-biological-spiritual incompleteness of man and woman. It is cosmic in its extensions because man is cosmic. Yet in the very roots of

18. Ignace Lepp, *Authentic Morality* (Macmillan, 1965).
19. P. Schoonenberg, *Man in Sin.*
20. H. Brentjens, "Evolutie-Heelal-Erfzonde," *G-3*, 15 (March, 1962), 89-92.

man's nature there lies hidden a radical fear of loving and uniting with others. Despite the fact that every man soon realizes as he matures that his happiness depends on others, we are all basically afraid to depend on others, afraid also to commit ourselves to another in love lest perhaps that other absorb us, destroy our personality or weaken our individuality. Because of our finite nature we have a vocation to unite with others even as we possess a radical incapacity to surpass ourselves or a fear of transcending ourselves which causes us to resist that divine vocation. Original sin, as seen in the finiteness of all creatures and their natural hesitancy or incapacity to remedy that finiteness, takes on a totally new meaning, but a meaning, just the same, which is in keeping with the essence of the doctrine of original sin.

Seen as a metaphysical evil, original sin is inherent not just in every man who as a finite creature must find his perfection and fulfillment in social and religious transcendence. It is also, as Teilhard de Chardin stressed, a general condition affecting the whole history of the universe and everything in it. The whole universe, as we noted in Part One, experiences a force of attraction which leads it to higher and higher levels of union. But there is also a reverse force which hinders and resists this attraction to unite. Synthesis and disintegration. As a-centric fragments, the atoms have a tendency to unite with other atoms to form molecules, but they also exhibit a tendency to further fragmentation, the phenomenon of entropy. The same holds true also for the molecular world and on into the realm of life. All nature resists the call to a higher union despite the fact that it is only in "the differentiated union," as Teilhard called it, that an a-centric or incomplete element can transcend its own limitations and affirm its full being as a finite creature in union with others. In a sense we only recognize ourselves when we admit that we are finite creatures who need others. We can only be fully ourselves when we humbly admit our limitations and accept joyfully and lovingly a union with others. If we are proud—the essence of original sin—we refuse to admit we are finite creatures who must unite with others. We claim to be God, totally self-sufficient, and hence we refuse to love. Enraptured in self, egotistic and idolatrous, we die the death alone.

In a very real sense, then, "original sin" is a cosmic phenomenon as well as a universal human phenomenon. While the resistance to union, to love, to the acknowledgement of our finite nature, and to a transcendence of self is quite characteristic of all levels of nature, it is only man who can freely and consciously ratify this unwillingness or incapacity.[21] Hence while the roots of "original sin" may stretch to the limits of the created universe, it is in man that "original sin," as a metaphysical evil, culminates.

In a number of his essays dating from 1922 till shortly before his death in 1955, Teilhard de Chardin considered the evil of death, of disintegration and resistance to union on every level of existence including the human, as an inevitable by-product of the progressive unification of the cosmos *in Christo Jesu*.[22] For Teilhard, all evolution is the history of a centrology, the gradual centering of all things on Christ in unions formed in love. Love is the only force that can unite without destroying the components. And since God, by classical definition, is the ultimate in love and good, any resistance to this unifying force on any level is evil. It is evil because it is a failure to recognize and affirm the true character of our situation as finite creatures; it is evil because it is a denial of

21. Thomas Aquinas, *Summa Theologiae* I-II, art. 26, q. 1 ad 3.

22. P. Teilhard de Chardin, "Note sur quelques representations historiques possibles du pêche originel," (1922); "Le Christ Evoluteur," (1942); "Comment je vois," (1948); Reflexions sur le pêche originel," (1947); essays unpublished at the time of this writing. See also "La Centrologie," (1944), in *L'Activation de l'Energie,* Volume 7 of the *Oeuvres de Teilhard de Chardin* (Du Seuil, 1963).

those very processes of love and union which alone can remedy our incompleteness and finitude. This is no arbitrary labeling of something as evil, no legalistic declaration; it is the very nature of things. On the subhuman level "original sin" is the expression of the natural forces of entropy. On the human level, man's fear of loving, his fear that in loving another he will give up his own identity or destroy the other, is but the conscious expression of this "original sin" to which there is no remedy except a "supernatural" assistance—though the adjective is not the best here—from the source of all love. In this light, "it is necessary that scandal come, but woe to him by whom it comes." While we often find ourselves affirming our existence as finite creatures and are fully aware of our hesitancy to fulfill ourselves in love of another, we nevertheless often freely and consciously ratify that basic inability of all nature. It should be obvious therefore that this view of "original sin" does not eliminate the necessity of avoiding sin, basically a refusal to love another, even though it does, from one angle, view this resistance to love as an inevitable by-product of the evolutionary process.[23]

Closely related to the idea of original sin as an expression of our finite nature and its inherent fear of self-transcendence are the very seminal suggestions of Henry Elkin, a clinical psychologist teaching at the New School for Social Research in New York. Dr. Elkin has linked "original sin" with the

23. Henry Elkin, "On the origin of the self," *Psychoanalysis and the Psychoanalytical Review,* 45:4 (1958-1959), 57-76; and "Psychotherapy and Religion," Connecticut Conference on Pastoral Counseling, *The Partnership of Clergymen and Psychiatrists,* The United States Public Health Service, State of Connecticut, Department of Mental Health, Connecticut Association for Mental Health, pp. 58-69.

This analysis by Elkin hopefully would shed some light on the very provocative but difficult study of original sin by R. C. Zaehner in *Matter and Spirit: Their Convergence in Eastern Religions, Marx and Teilhard de Chardin* (Harper and Row, 1963).

temptation every child experiences in its first six months, as its personality emerges from the chaos of primordial consciousness and is affirmed in the real world. Dr. Elkin maintains that every child experiences the "temptation" to self-idolatry, the urge to assert Self as omnipotent and numinously autarchic, or self-sufficient. The child must learn to affirm his personality in a social world and to admit his finite nature, his need for others. In this universal experience of the newborn child, Dr. Elkin feels he has touched on a concrete expression of the "original sin." We cannot examine here his approach in the detail it deserves, and will have to refer the reader to Dr. Elkin's own writings, and my analysis of these in an article entitled "The Emergence of Personality and 'the original sin'," in a forthcoming issue of *Darshana International* (India).

The metaphysical and psychological approaches to "original sin" touch certain aspects in the deeper understanding of the original sin. If we were to limit our picture to these aspects we would end up with a very incomplete, and thus false, picture of this reality. We would be like the seven sages who thought they understood the reality of an elephant when they had examined its trunk or leg. Consequently we must now turn to a third aspect of "original sin" to which the theologians have recently given much consideration. In this we will be relying primarily on the work of two Dutch theologians, Smulders, and Schoonenberg.

The essence of this third approach lies in the consideration of the original sin as no longer "an isolated moment in the history of mankind." Rather than limit the original sin to the single action of a unique couple far back in man's past, this reality is now viewed in the context of the solidarity of all mankind in the history of reprobation and salvation. Expanding the concepts expressed by John and Paul among others, Schoonenberg has given us a lengthy and scholarly presentation of "the sin of the world," that sinful state in which every man finds himself by the very fact of his birth into a rebellious mankind.[24]

The sin of the world is one of those biblical concepts that theologians and scriptural scholars have only recently studied. How can we describe it? Complex as this reality is, Smulders and Schoonenberg have summed it up in a single phrase as the *situation-état* of man, the situation-state in which each man finds himself as a result of his birth into a human race where sin, rebellion, hatred, egotism and selfishness are rampant. Mankind, according to Troisfontaines, is a social group in which the bonds of unity are so closely interwoven that one man's selfishness and sin automatically influences all other men. This would hold true for the very beginning of mankind where a small group of people lived within the family or tribal circle as well as for modern man with his Early Bird communication and jet travel. Selma, the Congo, and Viet Nam undoubtedly had their parallels in the society of Peking and Neanderthal man. This situation-state of man within an egotistic and self-centered humanity is what John and Paul referred to as the "world" or the "sin of the world."[25]

In the present theological understanding there seems to be a real parallel, or at least a harmony, between what we have traditionally called the "original sin" and the life of a man placed in a milieu infected with sin. Schoonenberg has tried to clarify the parallel by pointing out that whether we are talking about the classic concept of original sin or the sin of the world as modern exegetes see it, we are dealing in both cases with individual men and with mankind as a whole located in an

24. P. Schoonenberg, *Man in Sin.*
25. Roger Troisfontaines, *I do not die . . .* (Sheed & Ward, 1963), pp. 208-245, particularly p. 239. Neither the second French edition nor the English translation cited here contain the full original text of the first French edition, *"Je ne meurs pas . . . "* (Editions Universitaires, Paris, 1960).

existential situation or state. Most important is the fact that this situation-state is not something external to the individual person. By our integral role within a society, we respond personally to others in that same society. Our dialogue with the society in which we live is not an abstraction, an external condition, or an impersonal juridical relationship. Thus the sin of the world touches each of us in the very depths of our being. It is the ultimate in a personal, psychological and interior "situation" as Elkin, Smulders, Schoonenberg and others have shown so well in their own fields of specialization.[26]

Schoonenberg has suggested that we describe the situation of man within a sinning mankind as being both external to us or objective and at the same time within us as a situation or condition "which is born in me" as a person.[27] Recalling the metaphysical approach to "original sin" as our own finiteness and its corresponding natural fear to transcend oneself, Schoonenberg constantly refers to the "original sin" of a newborn child as a privation and impotence before the vocation of love. By this he means that the child does not contribute in any way to this passive situation; he is simply born into a sinning mankind. Later in life when his moral consciousness has awakened, he will undoubtedly ratify this situation in his own selfish actions. In all this it should be apparent that sometimes the scholars are groping for words to express what they are thinking. It is not always easy to find those words. For instance we might speak here of "the situation of being a human" as a better though still inadequate way of expressing the idea that we share in the sinful situation of mankind by the very fact that we are conceived and born within a sinning humanity. "Original sin" is, then, a "situation-state," constructed by all the willful sins of men, past and present, a situation-state into

26. Refer particularly P. Smulders, *La Vision,* p. 180-190, and H. Elkin, "On the origin of Self," and "Psychotherapy and Religion."

27. P. Schoonenberg, *Man in Sin.*

which each of us is born through our membership in the human race.

Our traditional theological explanation views "original sin" in the child as a passive state or habit, a view which would eliminate from it any idea of a voluntary act, an acquired attitude or even of an active habit. This same view can be applied to the explanations proposed by Schoonenberg and Smulders but with the additional insight that this situation-state indicates also the milieu which is responsible for this passive habit or state in which we find ourselves. From this viewpoint, the connection between "original sin" and our own personal sins is limited to an analogy since for us the voluntary element of "original sin" is totally absent. As a result, Schoonenberg would like to drop all reference to the volitional element in "original sin" and speak simply of *each of us as situated by the free decision taken by Adam and all mankind.*

Smulders' thought is in much the same vein, but he uses a slightly different terminology which in its own way adds a little more to our understanding of the new insights. Smulders prefers to describe the original sin as

the burden of sinfulness oppressing each man on account of his birth in and from this sinful humanity and arising from his internal solidarity with the human race. This solidarity precedes each man's personal sins even though it is ratified and appropriated freely and at the same time inevitably by the personal sins of each individual.[28]

—"freely and at the same time inevitably." Take any human being, no matter how holy he may be; give him ten years and somewhere in the course of those years he will give in to his selfish and egotistic urges in some way, freely and yet inevitably. In the depths of every man's heart there is hidden a secret unwillingness to love God and our neighbor, or as Smulders called it, a "don't want." This unwillingness is part of our being finite men. It is prior to any personal choice on

28. P. Smulders, *La Vision*, p. 183.

our part because it is the situation of being a member of the human race, though it is also the result of our own personal decision in which we ratify that original expression of egotism, that original rejection of love (God).[29]

While Smulders speaks of the basic unwillingness of every human which leads him to ratify the "original sin," Schoonenberg is not happy with this reference to the voluntary choice of man. He would like to avoid any reference to willing or not willing. In searching for an expression which will clearly place the situation-state of "original sin" prior to any personal choice of our own while preserving our freedom as individuals, Schoonenberg suggests that we speak of an incapability for loving or transcending oneself. From this viewpoint, each human being born into the sinful situation-state of mankind is *negatively* limited in his capacity as a free human being. According to Schoonenberg, "original sin" blocks our human liberty in its ascent to the "supernatural" life of love for he maintains that a true love of God and neighbor is impossible even on the "natural" level without the "supernatural" help of the Creator who alone can give man the strength and courage to transcend his own finiteness and commit himself in loving surrender to another. The potency to love is present but he suggests that man cannot develop it without divine assistance, without redemption from the powers of darkness.[30]

29. *Ibid.,* p. 188.
30. The question of the natural and supernatural states of man has been very clearly delineated over the years by eminent theologians. It has also been the subject of innumerable definitions of the Church, ranging from the days of Pelagius and Augustine to Trent and the First Vatican Council.

The question is posed today in a different light, and here the theologians have only recently begun to explore the implications of the basic truths behind the concepts of natural and supernatural, when these truths are viewed in an evolutionary framework. The pioneer work of Henri DeLubac *(Surnaturel)* was one of the first attempts to achieve a deeper insight into the question in the light of new knowledge.

In a very tentative way, what seems to be emerging from the works of such scholars as DeLubac, Schoonenberg, Rahner, Troisfontaines, Teilhard

Nature has been created in the image of God and in its own veiled way reveals the mysteries of eternity. Theology has two eyes, the eye of faith and the eye of natural perception which involves the whole man and his response or dialogue with the world around him. One of the definitions of the first Vatican Council tells us that we can gain a valuable insight into the mysteries of our faith by looking at analogous natural phe-

---

de Chardin, and others might be summarized as follows: The categories of natural and supernatural are authentic and valid in a philosophy of being. Their value in a philosophy of becoming is not certain. In the light of the summary given in Part Two, the fact that "there are no voids in the history of the salvation of mankind" becomes more than evident, as also the fact that every man is born with a supernatural vocation to love. This vocation to love, even in its most elementary and "natural" expressions, must be conceived as within and related intimately to the divine, even though the person may not even be conscious of a personal God or Christ. "The love which every man is called to give to his neighbor is not a purely human love. A first reason is that we do not fully love our fellow creature unless we love him in our Creator. The second reason is that *de facto* we are placed in the sphere of God's supernatural salvation, and no love for God or love for man corresponds with our present order unless it is in harmony with that divine salvific love" (Schoonenberg, *God's World,* pp. 64-65). Since mankind is *de facto,* from the very beginning, on the supernatural plane, and since we are now working out our theology in terms of a four-dimensional theology and philosophy of nature, it seems that the new insights into this question may be phrased not in terms of natural-supernatural, but rather in terms of *profane* and *sacral*. This new approach was given a provisional sketch in an essay on the psychedelics (R. T. Francoeur, "Cacti, Mushrooms, and the Mystical Life," *Spiritual Life,* 10:4 [1964], 255-62) from which we quote: "Since the whole universe is pervaded by Christ's redemptive power, since it is the created image of God and possesses a type of sacramental character or essence, and since mankind has always possessed a supernatural vocation, we may envisage a movement from the profane to the sacred. By this I mean that every thing and every man has a supernatural calling and destiny (to unite with God according to its level), but our consciousness of this vocation may vary in its depth. It, along with our awareness of a personal God, may be very confused and uncertain, in some cases even absent altogether—profane; or it may be very clear and distinct—sacred.

"That even this very human awareness of the cosmic and the Divine

nomena, and this is exactly what theologians of every age have done.[31]

In keeping with this tradition, Schoonenberg has tried to highlight certain aspects of the sin of the world, the situation-state of "original sin" by comparing it with a child born in a family and society where a particular virtue is unknown and unpracticed. In such a situation-state, the child is perfectly free but at the same time incapable of practicing that particular virtue for the simple reason that none of his associates are even aware of it. Neither the child nor his family know of this virtue, let alone realize how valuable it might be in their lives. The only way the child can become aware of this unknown virtue and its desirability, the only way he will be inclined to practice it, will be for him to come into contact with an influence totally foreign to the situation within his family. Only by meeting someone from another society which treasures this virtue will the child learn of it. In a way, he

---

Milieu is the result of God's calling—his prevenient grace as Augustine termed it—is evident even though it presents an existential paradox. Cosmic consciousness is the very movement of man towards God. If this consciousness is only a movement out of self to the world and fellow man, it remains profane. Yet it can easily become sacred and complete by an awareness of the attracting and centering power of Christ. Theologians from Paul to Bonaventure to Teilhard have stressed the all-pervading attraction of Christ, "in whom all things hold together." Man's movement (of self-transcendence) towards God and God's call to man: simultaneous phases of the redemption-incarnation!

"In this context the Christian life and grace can no longer be considered a static gift or a beautiful white garment. They must be seen as an encounter with the divine, a sharing of divine life, the presence and all-pervading attraction of Christ throughout the universe."

Along these lines, Schoonenberg's references to the sacred and profane in *God's World*, pp. 84-85, 114, 163-66, and R. C. Zaehner's in *Mysticism, Sacred and Profane* (Oxford University, 1960), are very informative. See also Henri DeLubac, *La Pensée religieuse de Pierre Teilhard de Chardin* (Albin, 1963), pp. 169-84.

31. H. Denzinger, *Enchiridion Symbolorum,* #1796.

must be transported into a new milieu and brought face to face with a new influence which will teach him this virtue and urge him to practice it. Somewhat the same experience can be attributed to the child born into the situation-state of a sinful humanity. This new-born child can only learn to love, to accept the vocation to a "supernatural" life of union with God and his fellowmen, if he comes into a personal encounter with the source of all love and transcendence, God. This personal encounter with Christ which liberates the child from the powers of darkness, death and hatred may come in two ways. It may come through a direct incorporation into the Mystical Body of Christ, the People of God, through baptism of water and by the example he sees in the lives of Christians around him. It may also come indirectly, namely, in a way that is not directly conscious of the Christian aspect of this incorporation and encounter with God, through what has traditionally been called baptism of desire and through the example of sincere and moral non-Christians. Either directly or indirectly the child must come into contact with Christ the Redeemer if the situation-state of "original sin" is to be shattered and the child freed to love.

In every analogy there are some details which limp and we should note a few limitations in Schoonenberg's comparison. He himself has pointed out three of these. His example is a child who finds it impossible to practice a particular virtue because no one in his society is aware of it. However, the situation-state of "original sin" affects our whole moral and religious life, our whole relationship with the Creator, because it affects our ability to transcend ourselves in love. Secondly, his example deals with a single child whereas "original sin" touches all mankind And finally, this situation-state affects man not only on the "natural" and purely human level but also on the "supernatural" level of his relationship with God. Since mankind has refused the covenant offered by the Creator with its bond of a sharing in the divine life of love, the solidarity of mankind in sin is such that every child born into this world arrives without this divine life, without supernatural (and Schoonenberg would say even natural) love which is the basis of divine life. Only through the sacraments, only through Christ ultimately, can the child be removed from this situation.[32]

There are, however, some problems raised by this comparison of Schoonenberg's. There is a question, for instance, whether the child is totally incapable of any act of love, natural or supernatural. It may be that Schoonenberg has not delineated precisely enough his use of the terms natural and supernatural. It may well be that this question will require much further study by the experts. One possible solution might be found in an examination of the situation-state into which the child is born. Conceding that the child is born with "original sin," both as a result of his finite nature with its concomitant fear of loving and as a result of his situation within a human community where the selfishness, hatred, and sins of the parents, family and community influence very deeply his capacity or rather ability to love—conceding this, we may be able to find an answer in the actual human situation. The finiteness of human nature and our fear of loving is basic, it is not altered or modified by anything within the social structure. But the milieu into which the child is born is subject to great variation. Thus a child may be born into a family and society where the good habits and virtuous life of the parents, their selfless love and generosity, form a situation-state which in many respects counterbalances the more general and widespread sinfulness of the world. This openness to love others with its implied humble recognition of our creatureship would, in the Christian family, be ratified and concretized in the personal encounter of the child with Christ through the sacra-

32. P. Schoonenberg, *Man in Sin*.

ment of baptism which incorporates the child into the Mystical Body. For the sincere and loving family in a non-Christian culture the same encounter with the Redeemer of all could be ratified and concretized by what has been traditionally referred to by Catholic theologians as "baptism of desire." If this be the situation, then the objection to Schoonenberg's claim that the child is totally unable to formulate any act of love, natural or supernatural, without the assistance of divine grace may be answered. This, however, must be given further thought.

If we choose to use the present situation of sinful mankind, as Schoonenberg does, both as a starting point for our explanation of "original sin" as well as a working hypothesis, we should be aware that not only are we sinful as a result of the sins of the first man (men) but also that our belief in the sin of the first man (men) is rooted in a consciousness of our own sinful condition. Ordinarily we think of Adam's sin as the cause or explanation of our own inclination to sin, but we should recall that the sacred authors formulated the story of Adam's fall only because they were so keenly aware of their own sinfulness.[33]

This parallel between the original sin and the sin of the world raises an important question for us. Should we attribute the "original sin" only to Adam, only to the sinful world and man in general, or to both? All of this brings us back to the problem of the preceding chapter, the monophyletic or monogenistic origin of mankind. Schoonenberg has answered our question by pointing out that nothing in the Bible would prevent us from seeing in "original sin" a situation resulting from *the sin of the first men and their descendants*. On the other hand, the teaching authority of the Church has, since Augustine, linked "original sin" with the first man of history. Yet even in these definitions and declarations the Church has

33. B. Willaert, "Aanlekeningen bij de erfzondeleer" in *Collationes Brugenses Gandavenses*, 6 (1960), 509.

never forbidden in any way our including the sins of later generations with the sin of the first man as the source and cause of the situation-state of "original sin." In fact, it seems logical that if we hold baptism remits personal sins, it should also in the case of a child be a remedy against the evil influences which arise from a closeness to his milieu, at least in so far as that situation consists in the absence of supernatural life and the capacity to love.[34]

Smulders does not at all like the isolation and limitation of "original sin" to the unique act of an original couple. His position is very well stated in *La Vision de Teilhard de Chardin:*

> Original sin [should be seen] not merely as a static reality, but as something that grows and develops . . . at the pace of mankind itself, somewhat like a parasite which once having penetrated the seed grows up with the tree and pervades it even to the tips of its roots and branches. . . . [In the enlarged framework of a personal and collective awareness of mankind's sinfulness, the original sin] is no longer an isolated moment in the history of mankind and thereby loses its exaggerated importance. It then becomes possible to look on original sin as a growing reality, growing at the pace of mankind itself, because each sinner gives it a new figure and impulse. . . . Adam's descendants not only inherit the sin of their ancestors, they assent to it [and ratify it] on their higher cultural plane with a maturer self-consciousness and more powerful command of their own will and of the world. As a consequence, the weight of inherited sinfulness increases; it grows and develops at the pace of the very development of mankind.[35]

As with Schoonenberg's views, we have here an attempt to deepen our understanding of "original sin" within the guiding spirit of the Church's magisterium. Hence the theologians

34. P. Schoonenberg, "Erfzonde en 'zonde der wereld'," *Ned. Kath. Stemmen,* 58 (1962), 77.

35. P. Smulders, *La Vision,* pp. 185, 178, and 193.

have been seriously concerned with the reconciliation or integration of their suggestions with the definitions of various Councils and popes. After examining very carefully the extension of the concept of original sin to include the sinful state of all mankind, in the light of the Council of Trent statement on original sin as being unique in its origin, Smulders concludes that the two are in no way conflicting.[36]

There is a very important advantage to this extension and clarification of original sin which we mentioned before when discussing the advantages of theological explanations worked out in the evolutionary perspective. Since the conception of "original sin" worked out by Smulders, Schoonenberg and others has been thought out in evolutionary terms, "the opposition between dogma and our contemporary evolutionary world vision ceases."[37]

Two questions are suggested by this summary and we must deal with them before we can make any kind of judgment on the views proposed here.

The first question is posed by the Augustinian intepretation of how the original sin is transmitted from the first man to us. Augustine, it will be recalled, maintained that the transmission was achieved through the sexual union, which necessarily involved concupiscence. When Schoonenberg equates the "original sin" with the sin of the world, he claims that procreation and the generative union are only an indirect cause of the transmission of original sin and its effects. The main element is not the fact that there may be passions and even selfishness involved in the marital union, but simply the fact that a child is conceived as a member of our human race. For Schoonenberg any speculation about the role of concupiscence and sexuality in the transmission of original sin is more

36. H. Denzinger, *Enchiridion Symbolorum,* #790; P. Smulders, *ibid.,* pp. 184-185, note 44.

37. P. Smulders, *ibid.,* p. 199.

than useless. The marital act by which we are conceived does not communicate to us a fallen nature; it does however introduce us into a situated mankind. If a man could be conceived without the benefit of sexual intercourse, he would still be conceived in the situation of "original sin." And as a result of that high-flying virgin birth achieved by the Gemini III astronauts when they added some chemicals to unfertilized sea urchin eggs and produced living embryos, we should be well aware of the possibilities of artificial virgin birth, ectogenesis, and test tube babies. Augustine never had to face the question of finding concupiscence in the test tube union of an egg and sperm!

The other question we have been leading up to is the role of Adam in this new perspective. If we insert Adam's sin in the sin of the whole human race, then we no longer consider the fall as an experience unique to the first man but rather as being more the whole history of man's rebellion over the past million years or more. This leads us to ask a further question about Adam. Does this first man in human history have any significance for us apart from the fact that he was the first in a long series? Our traditional explanations have taught that we received from our parents, and ultimately from the first human couple, a human nature that is profoundly altered as a result of the fall of our first parents. We are subject to death, our first parents were not. We do not have infused knowledge, our first parents did. We have to labor in the sweat of our brow, we bear our children in pain, our first parents were not subject to these inconveniences. Our assessment of the significance of Adam, then, depends on two points: our interpretation of "original sin" and our explanation of the effects of that fall. After posing the possibility of connecting the situation induced by "original sin," not with the sin of one single individual or with the first man in the chronological order, but with the sin of the world, Schoonenberg suggests that:

in such a case it might perhaps be of no importance exactly when and where sin entered the picture, and as a consequence, we could say that Revelation tells us nothing about the degree of self-consciousness and freedom of the first human generation.[38]

The question of the four preternatural gifts alluded to here by Schoonenberg in his comment on the degree of self-consciousness enjoyed by the first human beings is the second point on which our answer depends (see Appendix). Once we place the doctrine of "original sin" in the enlarged framework of a consciousness of personal as well as communal sin, the necessity of attributing a special role to the first individual or individuals in human history diminishes and, perhaps, even disappears.[39]

The Church has always considered original sin as a general and inescapable condition to which all men, except the Virgin Mary, are subject. If we are to accept the explanation of Schoonenberg and Smulders, then we must be able to find something in the sin of the world which is responsible for this inescapable situation in each man. We might also ask whether there should not be even in the first historic sin something that would be the cause of this inescapable character. However, as soon as we define the prime effect of "original sin" as the creation of a situation-state instead of a change in human nature, it would not seem necessary or even probable that there was anything in the first historical sin to give it an inescapable character. This inescapable character would be due rather to the multiplication of personal sins over the years, to the strengthening of that sinful milieu into which each of us is born. Yet if we were to admit this as the reason for the inescapable nature of "original sin," we would have to admit that it is more inevitable for some than for others, depending on

38. P. Schoonenberg, *God's World*, p. 83.
39. P. Smulders, *La Vision*, pp. 201-209.

the individual family or society into which the child is born.

Such a solution to the inescapable nature of "original sin" is not very satisfactory. It would seem that there should be somewhere in human history a unique and outstanding sin, which would be the culmination of the sin of the world and the expression of the refusal of all men to love their neighbor and Creator, so universal as to account for the inescapable nature of "original sin." If we are to seek a unique and outstanding sin in human history as the culmination of "original sin," Schoonenberg suggests we look to the historic rejection of Christ by the human race, concretized in the crucifixion. (Schoonenberg points out that several times in his book *The Lord* Romano Guardini refers to mankind's rejection of Christ as the "second fall," or more accurately as simply "the fall.") Thus Schoonenberg and others would view the crucifixion as the culminating point of the *active* original sin. In this context, he goes on to point out that salvation through Christ operates beyond the death of the Redeemer, through his glorification which is achieved only after his humanity had completed its earthly course. He then asks if this rejection of Christ might not be the reason preventing God from communicating himself and his salvation to us through the charism of his personal influence and the reason why he must communicate salvation to us through the mysterious signs of the sacraments. Such an interpretation would help us to understand better how baptism, which unites us to Christ, can also insert us into his death and lead us to eternal life.[40]

If we are to view "original sin" as the sin of the world, as a cosmic phenomenon coextensive with mankind and culminating in the rejection of the Christ, then we must also consider redemption as cosmic, as coextensive with all nature and centered in the incarnate God-Man who died on Calvary. It is

40. P. Schoonenberg, "Natuur en zondeval," *Tijdschrift voor Theologie,* 2 (1962), 199-200. (The insert in parentheses is from *Man in Sin.*)

interesting to note that for many Christian traditions, particularly in the East, Golgotha was situated at the center of the universe, since it was the summit of the cosmic mountain and also the place where the first man had been created and buried. The blood of the Savior fell upon Adam's skull.[41]

There is an intimate connection between the creation and redemption. It would then be a serious mistake to think of man's history as primarily one dominated by sin. From the very beginning Genesis links original sin with the promise of the Redeemer. The whole of the Old Testament is a dialogue between adulterous Israel and the faithful Yahweh, between the unfaithful bride and the loving bridegroom. The trouble has been that the Judaeo-Christian revelation has all too often been presented as a two-act drama: the fall with its sad consequences, and then the long wait for the Redeemer. In this view it is regrettable that the sins committed after Adam have been practically overlooked, with the result that the crucifixion of Christ seems to be only the fulfillment of a condition for our salvation required by the original sin of Adam instead of being required by the refusal of God's love by all mankind. As a result, the sin of the first man seems to take precedence over our own personal sins in the salvation drama. In this exaggerated emphasis on the original sin of Adam, our own personal sins have only an incidental relationship to the salvation wrought on the cross.[42]

Such a dichotomy between the fall and the cross is, in truth, *a historical optical illusion*: both sin and grace were present at the first moment of man's existence in a dialogue which continues down to the present moment. God's plan for salvation through Jesus Christ dominates the whole history of mankind. Sin never reigned unconditionally in the world.

As a conclusion to this exploration of the new insights into

41. M. Eliade, *Cosmos and History,* pp. 14, 30-31.
42. P. Schoonenberg, *Man in Sin.*

original sin we might best quote the definition and explanation offered by Schoonenberg when he said that "original sin" is

> a situation consisting of the absence of supernatural grace and the incapacity to formulate any act of love [self-transcendence] whatsoever, that situation in which man finds himself from the moment when and because he starts to exist as a man in a world whose sin has broken its alliance with God. . . . Original sin is the situation of an absence of supernatural grace to which the sacraments alone can put an end, and in which man finds himself because and from the moment when the alliance between man and God ruptured, a rupture rendered definitive by the rejection of Christ.[43]

Even more succinct is the conclusion of Dubarle:

> We see original sin now as a truly tragic and actual situation: no longer merely the loss of wonderful gifts at a great remove from our day and condition, but the moral and religious perversion in which every man finds himself inevitably plunged by reason of his birth into a perverted environment: ignorance of God, or idolatry and a more or less profound corruption.[44]

With this general setting, we must now pick up some of those threads which are still hanging in the air. It is time to examine the creation of man and his nature, once again setting the eternal truths in the new perspective of a four-dimensional evolving world picture.

43. P. Schoonenberg, "Natuur en zondeval," p. 199.
44. A.-M. Dubarle, *Biblical Doctrine,* p. 244.

CHAPTER 4

The Creation and Nature of Man

In the long history of man's attempts to articulate and ultimately, it is hoped, to explain the mystery of his origin and nature, two great systems stand out both as pioneer attempts and as the pattern for or basis of almost all subsequent thought on the problem in our Western culture. Plato and Aristotle were pioneers who have exerted a tremendous influence on all our Western attempts to understand the creation and nature of man for the past twenty-four hundred years. Expressed in ever new terminology, rethought and reworked, the perennial Platonic and Aristotelian views of man have molded philosophical, scientific and theological ponderings even when the philosopher, scientist or theologian has been completely ignorant of the source of the suppositions underlying his conclusions.

It undoubtedly is unfair to the original authors, but for the sake of clarity and brevity, we will attempt a simplification of the Platonic and Aristotelian views. This will entail our exaggerating the contrast between the two positions, based not so much on the original Platonic and Aristotelian views as on the extremes to which some of their more influential devotees in later centuries carried their basic intuitions. As a word of caution we might point out that the caricature presented here is more a contrast of Plotinus, Descartes and some scholastics than it is of Plato and Aristotle, for these later thinkers have had a more universal appeal for the common mind than the more restrained and moderate views of their Greek forefathers. It is usually the disciples who carry the logical or illogical weaknesses of a system of thought to their extremes, and it is usually these extremes that appeal more to the common man who has little inclination to pursue the tight and moderate views of the masters. Recalling this propensity of human nature, it is hoped that our over-contrasting here will give a clearer indication of the perennial influence of these two basic views of man, his nature and creation.

The Platonic approach to the mystery of man, particularly as articulated by Plotinus in the third century A.D., centers its attention on one essential aspect of the mystery. Like all attempts to explain or describe and define basic fundamental realities, the Platonic approach does not ultimately do justice to the whole mystery, perhaps because such a basic and fundamental reality as "matter and spirit" may prove essentially unexplainable and undefinable. Plato, and particularly Plotinus, saw man as a true dualism, a soul, god-like in origin and eternal, cast down into a bodily prison here on earth. Imprisoned within the body, the soul awaits its liberation from this material world into the timeless world of the spirit.[1]

Over the years this dualistic perspective has been repeatedly carried to its logical conclusions, in the thought of Plotinus and the Christian world. In many cases the extremes of this approach to the mystery of man have led to a whole series of related heresies, Manicheanism, Jansenism, Puritanism, among others. In these the soul of man is considered good because it is "like unto God, a spirit" while man's body is viewed with suspicion, if not condemned outright as basically evil, the work of the devil. In every age there have been some who

1. For the basic writings of Plotinus and Plato on the question of man's nature, body and soul, see *The Essential Plotinus,* trans. and commentary by Elmer O'Brien (Mentor, New American Library, 1964).

have gone the limit and proposed the existence of two gods, one good and one evil. This attempt to *solve* the mystery of evil in man ends by blaming evil, pain, suffering and sin on an evil god who has created man's body as a prison for the divine soul, created by the good god. The Albigensians of the thirteenth century were so consistent in their application of this dualistic belief that they totally condemned marriage and human sexuality as a tool of the devil, contrived as a trick to perpetuate the imprisonment of souls. The Cathari or "Clean ones" in this society were so convinced of this belief that they starved themselves to death in addition to remaining celibate. Thus they hoped to free the spirit from its dungeon. This religious group undergoes a periodic reincarnation in the Pyrenees, but we have more concrete and influential threads of this dualistic approach to man's nature in our New England puritan mentality, and a perennial current of anti-body, anti-sex, anti-marriage appreciation in the Catholic world. In the latter area, the influence of Augustine has been very potent. Converted from Manicheanism and a disciple of Neoplatonism, Augustine's views of woman, sexuality and marriage have often been carried to their extremes by intellects of less stature and perception. And, as with any "vulgarized" popularization, the ordinary man has unconsciously and unthinkingly gone more often to these extremes.[2]

The impact of Platonic and Neoplatonic dualism was later adopted by the scientific world through Descartes, thereby increasing its impact. Obviously, when this approach is carried to its extremes, the result is a complete distortion of man's nature. This distortion follows through into daily life where its appreciation of the world of matter makes it difficult to see how a man can want to become involved or committed to the

2. See "A history of Catholic thought on contraception," by Daniel Sullivan, in *What Modern Catholics Think About Birth Control,* ed. William Birmingham (New American Library, 1964).

progress of our material world. Nevertheless, the Platonic view of man has an appeal. Its approach does safeguard the spiritual aspect of man's nature.[3]

However appealing the Platonic description of man may be, it does not fully satisfy most because it fails to resolve the dualism of body and soul. In stressing man's spiritual side, the Platonic view forgets that man is a true duality and not a simple dualism. This duality is an essential *unity* of body and soul. In the Platonic dualism body and soul are two complete substances. Body and soul can exist apart from each other though they do form a temporary *union* in the living man. It is also difficult to see, in this system, how man is related to the rest of the world around us. Plato maintained that before we were born our souls existed in a heaven of pure Ideas. In this heaven, Ideas existed without any materiality and could be contemplated directly by our souls. The ideal Tree, Dog, Cat archetypes were contemplated in their pure form rather than as engrossed and individuated in matter. When our souls were imprisoned in our bodies we lost this contemplative ability and forgot the pure Ideas. Only when we perceive individual dogs, cats, and trees, the shadows of the pure Ideas, do we "remember" the archetypes on which they are modeled. For the Platonic tradition man is a union of an inanimate material element and a spiritual vital force, comparable to the union of a car and its driver.

Aristotle preferred to view man as the substance and form of a statue. While in Platonic thought the body is accidental to man's integrity and with the soul forms a *union of two complete substances,* Aristotle maintained that man is a *unity constituted by two incomplete substances,* a substantial form (the spiritual principle) and prime matter (a material principle). For Aristotle all material beings are composites, not a

3. Joseph F. Donceel, *Philosophical Psychology,* 2nd ed. (Sheed & Ward, 1961), pp. 245-50, 341-51.

union but a unity formed by prime matter and substantial form. All minerals, plants, animals and men are thus constituted, according to the hylomorphic theory devised by Aristotle and adopted later by Aquinas. In this system, the difference between mineral, plant, animal and man lies in the degree of perfection of the substantial form, "of its emergence from matter." As Donceel points out, minerals, which the ordinary person would call "matter," are already composites whose "substantial form is so entirely immersed in matter that it can give the mineral only its material existence and material activities. In man [the substantial] form emerges so far from matter that it can produce operations which are *intrinsically independent of matter.*" While there is a true analogy (with a foundation in reality) between the substantial forms and prime matter of a rock, a plant, animal and human, we cannot simply equate the body with prime matter nor the soul with the substantial form. As Donceel emphasizes, man's soul is more than a simple substantial form, it is a spiritual entity which functions as a substantial form.

Plants and animals actually lie between the two extremes of the mineral and human worlds. In both the substantial form cannot exist without matter, "in both it emerges enough from matter to produce some effects which are never found in minerals."[4] The plant soul or substantial form is material, which means either that it can be seen, touched, weighed or measured by the senses, or that in all its operations, and even "for its very existence, it is intrinsically dependent on matter." The plant soul is not material in the sense that it can be measured or weighed, but in its intrinsic dependence on matter. What this means is that the plant's substantial form depends on matter which is the co-cause of the plant's operations and existence. When a plant grows or carries on any metabolic function, its actions are not produced entirely by

4. *Ibid.,* p. 47.

the plant itself but involve the causal influence of matter. Every action of the plant is the effect of a dual causality, the being or form of the plant in question and its prime matter. And since prime matter is a real co-cause of the very existence of the plant soul, it cannot exist independent of it. Neither the prime matter nor the substantial form of a plant can exist alone; both together form the whole substance of the plant. Roundness cannot exist except in something round and that roundness disappears when the ball is flattened. A similar situation exists with the plant soul which is so dependent on matter that it disappears when the matter of the plant "dies" or disintegrates. The plant soul is replaced then by a mineral substantial form just as the roundness of a ball is replaced by its flatness.[5]

The philosopher of an Aristotelian-Thomistic tradition speaks of prime matter and substantial form. The ordinary person is not used to thinking in *ontological categories and abstraction,* so he immediately tries to concretize these two principles of being. This we commonly do in the light of our own experience when we equate our bodies with prime matter and our souls with some etherial, angel-like phantom. Such concretizing is totally contradictory to the hylomorphic theory, yet this is very frequently done by us who consciously or unconsciously have been influenced by the Cartesian picture of man. Our living body is already a unity composed of prime matter and substantial form, for neither of these two principles can exist alone.[6]

In the early seventeenth century Descartes returned to the Platonic and atomistic view of man's body and soul as two complete substances, though he left unsolved how the body

5. *Ibid.,* pp. 48-49.

6. On the question of a possible separation of man's component elements, body and soul, in the phenomenon of death, refer to our later discussions, pp. 268ff. and 282ff. On Descartes, refer: Donceel, *op. cit.,* pp. 246-47.

could influence or act on the soul—at one time suggesting that the pineal gland forms the connecting link and at other times claiming that any interaction is impossible. Malebranche, one of his successors, suggested an "occasionalist theory" which agreed that there could be no direct interaction, but that God used the occasion of our body seeing or sensing something to place a corresponding idea in our mind or soul. Leibnitz went further and claimed that God has freely established a harmony between the physical and psychic worlds, a "pre-established harmony" between body and soul which allows us to exist in two parallel but totally independent worlds. Spinoza added one more logical step towards a total pantheism when he suggested that we might compare God to a gigantic tree whose many branches grow in perfectly synchronized parallelism, not because freely established by an autonomous God but as the result of the absolute necessity of Nature who is god. Emmanuel Kant saw the problem and tried to solve it by returning to the hylomorphic theory of Aristotle and Aquinas, at least in part. His incomplete attempt restored the concept of man's nature being composed of two incomplete principles of being, even as it led to an agnostic attitude towards philosophy and the spiritual.[7]

At this point, we might note that all these approaches to the mystery of man have been worked out in a pre-Darwinian world vision where the dynamic evolutionary dimension is missing, or at least incompletely understood and accepted. In these views of man, we see the approach taken by philosophers who are concerned with categories of *essence* and *being,* rather than with *becoming.*

In this line, and remaining within the context of a *philosophy of being,* thinkers have found it difficult to accept, or better to explain, the evolution of man. We have already seen the problems involved in the evolution of man as a species,

7. *Ibid.,* pp. 247-49.

his *phylogeny*. We must now turn to the origin of man as an individual, his *ontogeny*. This, of course, raises the question of man's nature, for with the acceptance of Darwinian evolution we must now explain the evolution of the whole man, body and soul. Once the theologians and philosophers agreed, quite grudgingly in most cases, that they could not ignore evolution as a reality, they tried to safeguard the essentials of our Christian revelation. In keeping with their philosophies of being, which formed the basis of their theological explanations, they then conceded that we might allow a "mitigated evolution" in which man could trace the origin of his body back to a subhuman primate stock but in which God would still *intervene to infuse the human soul by a direct creation into this evolving body*. This direct creation of the human soul and its infusion would so modify the subhuman body that the whole man, body and soul, would begin his existence at the moment of conception.[8]

The moment of conception, the moment when man begins to exist as a human being, has been a problem for the philosophers and theologians. They admitted evolution, but tried to remain within their three-dimensional world and continue the dialogue. The problems that have resulted from this dual existence are particularly pertinent for us in our attempt here to look deeper into the origins of mankind and man the individual.

Once again let us use the historical approach and return to Aristotle's view of man. While Aristotle was quite anti-evolutionary in his conception of species and substantial forms, we must admit that certain elements in his thought, particu-

8. See for instance Adolphe Tanquerey, *Brevior synopsis Theologiae dogmaticae,* 22nd ed. (Benziger, 1929), I, p. 477. For a summary of the theological concensus of 1920 see E. C. Messenger, *Evolution and Theology,* pp. 80-84; or more recently, C. Vollert, "Evolution and the Bible," in *Symposium on Evolution,* pp. 105-106.

larly as adopted and explained by Aquinas, do *seem* to lend themselves to the *possibility* of an evolutionary interpretation by someone living and thinking in a post-Darwinian world view. *This,* however, *is an illusion,* for as we have noted the Aristotelian-Thomistic physics is totally static and anti-evolutionary.[9]

The Aristotelian explanation of the origin of the individual man is more than just a historical curiosity. It has a relevance here which we cannot ignore, particularly since Aristotle was a biologist and a philosopher who tried to expose the fundamental details of man's mysterious nature and origin. In his attempt to unite biology and philosophy, he tried to show the connection and relationship that must exist between the functions and structure of a plant, animal or man and its substantial form. Actions flow from and indicate the nature of a being's substantial form. Hence the substantial form of a flower, its vegetal soul, interacts with the prime matter to form a petunia plant. The same situation holds for the animal and for man. Quite obviously, a plant has no need for an animal or human substantial form (soul) for neither its structure, its functions nor its "purpose" warrant a principle of life higher than that of a simple vegetal soul.

This principle of philosophy Aristotle applied to his observations of the development of human beings and animals. A capable biologist as well as a naturally curious thinker, he observed the embryological development of many animals, and undoubtedly also of man. His explanation of the development of the chicken embryo in the egg is a classic example of observational and descriptive science. Integrating his philosophical principles with his science undoubtedly led him to a study of naturally or artificially aborted fetuses and embryos.[10]

9. J. Donceel, *op. cit.,* p. 62.
10. Bernard Towers, "Man in modern science," *The Month* (London), 217:1157 (January, 1964), 23-36.

In these studies he observed, as we can today, the development of a pre-animal or pre-human embryo from a vegetative mass of cells with no apparent animal functions at all, a series of stages which the embryologist today calls the zygote (fertilized egg), blastula (solid sphere of cells) and gastrula (hollow sphere) stages. Watching the development of animal eggs, the chick in particular, and noting the differences of aborted human fetuses and embryos, he could see how this vegetative mass soon took on a distinctly animal form and function. Then, after four or five weeks in the case of humans, he could discern a truly and distinctively human form.

To attribute to Aristotle such observations in the field of embryology is not unreasonable even with the primitive character of science three hundred years before Christ. It is only by admitting such experimental knowledge to a man who we know was an astute observer of nature, interested deeply in the origin and development of the chicken, that we can explain his philosophical deductions about the origin of man and the human soul. He proposed that the rational substantial form could not be present in the earliest stages of human development for the simple reason that the human form and function was not present till about four weeks after conception. But what would animate and direct the growth of the embryo before this phase, in those critical first four weeks? On the basis of his observations, Aristotle suggested that there might be a sequence of substantial forms in the development of the human embryo, a vegetative soul very soon giving way to an animal soul which ultimately yields to a rational, spiritual soul which takes over all the life-giving tasks of the lower life-principles and allows those activities which are strictly human. The difference Aristotle noticed in the development of male and female embryos has been confirmed by modern embryology. Today we know very well that all human embryos assume a recognizable masculine structure of the external genitalia at about forty days; only later, at about eighty days, does the female fetus begin to develop typically female structures. On this basis Aristotle claimed that the human soul was infused at forty days for the male and eighty days for the female. This theory of just when and "how" the human substantial form originates has been called the *mediate animation theory*. Here it is not a question of the direct or special creation of the human soul, but of when the soul is created and "infused."[11]

When the concept of evolution began to find its way into the popular and scientific worlds, many men feared that it would undermine the whole Christian foundation of life: if species could evolve, what would happen to creation? The dilemma was solved in much the same way man had tried to solve the problem of Time: by seemingly accepting the new idea but then quickly eviscerating it and going back to the old position. With their crude microscopes some scientists claimed they could see a tiny human body all curled up in the human egg or sperm. This *pre-formed* human being proved that evolution was impossible. If the individual human being does not really change and evolve (since he is "pre-formed"), neither can species change and evolve. Evolution is just a "jack-in-the-box," an unrolling of a pre-determined pattern, a *preformation*—much as Augustine had once suggested. The acceptance of preformation "saved" the Christian faith, but it also knocked the pins out from under Aquinas' and Aristotle's belief in the mediate-animation theory. If there was a human form present in egg or sperm, then there had to be a human soul present. Thus arose the idea of *immediate animation*,

---

11. *Loc. cit.;* see also E. Messenger, *Theology and Evolution* (Sands, London, 1949), pp. 219-333. An incredible pictorial history of the development of the human embryo was carried by *Life*, 58:17 (April 30, 1965), pp. 54-72A, "The drama of life before birth." This article has been expanded into a four-part series on "The Control of Life," *Life* 59:11 (Sept. 10, 1965) *et al.* which explains the possibilities of ectogenesis, virgin birth, etc.

the idea that the human soul is infused at the moment of conception.

The moment of conception of which the philosophers and theologians speak even today reveals a basic pattern of thought, a dimension, a world vision, rooted in categories and essences. But the moment of conception, like everything else in our evolving world, has proven to be more a process than a simple black-and-white point in time. Modern experimental embryology, with its time lapse photography, has shown quite clearly that the "moment" of conception actually lasts about half an hour from the formation of the fertilization cone when the sperm head penetrates the egg until the egg and sperm pronuclei finally fuse to form the zygote.

If the human soul is given at the moment of conception, if the soul is specially created and infused at the moment of conception, then how can we explain the development of identical twins who come from a single egg which splits into two some hours after fertilization? Can it be that a human soul also splits in two, or can two human souls animate that single fertilized egg before it splits?

Beyond this problem, which is quite natural, we must also face now the question of artificially induced twinning which the scientists have already accomplished with the frog and bird. If the scientist can divide a two or four-celled sea urchin blastula into two or more separate and identical embryos, if he can do the same with duck embryos to produce twins at will, we must face the possibility of this soon being done with humans. Already we can induce the conception of quintuplets with the "birth control pill" by utilizing its rebound effect. And within not too many years we may be facing ectogenesis, in all its ramifications. "Test tube babies" are no longer the shocking newspaper sensations they were a few years ago when Dr. Petrucci induced the fertilization of a human egg in a test tube and managed to keep it alive in an artificial womb for twenty-eight days. Similar experiments have been carried out in a number of universities and medical centers around the world in attempts to learn more about human development. The artificial womb, which is essential for successful ectogenesis, has already been developed in a pilot model by scientists working at the University of Alberta in Canada. A combination heart and lung machine, it has already been tested on near-term sheep and may soon be adapted for the benefit of premature human babies whose lungs are too weak to support their frail lives. Aldous Huxley may have been indulging in a bit of science fantasy some years ago when in his *Brave New World* he described the Decantation Room where babies, conceived artificially, could be raised under ideal conditions until the day came for their decantation or "birth." In *D'Alembert's Dream,* Diderot spoke of a "warm room with the floor covered with little pots, and on each of these a label: soldiers, magistrates, philosophers, poets, potted prostitutes, potted kings . . ."

In the future a mother who has difficulties carrying a child full term might conceive in the normal way and then have the doctor induce a premature delivery at two or three months so that the child can be raised in an artificial womb without any danger of miscarriage. Even if this practice were accepted as moral in the future, we do not have such equipment at present. The problem today is to explain how nearly one-half the human eggs fertilized in the normal course of nature never reach full term and are spontaneously aborted, most of them before the mother is even aware she is pregnant. How can we reconcile this with the universal salvific will of the all good Creator? Are we willing to admit that fully one-half of the human beings conceived never have the slightest chance of participating in the redemptive powers of Christ's sacraments? We must also face the reality of Providence in the thousands of artificial fertilizations that occur in universities and hospitals every day which, for lack of effective artificial wombs, cannot today be carried to full term. One hospital on the East coast has over ten thousand such fertilizations a year!

Perhaps it might be more sensible to return to Aquinas' theory of mediate animation and look on these very young and undeveloped embryos as only pre-human or pro-human.

The question now arises, do we want to return to Aquinas' view or do we have other alternatives? Is it simply a choice between Plato and Aristotle, or between mediate and immediate animation theories? In trying to describe the ultimate mystery of man's nature we can easily point out the superiority of the Aristotelian-Thomistic view over the Platonic and Cartesian approaches. But we must also admit that it does not explain the mystery, and that it has been worked out in a pre-Darwinian three-dimensional world vision. Even in that world vision we can validly ask the question whether it is the only view possible. A number of times we have recalled the warning of Aquinas with which we opened the second part of this book:

> Since the divine Scriptures can be set forth in many ways, no one should cling so insistently to any one explanation that if this should be proven false with certitude we would still presume to assert that this is the sense of Scriptures. Such declarations would expose Scriptures to the derision of unbelievers and close the path of faith to them.

Even in his own day, Aquinas admitted his views and explanations were not the only ones possible, though some of his students are not always so humble. There may be other explanations of man's mystery worth examining.

One view of man that particularly comes to mind in the context of our present study and in the light of our survey of cyclic and linear time in the first part of this book, is the biblical conception of man's nature. The Hebrews were not a philosophical people, they dealt with the living world in all its down-to-earth passion. They knew and experienced man not in the abstract categories of metaphysical speculation but in all the vibrance of human passion. The biblical mentality saw man as a "living soul," for "Yahweh formed man from the dust of the ground and blew into his nostrils a breath of life; and man became a living soul" (Gen 2:7). If we try to see this in Platonic or Cartesian perspectives, we lose the whole meaning of the biblical message about man's nature. First of all there is no word in Hebrew for what the Platonists and Cartesian thinkers would call the "body." Beyond this, the Hebrews made no dichotomy between what the Greeks called man's body and his soul. Instead they spoke of two aspects in the mystery of man, his *nephesch* or breath of life and the dust of the earth. These two aspects of man are not the equivalent of the Greek body-soul even though the Septuagint translates *nephesch* by the Greek word *psyche*. *Psyche,* in Platonic thought, is fundamentally dualistic, arising as it does from an Orphic tradition, which was later carried over into Cartesian dualism. For the Hebrew, these two aspects of man's nature together comprise his soul or flesh.

> Unhampered by the body-soul dichotomy, the Hebrew calls this tangible, sensible, expressive, and living reality that is man, a soul. I perceive, not a "body" which contains a "soul," but, directly, a living soul. Within the sensible that I am shown I may decipher all the wealth of its intelligibility. This soul is visible to me because it is within the world, fed on the world's elements which in turn cause it to *be* flesh. The essence of this flesh which is man, is the soul. The soul gone, there is no "body" left; nothing is left. Nothing but the world's own dust.[12]

There is a dialectics in the Hebrew view of man but it is definitely not the Greek body-soul dualism, even though the popular view of biblical references to flesh and spirit equates

12. C. Tresmontant, *Hebrew Thought,* p. 94.

these with the Platonic and Cartesian body and soul. The dialectics and opposition that the biblical writers testified to between flesh or soul and the spirit is unique.

> The opposition of flesh to spirit is an opposition between two *orders*. Flesh . . . is man's index of frailty, that frailty that comes of being made of dust. The spirit is man's participation in the supernatural order. The spirit summons him to the destiny of a god according to what is written: "Ye are gods" . . . With the *ruah,* which we call "spirit," biblical anthropology unfolds a new dimension specifically its own. . . . The *pneuma* [spirit or *ruah*] is in man a supernatural part, a participation in the supernatural order. The spirit is, within man, a permanent substantial invitation to a change, to a supernaturalization, that will permit created man to partake of his Creator's uncreated life.[13]

The flesh is not the equivalent of body since it is commonly used as a substitute for soul, the two terms being equivalent expressions for the whole man who is both *nephesch* (breath of life) and dust of this world. It is the whole man, the flesh, the soul, who is weak and rebellious against God. The flesh is an index of man's frailty. In the New Testament the "flesh" becomes the index of man's proneness to rebel.

In the New Testament this dialectics of flesh and spirit is expanded and developed by the evangelists and apostles. The distinction of body-soul as a material and a spiritual element united in man came into the Judaeo-Christian world first and only very vaguely during the Babylonian exile. It was not until the third century of the Christian era that Neoplatonic thought was successful in introducing the distinction effectively into our thought. Later because of our undercurrent of Cartesian-Platonic connotations and our difficulty in finding the proper words to translate the unique terminology of biblical thought, the Christian mentality slowly lost almost all of

13. *Ibid.,* pp. 108-109.

the biblical insight into man's nature. Without scientific exegesis and literary analysis to clarify the real significance of the biblical view of man, that view was soon drowned in the Greek metaphysical world vision.

The confrontation of the biblical view of man and the Greek philosophical appreciation of man brought many problems. The risk of misinterpretation was enormous particularly on the part of thinkers trained in the Greek schools who found the world view of the Hebrews (with its linear time) so alien to their own. An instance of this, on which we will comment more later, is the question of man's state after death. In the New Testament we find many references to the "resurrection of the dead" but only a few to the "resurrection of the body" (as in 1 Cor 15).

When the New Testament writers spoke of the resurrection of the dead they meant the resurrection of the whole man, *nephesch* and dust. As the Christian world came into contact with Greek thought, the councils and Fathers of the Church tried to avoid a Platonic interpretation which would limit this resurrection to the liberation of the immortal soul from its bodily prison and its entrance into the timeless realm of the empyrean. To make this distinction between a pagan and the Christian view clear, the councils began to stress that the whole man would rise, with his body as well as his soul. The acceptance of Greek philosophical terminology was necessary in order to avoid any pagan dualistic interpretation of the resurrection of man.

The adoption of Greek terminology and a failure to understand the biblical thought has led to many pseudo-problems, particularly that one so often raised by young inquirers: How can our souls possibly recover all the elements of our bodies after the resurrection especially when these have been scattered over the earth's surface or assimilated directly or indirectly by other human beings?

The problem arises, as Tresmontant has pointed out, from our attempt to think about the resurrection in terms of a dualistic system where body and soul are seen as two complete and separable substances. In the biblical context, the problem does not exist. Since the soul is the essence of our body, since the *nephesch* and dust of this world are but one, the resurrection of our bodies means the resurrection of our souls, the resurrection of the whole man. The bio-chemical molecules we absorb into our being are quite anonymous. My eye, my leg, my skin are not composed of molecules and atoms bearing my own personal label on them; they are rather "this very self, this soul that I am, that has assimilated them and informs them from within."[14]

One of the main characteristics of all dualistic thought is to conceive of two things where in actuality there is only one. In this line, the distinction of body and soul in man led Plato and Descartes to see these as two physical realities. Aristotle and Aquinas held an opposite tack, namely that these two could not be distinguished as complete and separate physical realities though they could legitimately be seen as two distinct *metaphysical principles of being*.

In this context all sorts of confusions result from our discussions of the death of man, and his resurrection. When the death of man is described as a "separation of body and soul," we commonly think in dualistic terms appropriate to Plato and Descartes rather than Aristotle and Aquinas. Yet even with Aquinas' view of man's death and resurrection there are problems today. He would have us see in the living organism a potential multiplicity within a real unity of body-soul. This potential multiplicity, which we can talk about only in the abstract when we speak of a living organism, is the "matter" or "body" of concrete living beings. Death, as a separation of body-soul, actualizes this potential multiplicity. When the

14. *Ibid.,* p. 106.

body separates from the soul, it no longer is a body, only a corpse, for body and soul are metaphysical principles of being, not concrete physical realities.[15]

This may seem like double-talk to some and "heresy" to others but the thought of Aquinas is quite clear and very orthodox even though all too often totally misunderstood. For this reason we will have to return to this topic of the death and resurrection of man—even though that return will be only a brief sketch of some possible interpretations and in no way a total answer to the question. But we will return to the concept of man's death only after we have attempted to move out of the three-dimensional world vision in which all of the foregoing remarks on man's nature were constructed and into the four-dimensional world view of evolution.

In commenting on the mind of Aquinas and his approach to nature, Sertillanges has noted that the idea of evolution is totally alien to the thought of the Angelic Doctor:

> Consequently, one cannot say that the closed system of Saint Thomas constitutes a metaphysical or religious narrowness. *The narrowness is completely in the biological and cosmological order*. It arises from experimental science and neither religion nor metaphysics depends essentially on experimental science.[16]

Here is the strange dichotomy of Thomas Aquinas: his metaphysics and theology are perfectly compatible with our four-dimensional dynamic and evolving world vision, but his whole philosophy of nature is "hopelessly static."[17]

Typical of Aquinas' openness to the evolutionary dimension is the famous passage which deals with the origin of the human soul, so frequently cited in discussions of human origins.

15. *Ibid.,* pp. 87-92.
16. A.-D. Sertillanges, *L'Univers et l'Ame* (Paris, Editions Ouvrières, 1965), pp. 20-22.
17. J. F. Donceel, *op. cit.,* p. 62.

Everything therefore which is moved, in so far as it is moved, tends to become assimilated to God, in order that it may be perfect. But a thing is perfect to the extent to which it is actual. Hence the intrinsic tendency (*intentio*) of anything which is in potency is to become actual by means of change. Hence the more evolved and the more perfect an act is, the more completely does matter tend towards that act. For this reason matter tends toward the last and most perfect act of which it is capable as to the ultimate end of generation.

Now, in the actualizations of forms, there is a certain gradation. For prime matter is first in potency to the form of an element, and when it exists under the form of an element, it is in potency to the form of a compound; considered under the form of a compound, it is in potency to a vegetative life-principle, for the soul is the act of such a body. Again, *the vegetative soul is in potency to a sensitive, and the sensitive soul to an intellectual soul.* . . . Hence the ultimate goal of all generation is the human soul, and matter tends to this as to its final goal.[18]

Aquinas' philosophy of nature may have been "hopelessly static," but certainly his whole metaphysics of nature calls out for an evolutionary interpretation and world vision. That Thomas could not reconcile this dichotomy is no fault of his. As Sertillanges and many others have pointed out, philosophy and theology can learn much from the natural sciences, but ultimately their premises come from a source other than experimental observation. In the days of Aquinas the natural sciences offered not even the slightest hint that the world of nature was evolving. That Thomas came to express certain philosophical conceptions quite amenable to the evolutionary

18. Thomas Aquinas, *Summa Contra Gentiles*, III, 22. See also J. F. Donceel, *op. cit.*, pp. 62-63; and John L. Russell, "Teilhard de Chardin, *The Phenomenon of Man*, II," *The Heythrop Journal*, 2:1 (1961), 3-13. This quotation from Aquinas was used by Teilhard as a caption for his essay "La Paleontologie et l'Apparition de l'Homme," in *Revue de Philosophie*, (1923), reprinted in *L'Apparition de l'Homme*, volume 2 of the *Oeuvres de Teilhard de Chardin* (Editions du Seuil, 1956), pp. 51-82.

dimension is due to his reliance on biblical thought which as we have seen is linear and historical in outlook.

Our Platonic and Cartesian thought patterns make it very difficult to appreciate this real dichotomy in Thomas' thought, for almost imperceptibly these pervading atmospheres of thought lead us to view Thomas' prime matter/substantial form in dualistic terms, and thereby ignore the fact that his metaphysics and theology call out for an evolutionary world vision to complement it. Donceel has well stated the danger:

> Almost unavoidably, we image the spiritual I dwelling in the innermost recesses of our material body or subtly permeating all its parts. We must keep reminding ourselves that without the soul the body is nothing. The body is continually held in being by the soul. On the other hand, if we try to think of the spiritual I as separate from the living body, we are imagining something which does not exist. I am continuously embodying myself. Embodiment, or incarnation, is not something which happened to me once, when the soul slipped into the body; it is coextensive in time with my existence in the world. The way I exist is: embodying myself. I am a spirit continuously secreting a shell of corporeity; but it is a living shell, in which and through which this spirit inserts itself into the world of matter, undergoes its influences and acts upon it. From a certain point of view my soul is nothing but this living shell of corporeity, exhausts itself entirely in its production (i.e., my soul as substantial form); and in that sense I may say that I am my body. From another point of view my soul transcends the body, without which it cannot exist in the world. The comparison with the shell must not be carried too far. A shell is something solid and subsistent, which continues to exist after the animal has died. Better, then, to compare the body to the glow of a lighted bulb. That glow is not the same thing as the bulb; yet the lighted bulb cannot exist without it, and it cannot exist without the bulb, by which it is continually kept in existence. So our soul continually surrounds itself with the glow of corporeity; only thus can it exist and act in this world.[19]

19. J. F. Donceel, *op. cit.*, p. 449.

We have already seen that at least four philosophical conceptions of man's nature have been accepted at one time or other in the orthodox Christian tradition, the Hebraic, Platonic, Aristotelian-Thomistic, and Cartesian. Each of these was worked out in the three-dimensional philosophy of nature common before Darwin, though the Hebraic is more religious than philosophical in its linear orientation and the Thomistic view cries out for an evolutionary physics.

Can we now incorporate our modern evolutionary understanding of nature and the universe into our theological and philosophical understanding of man's nature? If we do, might we resolve the dichotomy of a dynamic linear metaphysics and theology joined with a static philosophy of nature in the thought of Thomas Aquinas? If we do, might we not also find need and use for a new terminology to express the new and deeper insights. And as we will see, we might find some interesting insights into such realities as death, resurrection, hell, purgatory and particularly creation.

Shifting to the evolutionary dimension of thought is not easy. It stirs up all kinds of fears in the hearts of the timid or inflexible. As Ignace Lepp noted in the *Psychology of Loving:*

> The human being is indissolubly composed of body and soul, matter and spirit. This is so true from the Christian point of view that the renowned Cardinal Saliège has had the courage to declare publicly that it is difficult for him to believe in a real distinction between the two components of the human composite. It would be wrong to be scandalized at this and cry heresy. Theologians and philosophers who consider the body and soul separately are looking at them *from the point of view of essences,* while the Archbishop of Toulouse sees them *in a perspective that is existential* [*evolutionary*]. Existentially, there is nothing human that is not simultaneously— although in different degrees—both matter and spirit, both body and soul.[20]

20. Ignace Lepp, *The Psychology of Loving* (Helicon, 1963), p. 21; (Mentor Omega paperback, 1965), p. 31.

Here the contrast between the two world concepts is very clear. Yet there is in the Thomistic view of man's nature an essential insight,

> that is still valid and important although it can no longer be accepted in the precise form in which it was understood by Aristotle and St. Thomas. It needs modification along lines indicated by Teilhard de Chardin.[21]

This comment by John L. Russell was echoed by Teilhard himself when he pointed out the true value of the Thomistic approach to the nature of man.

> Transported into a universe in which duration adds a further dimension, the [Thomistic] theory of matter and form becomes almost indiscernible from our speculations today on the development of nature.[22]

Teilhard, of course, never intended to "give an explanation of the world, but only an introduction to such an explanation." Even in this introductory attempt, Teilhard was convinced he could only make a minor, if important, effort indicative of the path we will have to follow in the future if we are going to understand man and his role in nature. "It is up to others to try to do better."[23] Before we can examine the efforts of others to do better, following his lead, we should perhaps see what Teilhard himself had to say about man's nature within the context of cosmic and convergent evolution outlined in Chapter Four of Part One.

Starting at the very bottom, Teilhard maintained that all

---

21. John L. Russell, "The principle of finality in the philosophy of Aristotle and Teilhard de Chardin, I, *"The Heythrop Journal,* 3:4 (1962), 347.

22. A statement by Teilhard, cited without reference by A.-D. Sertillanges in *L'Univers et l'Ame,* p. 38.

23. P. Teilhard de Chardin, *The Phenomenon of Man,* pp. 29 and 290. Also see Maurizo Flick, "Theological Problems in 'Hominization'," *Theology Digest,* 13:2 (1965), 122-127.

created reality is basically energy of some form or other.[24] Groping for a way to express this basic reality, Teilhard settled on the general term "cosmic stuff" or more often *Weltstuff* which he borrowed from the German philosophers of nature. Teilhard was very much aware that he could not use the out-of-date and over-nuanced philosophical language of a fixist, three-dimensional world vision without running the serious danger of confusing his thought with a lot of alien and even contradictory nuances stirred up in the minds of his readers by familiar terms.[25] The German *Weltstuff* is a term not too familiar to the ordinary reader. This would allow Teilhard to give it his own specific meaning without danger of being too misunderstood. Thus it would indicate what we ordinarily call matter but with the added nuance of a superior organicity or capacity for a higher activity than that possessed by simple, dead, inert matter. Cosmic stuff is, for Teilhard, the dynamic evolving reality we know both in our own nature and in the world around us. One of the weaknesses in the dynamic but fixed (cyclic) nature of Aristotle's world was the fact that he claimed the inorganic world lacked any natural structure, immanent activity, psyche or finality. This is not true for Teilhard.[26] Teilhard used *Weltstuff* as a metaphor suggesting a concrete and basic reality capable of being organized into a higher interiority or consciousness, or of disintegrating into a cloud of dust and ashes.[27]

Once Teilhard set the universe, all cosmic stuff, in an evolu-

24. Walter J. Moore, *Physical Chemistry,* 3rd ed. Chapter 19, "High Polymers" (Prentice Hall, 1962).

25. Karl Rahner, *Theology of Death* (Herder & Herder), p. 31.

26. See particularly the two articles, each in two parts, by John L. Russell, already cited from *The Heythrop Journal.*

27. Jean Onimus, *Pierre Teilhard de Chardin ou la Foi au Monde* (Paris, Plon, 1962), pp. 80-92; also Madeleine Barthelemy-Madaule, *Bergson et Teilhard de Chardin* (Editions du Seuil, 1963), pp. 239-54, 295-302, 112-28.

tionary perspective, he tried to approach the nature of this reality as a phenomenon within the dynamic process of evolution. He avoided any attempt to give a philosophical analysis based on the *philosophy of being:* "Of set purpose, I have at all times carefully avoided venturing into that field of the essence of being."[28] Actually he ended up analyzing nature in terms of a philosophy of process, but it is well to note his approach.

> I do not seek to define the nature of either Matter or Spirit. I am simply saying, without going beyond the level of physical appearances, that probably the greatest discovery made by our century has been the recognition of the fact that the march of Time has been measured principally in terms of a gradual coming together of matter into higher and higher groupings, . . . a gradual coming together of matter in groupings of increasing interiority, centeredness and freedom, all in the course of Time.[29]

Numerous quotations about the two aspects of cosmic stuff, the Within and Without of things or more classically Matter and Spirit, can be drawn from a wide range of Teilhard's writings. Here we might cite only two, the first from his "Essay on a Personalistic Universe" where he wrote: "Concretely, there is not Matter and Spirit. There exists only Matter becoming Spirit for there is in the World neither [pure] Spirit nor Matter. The 'Stuff of the universe' is Spirit-Matter."[30] The second statement is cited by Jean Onimus from an untitled essay written in 1950: "Matter and Spirit, in no way two things, but two faces of the same cosmic stuff."[31]

These statements may sound strange and even "heretical," but before we reject them outright, let us recall that we have

28. P. Teilhard de Chardin, *Phenomenon of Man*, p. 29.
29. P. Teilhard de Chardin, *The Future of Man*, p. 66 (Author's translation).
30. P. Teilhard de Chardin, unpublished essay.
31. Jean Onimus, *op. cit.*, p. 81.

changed our whole perspective. We have added a new dimension of thought to our portrayal of the world around us and this dimension can alter a great many things. Ever since the beginning of human history, man has incessantly pondered and discussed the co-existence and opposition of Matter and Spirit, body and soul. In the terms of the earliest philosophers it came down to a discussion of plurality and unity, a problem which has plagued all philosophies, all religions, and all science. Today it seems we are moving towards a solution to the problem which consists, as always seems to happen in the case of the most irritating paradoxes, in recognizing that the question has been wrongly stated in the first place. There is, in fact, no contradiction or opposition between matter and spirit, the body and the soul, the one and the many, if we view them as existing in a flux or process of personalization. Both poles are simply two phases, or more exactly, two senses of the same reality which surrounds us and is within us. Matter and Spirit contradict each other only if we isolate them or try to symbolize them as fixed, abstract and, in fact, unrealizable ideas: pure plurality and pure simplicity. In reality, in nature, Matter and Spirit are inseparable; one does not exist without the other, "and this for the good reason that spirit seems to appear essentially as the result of the synthesis of matter."[32] Here, of course, we are not speaking of God, but only of created nature. We are also using the concepts of matter and spirit in their broadest sense, in keeping with the analogy of being suggested by Thomas Aquinas as the foundation of philosophy, a principle to which we referred in our summary of Teilhard's thought in Part One.

By force of logic and consistency, a philosophy of nature that is based on static or fixed immutable essences must be dualistic. A philosophy of being or essences can only define

32. P. Teilhard de Chardin, "Sketch of a Personalistic Universe," in *L'Energie humaine*, Vol. 6 of *Oeuvres de Teilhard* (de Seuil, 1962).

by opposing two ideas; it can only explain an idea by using antinomies. In the fixist philosophies of nature the question of the one and the many, of matter and spirit, and of man's body-soul nature, are placed at opposite poles, poles that are not dynamically related and interpenetrated but rather contradictory and exclusive of each other: black and white! Either the spirit exists or it doesn't; either a thing is alive or it is dead; something is either a plant or an animal.

> In the realm of the Cosmos, a ruinous dualism has unavoidably been introduced into the structure of the Universe. On one side, the Spirit—on the other side, Matter; and between the two, nothing but the affirmation of a verbal interdependence between Matter and Spirit, all too often comparable to a slavery of the body to the soul. All this because *the two terms, arrested and fixed, have lost all genetic connection.*[33]

The biologist, of course, chuckles over such categorical thinking and smilingly offers the three-dimensional philosopher a culture of Euglena, flagelated algae, slime molds, or a tube of artificially synthesized DNA. In the fixist world vision, there are degrees of being, but no movement from one level to another: the Great Chain of Being in all its static glory.

Being a modern scientist, Teilhard, of course, did not see matter and spirit, body and soul, as isolated categories. He descended from the realm of three-dimensional metaphysics and tackled the problem on the level of living phenomena. Perhaps, despite his claim not to be a philosopher, he ultimately has led us to substitute a philosophy of becoming for a philosophy of being. In any case, the question of matter and spirit takes on an entirely new face in an evolutionary world.

> From the depths of Matter to the highest peak of the Spirit there is only *one evolution.*[34]

33. P. Teilhard de Chardin, "From Cosmos to Cosmogenesis," *L'Activation de l'Energie,* p. 266. Cf. Chapter 4 of Part I, *supra.*
34. P. Teilhard de Chardin, *The Future of Man,* p. 23.

Since the whole universe and everything in it, all cosmic stuff, is a single evolutionary process exhibiting a general pattern of recurrence within the ascending spiral of increasing complexity-consciousness, we must now see where man's body-soul nature fits into the picture. In looking at the origin of individual man in the evolutionary dimension, let us keep in mind Teilhard's various groping attempts to express the reality of that evolution: his equation of evolution with a growing consciousness, complexity, love, liberty and freedom, centreity, personalization and hominization. In this process of evolution, Teilhard saw spirit emerging from the synthesis of matter, consciousness expanding out of a growing complexity, psychic energy gradually gaining ascendance over the tangential or material, all within a process of amorization, personalization, centration and hominization.

"Spirit being no longer independent of matter, or in opposition to it, but laboriously emerging from it under the attraction of God by way of snythesis and centration,"[35] we must now see how this applies to what we have traditionally known as the "special creation" of man's soul. It is commonly known that the Catholic view of evolution must allow for the *immediate and direct* creation of the human soul and its infusion by God.[36] There is also the Dogmatic Constitution prepared for the First Vatican Council which, while never formally discussed or accepted, clearly maintains that there is an "essential difference" between the body and soul of man.[37] The problem seems to be clear in the light of all we have said thus far, and the solution just as clear. The Greek concept of man as composed of body and soul, and the whole hylomorphic theory of nature has been worked out on the basis of a philosophy of being. Granting the premises of this world view,

35. *Ibid.,* p. 93.
36. C. Vollert, *op. cit.,* pp. 104-106.
37. Denzinger, #1702.

premises which are not contained in revelation but derived rather from a particular philosophical tradition and a particular scientific view of the world, we can admit the validity of that view. It is and has been a valid and useful approach to the truth. *In the context of that view, we must maintain an essential distinction between body and soul.* We must also maintain that the spiritual soul of man is directly and immediately created out of nothing by God and infused at the moment of conception.

Are Teilhard de Chardin, Cardinal Saliège, and many others heretics, then, when they suggest that spirit laboriously emerges from matter under the attraction of God in the evolutionary process of synthesis and centration? If we judge them on the basis of a philosophy of being, the only answer we can give is a definitive "yes." But we must realize that they are not talking in terms of a three-dimensional world vision or in terms of essences and categories of being. They are speaking from a totally different viewpoint and must be judged in that light.

Karl Rahner has frequently spoken of our out-dated philosophical terminology in strong terms. Of this inadequacy Teilhard was very conscious and his constant search for a better way to express his ideas, his incessant groping for new terms to encapsulate what he was thinking, testify to this. Undoubtedly his search was not always successful nor were his choices of neologisms always the best. But this is hindsight, based on studies and work by eminent scholars who took his inspiration and in the ten years since his death have advanced and clarified those revolutionary insights into the theology and philosophy required by a four-dimensional world vision.

Today, scholars such as Schoonenberg, Smulders, Lepp, Troisfontaines, Rahner, and others still use the terminology of Aquinas and Aristotle to a greater or lesser extent. Sometimes this is for convenience's sake, at other times it is an indication that the author has not stepped fully into the four-dimensional world of thought. But in all these men there is a sincerity of purpose and an openness of mind. What we give here is a broad and brief summary of their views of man's nature, body and soul, in post-Darwinian theology-philosophy.

First of all, it might be interesting to inquire whether Teilhard's basic insight into matter and spirit in man can be reconciled with classical doctrinal statements by the teaching authority of the Church. Five years ago, when the new insights were only beginning to be explored, J. Edgar Bruns tackled the question in an article in the *Catholic World:*

> Perhaps Père Teilhard would say that the word "essentially" in the Vatican definition can be interpreted in terms of a "genesis" (a birth or emergence) and thus avoid the perils of anathema. Only the Church could judge the legitimacy of such an interpretation.[38]

Today it seems that the question remains open to discussion particularly since such eminent theologians as Rahner, Troisfontaines, Smulders and Schoonenberg have extended and clarified Teilhard's basic conception.

When we move into the evolutionary dimension, the classic Greek concepts of body and soul lose their significance. For this reason, many theologians today prefer newer and less confusing terms such as for body, "materiality," "corporeity," "dependence on others," or "the principle of dependence." Instead of soul, many now speak of the "person," "being-in-oneself," the pole or principle of being which makes me distinct from all others. *In this context,* and recalling Teilhard's characterization of evolution as a process of the emergence of spirit out of materiality, of freedom out of necessity, of personality and the human individual out of materiality, we can

---

38. J. Edgar Bruns, "God Up Above—or Up Ahead?" *Catholic World* (New York), 191:1, 141 (1960), 23-30.

see that it may not at all be heresy to speak of personality (soul), that which makes me me, emerging out of a necessary dependence on others. As a bipole unity I express my freedom and liberty, my personality and spirituality in a gradual process of conception, embryonic growth, birth, infancy, childhood, adolescence, and adulthood. There may be and undoubtedly are critical stages in this emergence of my personality: conception which is the first step in the affirmation of myself as distinct from my parents, birth with its declaration of biological independence at least in part, adolescence with its agonizing step into the adult world where it is hoped I will learn to be a full person. In all this long tedious emergence of my personality and being-in-oneself, I gradually emerge from the necessity of dependence on others, at first a biological liberation but soon followed on other levels of personal existence. In a three-dimensional world vision it is heresy to think that the spiritual soul of man can evolve from matter, but in the four-dimensional world vision we can, it seems, speak of personality emerging from materiality.[39]

In this context according to Rahner, Schoonenberg and others, we can still maintain the essence of the Christian revelation. But to do so we must clarify our concept of creation. Only then can we integrate the emergence of spirit out of materiality with the classical expressions of man's nature and origin found in the Church. Only then can we move on to some of the implications this holds for the conception of death, and what follows, namely heaven, hell and purgatory.

Theodosius Dobzhansky touched the heart of the problem when he remarked that "Evolution is the method whereby Creation is accomplished."[40] In the post-Darwinian world,

39. P. Schoonenberg, *God's World in the Making*, pp. 11-48; P. Smulders, *op. cit.*, pp. 71-100.

40. Theodosius Dobzhansky, *The Biological Basis of Human Freedom* (Columbia University Press, 1956), p. 124.

free at last of all those immature and unChristian fears about evolution being a denial of God, *evolution means creation,* evolution is simply God's plan and method of creating.[41]

Recently Paul Chauchard published a work called *La creation evolutive* in which he speaks of God creating an evolving world, a creation which when taken "terminatively" coincides with evolution. To equate evolution and creation we must get rid of a concept of creation all too common in pre-Darwinian thought and even today. Such expressions as "in the beginning" and "out of nothing" must be clarified in the light of what Schoonenberg calls a "more complete grasp of divine creation" based on Revelation and reason.

"In the beginning." Schoonenberg clearly points out that the biblical concept of God as Creator arose among the Hebrews out of their personal experience of him as their God, the Yahweh who had chosen them out of the gentiles and made a covenant with them. This salvation experience led them to the belief in the creation "in the beginning." In discussing God we have not maintained the same balance. We have forgotten that God is the God of history and more, that "my Father works even till now." Throughout the Bible, God's creative activity is something that is constantly going on. Scripture does not restrict creation to the beginning of time and oppose it to the activity by which God sustains, supports and governs this world. God is pure act and thus to oppose the idea of creation and Providence is unbiblical and poor theology. It does make, however, for facile and popular sermons! If we consider creation from man's viewpoint, a similar clarification is necessary, for to be a creature means to be totally dependent on God's transcendent causality, even in our personality (that which makes us unique persons distinct

41. John A. O'Brien, *The Origin of Man* (Paulist Press, 1947), pp. 33-38. Though now quite dated, the general approach of this pamphlet still makes it worth reading.

from all others). "Like any other being in the entire world, we are dependent on God even in that aspect in which we are independent of the rest of the world," our personality.[42] "In the beginning" can be a very misleading phrase. What it actually means is that God is above and outside time and this world.

> That is why the world, in all its duration, in all its unfolding and fullness, has its foundation and source in God's creative act. God creates in the beginning, that is, from His eternity, from Himself, and this relation of God and the world remains always the same.[43]

Creation *"out of nothing"* must be similarly clarified. Out of nothing signifies fundamentally God's transcendent causality. It is this transcendental causality that is the basis for the whole world and for everything in it. It is the cause behind every coming-to-be of one reality out of another. *"It is from nothing that God makes one thing emerge from the other."* God, in other words, is the Creator of an evolving world, a world in the process of personalization, hominization, centration and amorization.[44]

Admitting these clarifications we might still not have a true picture of the equation of creation and evolution. We could, for instance, follow the preformation path of Augustine and overemphasize "in the beginning," thereby limiting creation to the beginning and allowing evolution only a secondary role of "unrolling the preformed seminal pattern." A second mis-

42. P. Schoonenberg, *God's World*, p. 27. It is quite probable that the "in the beginning" of Genesis 1:1 does not refer to what happened at creation in the present theological sense of that word at all. There seem to be two ideas of "creation" in the Old Testament: the first in Genesis 1 where God *definitively* orders the world-stuff ("chaos"), and the other in Isaiah and the prophets where God overcomes the chaos but must constantly keep it in check.

43. *Ibid.,* p. 28.

44. *Ibid.,* p. 31.

interpretation of the union of creation-evolution is much more common: the special creations or interventions of God. Here God's continual creative activity is broken up into a whole series of ever new interventions and special creative acts. To think in these terms is not to take God's creative activity and his total transcendence as well as his immanence seriously. If God creates always, if he works in and through the laws of nature and evolution, then he does not have to supplement by some special creation or intervention for the deficiency of lower causes in nature which he has established in an evolving world. "He brings the world to realization in such a way that the higher really emerges *from* the lower."[45]

> If God does not create by intervention from outside, the same must be said about the creation of the human soul. We are quite willing to profess the "immediate creation" of the human soul, but we should divest that statement of all dualistic connotations. . . . The soul [if we use the old terminology] is the principle and the "pole" of personal being-in-oneself, and materiality is the principle of being-dependent. No matter how much man is connected with, and dependent on things, he is, as a person, by virtue of his spiritual soul, in-himself, free and self-realizing. The same must be said about his origin. *Now it is precisely this aspect, as caused by God, that is expressed by saying that the spiritual soul is created.*
>
> The expression "the soul is created by God" means that the soul is the principle in virtue of which man in his coming-to-be is independent of his parents and caused only by God. And again, this holds good not only for man's origin but also for his continued existence. . . .
>
> Hence the creation of the human soul is neither more nor less than the beginning of a new person in a whole world, which is constantly created by God as a world in which there is an increase of human persons. *And the creation of the*

45. *Ibid.,* p. 31.

souls of the first human beings was the coming-to-be of persons in a world which, under God's creative causality, had reached the apex of its evolution.[46]

The special intervention on God's part to create and *infuse* the human soul at the moment of conception has led to a multitude of misinterpretations and false ideas. Sertillanges has pointed out that Aquinas' use of the term "infusion" is not at all a happy choice. While excusing Thomas' choice of the word as a concession to the difficulties of language, Sertillanges nevertheless clearly equates this special creation and infusion of the human soul with the *immanent action of God within nature. Creation = evolution.*[47]

Every newness of a being that exists in itself, outside of its causes, and *a fortiori* the newness of a higher being, shows that this world does not have its ultimate explanation in itself. Coming-to-be looks forward to fullness of being, and the ascent looks forward to the summit on which that fullness is realized. Far from being a difficulty that militates against the existence of God, evolution is a proof for His existence.

In this way evolution leads us to God. At the same time, it also completes our notion of God's creative activity. A static image of the world makes us approach God's creative activity principally from the standpoint of efficient causality and the exemplary causality connected with it. God makes everything as it is; he forms the nature of the things that are and makes them reflect something of his own being; he makes man to be an image of himself, and leaves traces of himself in the rest of the world.

An evolutionistic image of the world adds something to this picture and makes us see God's final causality within it. God not only makes beings, he also moves them in their ascent. He both propels and attracts them. The ascent toward man is the growth towards God's image. The history of man-

46. *Ibid.*, pp. 31-32.
47. A.-D. Sertillanges, *op. cit.*, pp. 42-44, 56-60.

kind is, at least from God's standpoint, an increasingly clearer and fuller development of that image.[48]

The idea of God creating and *then* infusing the human soul can and has very easily led to the grossest misinterpretations of man's nature. It implies, for instance, the Platonic pre-existence of the human soul along with its exile in the body, an exile shattered only at death when the soul is freed from its corporeal prison. This, and many other un-Christian interpretations, have arisen from the juxtaposition of dynamic linear Judaeo-Christian philosophy and theology with a fixist, cyclic philosophy of nature drawn from the pagan world.

A possible solution, as we have seen here, is to adopt an evolutionary philosophy of nature and then rethink our theology and philosophy in terms of this new world vision. The dangers of a Platonic or Cartesian dualism are clearly avoided

48. P. Schoonenberg, *God's World*, p. 33. In a letter to the author, Schoonenberg made some important distinctions regarding the animation of the human embryo and the creation of the human soul. "The second question is that of the moment of animation or—less dualistically expressed —the moment of hominization. And it is here that I don't feel quite happy. Is it not a little oversimplified to say that the first life and the first soul of the human embryo are simply vegetative? Surely, this is partly true, but is all said by so speaking? For on the other hand: is not the human embryo (like the human sperm and the human ovum) a reality effected by *human* generation, by the generative act of beings that have already reached the *human* level, an act directed to the birth of another *human* being, etc.? Biologically speaking, is there not already the *human* pattern of chromosomata? I agree in calling the young embryo pre-human (or pre-personal), but the pre-humanity seems to me not quite the same as the pre-humanity of plants or animals. (It is again analogous to them here, I think.) So I would say, there is from the beginning an increasing humanization that includes the phases of pre-human life and yet remains a process that is determined by its human origin and human term."

In the first part of the letter, Schoonenberg agreed with the author's and Teilhard's equation of "special creation of the human soul" with "God's continuous creation of an evolving and self-surpassing cosmic reality," a creation by *genesis*. See also P. Smulders, "Une metaphysique de la creation," in *La Vision*, pp. 90-97; and Jean Onimus, *op. cit.*, pp. 88-92.

in the new perspective of a totally evolutionary theology-philosophy-science such as has been suggested by the writers constantly referred to throughout this book. A perfect instance of this is the question of death. Instead of seeing the death of man as "separation of body and soul," which can easily imply the escape of the soul from its prison, human death in a four-dimensional world takes on a new and deeper meaning, much more in keeping with the total view of Christian revelation and much more in keeping with biblical thought.

As prologue to a few comments on new insights into the phenomenon of death, let us set in contrast the Platonic-Cartesian "exile" and Teilhard's view of man whose spirit or Within gradually emerges from his materiality.

> There is nothing, not even the human soul, the highest spiritual manifestation we know of, that does not come within this universal law [of evolution]. The soul, too, has its clearly defined place in the slow ascent of living creatures towards [total] consciousness, and must therefore in one way or another *have grown out of the general mobility of things.*[49]

To quiet any still unsettled fears about the emergence of man's personality (soul) out of his materiality, let the reader be assured by Sertillanges' remark that this equation of the special creation of the human soul with God's divine action manifested immanently within the laws of nature and evolution is *in perfect accord with the Thomistic metaphysics of nature* when complemented by an evolutionary philosophy of nature. "Matter is only for the spirit; from its very goal and destination, it ascends to the spirit."[50]

But is this emergence of the spirit from materiality, of which Teilhard and others speak, not the same as the Platonic deliverance? It could be, if we forget a basic premise of Thomistic philosophy. Prime matter cannot exist without

49. P. Teilhard de Chardin, *Future of Man,* p. 13.
50. A.-D. Sertillanges, *op. cit.,* p. 59.

being in union with substantial form, and vice versa, substantial form cannot exist without being in union with prime matter. This is also the view of Teilhard and others who have explored the implications of an evolutionary philosophy of nature, perfectly in keeping with the best of Thomistic philosophy and biblical theology.

But, if spirit can never fully separate from materiality, if, in the true approach to Thomistic hylomorphism, substantial form cannot exist without prime matter, then how can we speak of a man's death as a "separation of body and soul?" This is exactly the question asked by three theologians in recent days, Karl Rahner, Roger Troisfontaines, and Ladislaus Boros. The answers they have offered are quite different and only proposed as suggestions for further discussion, but it may prove helpful to the reader to summarize their suggestions briefly in the light of the foregoing presentation.

Rahner's view is presented in his essay on *The Theology of Death*.[51] His approach is very Thomistic and classical despite its precise and careful distinctions of the true Thomistic view from all the accretions of centuries of Neoplatonic and Cartesian influences. Rahner would maintain that the human soul does not become a pure spirit after death, totally cut off from all material reality. He points out that a substantial form is destined to inform or be in relation to prime matter. Thus, after death our souls retain a transcendental relation to matter as such. This transcendental relation is not something just tacked on to the soul, as it would be in the Platonic or Cartesian view, but something belonging to the very essence of the human soul. Only recently have the theologians begun to examine the nature and character of this transcendental relationship between the soul and matter after death.

Rahner suggests a solution to the problem by asking if death might be considered, not as a total separation of the

51. Karl Rahner, *Theology of Death,* especially, pp. 21-39.

body and soul, but rather as a shift in the relationship between my soul and prime matter. Can death be considered as an opening up to matter rather than as a separation from it? Can we say that at the moment of death my soul transcends its limited informing power with this small parcel of prime matter which, with it, constitutes my body and opens up to embrace all prime matter? Instead of becoming *acosmic* at death, the soul may become *pancosmic* at the moment of death.

During this life my soul is united with prime matter to form my body, but prime matter is a universal phenomenon, pervading the whole material universe. Thus, in a real way, my soul is related to all the universe even during this life; it is pancosmic even now. Yet because of the limitations of this life, this pancosmic relationship is obscured by my soul's information of this particular portion of prime matter which has become my body. This, of course, does not mean that at death the whole universe becomes my body! or that the soul becomes present throughout the world. Just what the implications of this pancosmic relationship are we do not yet understand, but Rahner presents two ideas worth mention here. The pancosmic relation of the soul might mean that

the soul which has thus, in death, by giving up its limited bodily shape, opened up to the whole, does in some way influence the totality of the world, not only of the material world, but of the world considered as the foundation of the personal life of the rest of men, as beings composed of body and soul. . . . We might also mention here in passing that, on the basis of this hypothesis certain parapsychological phenomena, now puzzling, might be more readily and more naturally explained.[52]

Roger Troisfontaines has taken a somewhat different approach to the phenomenon of death in his book *"Je ne*

52. *Ibid.,* pp. 29-30.

meurs pas . . . " His premise is the same as Rahner's, namely that man's substantial form cannot be totally separated from his body or prime matter. But he approaches the question by asking what the gift of immortality meant for Adam. He suggests that it was God's intention that the first man experience a *peaceful transformation* and immediate resurrection of the whole man into the openness and fullness of the beatific vision, a *death-transformation* that would have been a joy and consolation to all mankind because it would have been visible to all. But because of man's sinful rebellious pride, this intended death-transformation has become a *death-rupture,* the violent, agonizing, painful rending of man's nature, the death-rupture of a sinner who hates God and man. Into this picture we must incorporate the universal redemption of Christ. On the cross, Christ took upon himself the burden of all our sins, suffering to the excess the death-rupture of the sinner in our place. For this reason, as we draw close to Christ and become personally joined with him in love, we can approach and perhaps experience to some extent death as a peaceful transformation. However, since each man experiences also "original sin," our experience of death as a transformation cannot be fully enjoyed. Even the most perfect saint, even the Virgin Mary, does not share fully in the *visible* death-transformation intended by God for man. Man, body and soul, resurrects at the moment of *real and absolute death* in the Troisfontaines hypothesis. Troisfontaines distinguishes between three types of death: *apparent death* when life has not been wholly extinguished and can often be restored through stimulation or artificial respiration; *real but relative death* (clinical death) in which life is suspended and can only be restored rarely through the extraordinary interventions of medical sciences; and *real and absolute death,* the point of no return and immediate resurrection of the whole man. On the cross, Christ experienced real but relative death; it was only at the moment of his resurrection that he underwent real and absolute death. Thus Christ's death and resurrection are simultaneous. As the Second Adam and the prophet of what is to come, Christ also experiences a visible and consoling resurrection in which the apostles and holy women could share when they saw his glorified body. The rest of men, no matter how close they are to God, may share the death-transformation into the beatific vision immediately at the moment of death, but their resurrection is still hidden from men's eyes.

In the pancosmic theory of Rahner, the soul comes, through death, into some relationship with the materiality of the whole universe. This radical unity of all cosmic matter Rahner calls the "heart" of the world and suggests that Christ's descent into "hell" (limbo) is simply his establishment of union between a redeemed universe (and mankind) and the God of love, a reshaping of the whole cosmic order through the cross.[53]

Ladislaus Boros is not exactly happy with this hypothesis of Rahner's, though he thinks Rahner has a basic insight for further fruitful thought.[54] Boros would like to go further along this path, somewhat as Troisfontaines does. He suggests that Christ's resurrection has opened the parousia and given man the possibility of resurrection. In this sense the parousia and last days have already begun, why then cannot resurrection take place at the moment of death? In keeping with our classic idea of the general resurrection at the end of time, Boros suggests that the risen man, body and soul, requires a transfigured universe, totally free of sin, something which will only be

---

53. Jean Galot, "Christ's Descent into Hell," *Theology Digest,* 13:2 (1965), 89-94.

54. Ladislaus Boros, *The Mystery of Death* (Herder & Herder, 1965). An excellent summary, incorporating some of Rahner's views, appeared in *Herder Correspondence,* 2:4 (1965), 131-35, entitled "The last things in recent theology." See Paul Barrett, "A Theology of Death," *New Blackfriars* (London), 46:536 (1965), 266-74.

achieved at the end of time. Hence man's resurrection is real at the moment of death but incomplete. This inchoate resurrection, invisible to us now, will only be perfectly accomplished at the end of time. "The end has come but it is not yet manifest."

Rahner's pancosmic relationship brings into focus the great image of the Eastern Churches, Christ the Pantocrator. In death, man encounters Christ in the universe ("hell," limbo) for the cosmos is Christocentric. This is a point brought out by Teilhard de Chardin and many recent scriptural studies which show the whole universe as oriented towards Christ and fulfillment in him. Death is, then, a birth into a world transparent to Christ, its Lord. The risen Christ, the glorified Lord fills our universe with his merciful love and through death man encounters Christ. This is emphasized repeatedly in the New Testament where death is seen as a manifestation of Christ, the Lord's coming.

Viewing man's nature in this light of evolution and particularly in relation to the phenomenon of death clarifies a number of pseudo-problems; it also sheds a new light and meaning on some traditional pictures. Boros maintains that it is now possible, given our evolutionary perspective of things, to replace certain inadequate or unworthy portrayals of purgatory with a conception that is more in keeping with divine majesty and our modern world view. Purgatory, he suggests, might be conceived as a *momentary* occurrence, associated with the quality and intensity of the decision to love accomplished at the moment of death. In that case, our encounter with Christ constitutes the final purification. To meet his pure gaze, to see Love face to face, would be the fulfillment of our capacity for love. And in this encounter, so penetrating our whole being, all the remains of our secret selfishness and sinfulness, the *reliquia peccati,* would be destroyed. The deeper and more stubborn the layers of our egotism, the more painful will be the purification of that *instant*. Thus, the concept of time spent in purgatory would be replaced with the different degrees of intensity or suffering each person would experience in *the purifying and maturing instant of his death-transformation*. Purgatory becomes, then, the momentary agonizing growth or maturation which at the instant of death makes us pure enough and mature enough to love perfectly, the final step in our personalization and human development.[55]

In our encounter with Christ at the moment of death-transformation, we come to know him clearly in the full revelation of his love. But a man can persist in his idolatry and expressly refuse Christ. In the ultimate rejection, a man totally isolates himself from his God, from other men, and from the universe. He stands alone, destitute and cut off from all. In the hypothesis of Boros, a man has his full personal freedom at the moment of death. He is in complete possession of himself as a person, and thus, in a way far different from what is possible in our daily lives, capable of expressing and affirming himself in a totally unified act. If that act is a refusal, then our radical choice is definitive. That decision is me as I choose to be once and for all. Eternally I will, then, remain what I choose to be at that moment. Christ has not refused me, I am the one who has refused to love. Once and for all this eliminates that theological crudity of "Christ condemning a man to hell." Hell is seen now not as an eternal punishment for some violation of a law a long time ago and now, perhaps, bitterly regretted. Hell is sin itself, idolatry and the refusal to love, ever present and affirmed by the whole person, an enduring rejection of Christ who is love. In fact, if God were to stop loving the damned, hell would no longer be hell for the pain of hell is the knowledge that we are incomplete finite creatures who must love God, man and the universe coupled

55. L. Boros, *Mystery of Death,* pp. 132-33.

with the acute realization that we are so self-centered, so egotistic and selfish that we are unwilling to love. The rejection of love is hell.

As Boros exposes his insights into the mystery of death and the last things, it soon becomes evident that we can no longer consider hell, as it were, a special place "down below," bubbling over with fire and brimstone. In the perspective suggested by Boros, hell is a place, the same world in which the blessed also live in their happiness, our world transformed and glorified. God, he maintains, cannot create an evil place any more than he can create anything else evil. It is the sinner who is out of place, a misfit and alienated from all. The damned live hatefully and unhappily in a universe transparent with love (God). Boros points out that the deliberate idolatry of the damned, their refusal to love, has placed them in a double discord, a state of internal conflict with themselves and a state of enmity with the universe and all in it. If the damned could be totally separated from all others in actuality, they would not suffer at all from their separation from God, man and the universe. But because they must associate with those they refuse to love, they continually make their own hell. Jean Paul Sartre's play *No Exit* is a perfect example of this hellish existence.

Returning to our main point in this chapter we now find that we can surpass the old categories of body and soul, and see man, his nature and destiny, in a new light. As long as man was regarded as an essentially static being, established in the fullness of his essence and personality from birth, his activity in this world was only an accidental accretion tacked on to his nature. Death could, then, only be seen as an unpredictable moment somewhere in our future with no essential bearing on man's nature or life. Once we step into the four-dimensional world and view man as a dynamic reality we become more conscious of ourselves as a personal "becoming." And our becoming a full person, of course, takes place within the community of man and the cosmos. Thus while affirming our personalities, we also find we cannot live in isolation. True, our personality emerges from materiality or the necessary tyrannical dependence on matter or others. No man can live in isolation and be fully human, for each of us is a center of activity within the society of man. Since all creation takes place "in the beginning" or, as Augustine interpreted this, "in the Logos," creation cannot only be equated with evolution and the emergence of personality out of materiality, but also with the real extension of the Incarnation of Christ (love).[56] Even better, we might say that all creation-evolution-redemption is ultimately the transubstantiation of the universe and mankind into the Body of Christ. "The theology of death is basically an extension of the theology of the incarnation, for death is a very important phase in the emergence of our personalities."[57]

As we learn to affirm our being-in-oneself within the context of God's world and human society, we learn also to transcend the *necessity* of depending on the other. Through a loving recognition of our own condition as finite creatures, we soon learn humbly and freely to accept our place within a world converging on the Christ. In humble love, we learn to embrace the other, nature, neighbor and Creator. Tyrannical dependence has become loving embrace. Thus does personality emerge from materiality, no longer in a Platonic flight—for in this loving embrace materiality, our dependence on others, is transformed and "glorified" by love.

It was Paul who reminded us that "all creation groans and travails in labor until now," awaiting the redemption of the children of God. Creation was not completed "in the begin-

56. A.-D. Sertillanges, *op. cit.,* p. 31.
57. P. Barrett, *op. cit.*

ning," it continues to this day and until the fullness of Christ is achieved.

> . . . we find ourselves [by simply having followed the "extensions" of the Eucharist] plunged once again precisely into our divine milieu. Christ—for whom and in whom we are formed, each one of us with his own vocation and individuality—Christ reveals himself in each reality around us, and shines like an ultimate determinant, like a centre, one might almost say like a universal element. As our humanity assimilates the material world, and as the Host assimilates our humanity, the eucharistic transformation goes beyond and completes the transubstantiation of the bread on the altar. Step by step it irresistibly invades the universe. It is the fire that sweeps over the heath; the stroke that vibrates through the bronze. In a secondary and generalized sense, but in a true sense, the sacramental Species are formed by the totality of the world, and the duration of the creation is the time needed for its consecration.[58]

Even more cogent is the expression Teilhard gave this vision of the world in an as yet unpublished essay written just a few weeks before his death on Easter Sunday, 1955, to which he gave the title *Le Christique,* "the Christic Vision":

> In the wondering gaze of the believer, it is in the mystery of the Eucharist itself that Evolution is prolonged indefinitely in a veritable universal "transubstantiation" where it is no longer only over the sacrificial bread and wine, but, indeed, over the totality of joys and pains engendered by the Convergence of the World in its advances that the words of consecration fall—and over these that the possibilities of a universal communion descend as a consequence.[59]

58. P. Teilhard de Chardin, *The Divine Milieu* (Harper & Row, 1960), p. 104. See also K. Rahner "Christology and an Evolutionary World View," *Theology Digest,* 13:2 (1965), 83-85. One of the finest studies of Teilhard's Christology has been done by Pietro Bilaniuk in the Teilhard de Chardin Conference 1964 *Proceedings,* of the Human Energetics Research Institute (Fordham University, 1965).

59. Cf. Cuenot's biography of Teilhard (Helicon, 1965), p. 450f.

Here we face the fulfillment of man's deepest nature and also the completion of the universe in its tortuous evolution. Here we face the New Heaven and the New Earth of which John the Evangelist spoke so eloquently in the Book of Revelations. Since our earthly life is only a preliminary and our earthly death only a birth-transformation, our real task must be to shape this earthly life in the light of the heavenly reality such as we can know it. We know that everything in this world is God-given and that the very cosmos is Christocentric, hence every facet of a truly human life should reveal something about the fulfillment of our humanity in heaven. Our longings, our aspirations, our self-transcendence, all the limitless horizons that open before our minds, the very thirst for something new and complete—all these are pointers, according to Boros, indicating to us just what the hope of heaven can mean. Thus he maintains that we should have no hesitation in depicting heaven in human terms that appeal to us. In support of this he points out the example of Christ who promised men the kingdom of heaven in images that most appealed to them as the human beings they were. To the Samaritan woman he promised fountains of living water; to the people of Capharnaum, he promised bread; to a shepherd, flocks and green pastures; to the merchants, the pearl of great price; and to all of us, he promised an eternal banquet and wedding feast. Later on, the apostles promised the Greeks knowledge, wisdom, and a *polis*. What Boros is getting at is a solid reaffirmation of the biblical concept of heaven and rejection of the Greek idea of contemplation, a reaffirmation of the Christian belief that all things in this world are sacred, created in the image of the Logos. "For those who know how to see (Christ and the divine Diaphany), nothing here below is profane," as Teilhard expressed it. No one can escape the cosmic presence of the risen Lord, nor the infinite perspectives in which our human existence is set. Heaven is not, therefore, up in "the pink clouds."

In the ascending spiral process in which our universe converges on Christ, mankind achieves its fullest expression. As our personality emerges from materiality, at the same time it lovingly embraces that same matter because it bears the imprint of the Divine who perfects and completes our personality through this brute, cosmic matter. In the humble embrace of love, matter is transformed and "glorified." As Teilhard wrote in his "Hymn to Matter":

> To attain you, Matter, we must, detached from a universal contact with everything that stirs here below, feel the particular form of everything we possess vanish bit by bit between our fingers until we stand at the threshold of the sole essence of all stabilities and all unions.
>
> We must, if we wish to possess you, Matter, sublimate you in our suffering after having voluptuously clasped you in our arms. *You reign, Matter, in the serene heights where the Saints imagine they can avoid you—flesh so transparent and so mobile that we can no longer distinguish you from spirit!*[60]

The implications of the evolutionary or four-dimensional philosophy of nature which we have explored here may well shock some readers. If so, let me simply point out and underline a statement of Pierre Schoonenberg:

> We might perhaps say that *the acceptance of evolution is demanded precisely by what the Encyclical,* Humani Generis, *calls "the philosophy that is accepted and recognized by the Church."*[61]

60. P. Teilhard de Chardin, "Hymn to Matter," in *Hymn of the Universe* (Harper & Row, 1965), pp. 7-71 (Author's translation). See Robert T. Francoeur, "The Cosmic Piety of Teilhard de Chardin," in *Cosmic Piety*, ed. Christopher Derrick (P. J. Kenedy, 1965), pp. 99-118.

61. P. Schoonenberg, *God's World*, p. 7.

The evolutionary dimension of thought is both scientific and biblical. The evolutionary perspective is the only one acceptable to modern science. It is also the only approach to nature and the only philosophy of nature that is acceptable today for the theologian and philosopher.

The Fall of Man

In sketching the broad symbol of the Garden of Eden the sacred authors made use of a number of small details, each containing a religious truth. Over the years catechetical and popular traditions have added much to the delineation of these germinal elements. The very simple story of the first man has been so elaborated on that it is now quite common to find in Roman Catholic catechisms a detailed description of the four so-called preternatural gifts which the first man is supposed to have lost as a result of his proud rebellion in that "Never-never Land" of Eden (as John L. McKenzie has termed it). Most of this delineation came from oral folklore and imaginative speculation, particularly during the middle ages.

The four privileges we will treat briefly here have been labeled preternatural to indicate that they are not truly *super*natural or directly involved in divine grace, which is a personal sharing in the divine life totally beyond our natural human capacities. While we may not possess these gifts today as they have been classically described, they do not lie totally beyond the reach of our human nature. Traditionally they have been listed as freedom from ignorance (infused knowledge), immunity from death (immortality), freedom from the tyranny of the passions (concupiscence), and freedom from pain and suffering.

When the Christian scholar of the second and third centuries after Christ tried to analyze the condition of the first man, he turned to certain principles in Greek philosophy which seemed to fit the situation. Thus Philo, the "Jewish Plato," had stated in his *De opificio mundi*, #40, that an ancestor must contain in himself all the perfections enjoyed by his descendants. Applied to Adam, this principle of Greek philosophy meant that Adam had to possess all the knowledge of all his descendants when he dwelt in Eden. Yet no definition of the Church or dogmatic statement has ever made this privilege of early man a part of the deposit of faith. Since it has been based solely on a principle of Greek philosophy, theologians today see no problem at all in denying to the first men any infused or special knowledge whatsoever beyond the simple human reflection necessary for a morally responsible action.[1]

The other supposed privileges of the first man are not so easy to integrate into our picture of man evolving from an animal stock monophyletically. In the case of the gifts of immortality, freedom from concupiscence, and immunity from pain and suffering, the Church has clearly spoken, indicating that both sanctifying grace and these gifts were lost as a result of original sin.[2]

Since science has proven beyond doubt that animals died long before the first man appeared on earth, we cannot take literally and without qualification Paul's statement that death entered the world through the sin of the first man. To solve the problem, theologians today suggest we clarify our understanding of death in the light of biblical thought. They suggest that we distinguish two aspects or elements in death when

1. Ernest C. Messenger, *Two in One Flesh*, II, p. 6; M. M. Labourdette, *Le Pêche originel et les origines de l'homme* (Alsatia, Paris), p. 174; P. Smulders, *op. cit.*, p. 197.

2. H. Denzinger, *Enchiridion Symbolorum*, #788ff.

applied to man. The first element is a purely natural one resulting from our nature as finite "composite" creatures, composed of a material aspect which is subject to entropic decomposition and a spiritual component, the source of my unity, personality and "being-in-myself." Considering death as an *ontological reality* we find that it is a purely natural phenomenon to which all created life in this world is subject. Death as an ontological reality is universal and inescapable. The other aspect of death seems to arise only with the appearance of mankind and results from man's decision to stand alone, to assert his numinous autarchy in an act of self-adoration or idolatry. This is death as a *relational reality,* the existential product of man's pride. The death of the sinner is totally different from the death of a friend of God because of the relation that each experiences with his Creator. The one fears death and judgment because he hates, to a greater or lesser extent, the very source of all love. The gift of immortality might mean, as Troisfontaines suggests, that God *intended* all nature and mankind in particular to share in the beatific vision, in the fullness of life with him. God would then intend man to *transcend* the limitations of his nature, to mature and open himself to the fullness of love in a peaceful, glorious *death-transformation.* This would be possible for a man open to love. But for a sinner who rejects love, death becomes a painful experience, a *death-rupture.* As Lyonnet puts it, all men must die because all of us, like the first man, are sinners and have rejected God. Our death then has become a death-rupture.[3]

This death-rupture was par excellence the death Christ chose to experience in our stead. By uniting ourselves to him

---

3. A.-M. Dubarle, *Biblical Doctrine,* pp. 11-21 and 81; Karl Rahner, *On the Theology of Death,* pp. 21-62; R. Troisfontaines, *"Je Ne Meurs Pas . . .",* pp. 153ff.; S. Lyonnet, "Le Sens de *eph'oi* en Rom. 5:12 et l'exégèse des Pères grecs," *Biblica,* 36 (1955), 437-56.

and sharing in his redemptive love, can we perhaps experience to some small extent that glorious death-transformation intended by the Creator as the door to a fuller life?[4]

Troisfontaines does not find the distinction between natural and preternatural meaningful, and Smulders has suggested that the first humans *never actually received any of the so-called preternatural gifts.* In the light of this, we might say that the privilege of immortality is not so much an immunity from biological death as it is a freedom from the tyranny of a death-rupture. Thus the death of a saint may well embody, to some extent, the gift of immortality "offered" by God to mankind. The same may be said for the privilege of freedom from pain and suffering, since these are *part and parcel of any growth or birth.* Certainly we must admit that mankind is only in his infancy, just beginning the process of hominization as Teilhard would say, and that the mystical body of Christ is still awaiting its full maturity which will come only at the parousia. As Smulders has noted, the privileges of the first men must be looked upon not as a radical break with our animal predecessors but rather as potentialities in the line of our human vocation and destiny. As man becomes more like to God and "spiritualized," he may well develop these potentialities by making his death more and more a death-transformation, and by gradually conquering pain and suffering as much as this is possible in a world involved in an evolutionary birth.[5]

The common explanation of the privilege of immunity from concupiscence was also worked out during the middle ages. It claims that the human nature of the first man and woman was so harmoniously constituted that man's "lower faculties," his emotions and passions and appetites, were totally subject

4. P. Smulders, *La Vision,* pp. 197-198.
5. R. Troisfontaines, *op. cit.,* pp. 153ff.; P. Smulders, *ibid.,* pp. 197, 199; E. C. Messenger, *Two in One Flesh,* II, p. 4.

to his "higher faculties of intellect and will." Sexual desire, passions and emotions in Eden were inconceivable to them. Adam would have mated "chastely" with his wife for the sole purpose of procreation, and without any passion or sexual pleasure disturbing his higher faculties. Deeply embedded in this explanation are all kinds of Augustinian influences, rooted in Augustine's idea of the transmission of original sin through the passions and concupiscence of the sexual union. The theological context in which this common explanation of Adam's immunity from concupiscence arose is vital, for that context found it impossible to accept man's sexual nature and to integrate our "animal passions" into a balanced and human spirituality. It took the theologians twelve centuries to agree that marriage is a sacrament even though it involves sex, and nineteen centuries to realize that human sexuality and passion have a valid purpose beyond mere procreation.[6]

Today, when we do not merely tolerate or condone human sexuality and passion but accept it as a valid, integral and valued part of our nature, our explanation of this privilege has changed drastically. Karl Rahner does not place concupiscence in man's body, his rebellious passions or lower faculties. He prefers to see it as a tension or conflict resulting from the emergence and expression of the whole human personality within a social context. Man spontaneously tends to affirm and express his personality in an *absolute* sense—the temptation to self-idolatry. But if man is to use his freedom properly he must learn to accept his place within a community, to realize

6. Albert the Great, *Summa Theologiae*, II, Tract XIV, p. 84; Augustine of Hippo, *De Nuptiis et Concupiscentia*, lib. 2, c. 21, *P.L.*, 44, 457. See also *Genesi ad Litteram*, lib. 9, cc. 3-5; 8, *P.L.*, 34, 394-5; 398; and Antonio Piolanti, "Original Sin," in *Sin: Its Reality and Nature: A Historical Survey*, ed. by Pietro Palazzini and Salvador Canals (Scepter, Dublin, 1964), p. 133; Sylvius, *In Summa* ("Commentary on St. Thomas"), I, q. 98, art. 2; Suarez, *In Summa S. Thomae, in loc. (Summa Theologiae*, I. q. 99, art. 2, ad. 3.).

he is not absolute and that his personality is finite. There is then a conflict and tension between man's spontaneous impulses and the freedom of his personality expressed within a society.[7]

Rahner has accepted the reality of a state of innocence during which the preternatural gifts lay *dormant* prior to Adam's original sin. Such a suggestion seems unnecessary, and we find Smulders' approach much more intelligible and satisfying in the light of modern science:

> The privileges of the first men have to be looked upon not as a radical break with their animal prehistory but rather as potentialities in the line of human vocation and destiny. [We can maintain that] the first man received these privileges only in potency and with a mission to develop them rather than as already perfect and complete gifts.[8]

Vincent Cronin has made an interesting suggestion in a brief essay entitled "The Noosphere and Extrasensory Perception." Working only from Teilhard's concepts of the Noosphere and human convergence, he suggests that as mankind continues to evolve psychologically and becomes more human new and more direct modes of communication may be developed— mental telepathy, extrasensory perception and the psychedelic experience being some possibilities. It would be interesting to link Rahner's passing comment on ESP, Cronin's idea, and Smulders' view of the preternatural gifts.[9]

---

7. See Teilhard de Chardin, "La Centrologie," in *L'Activation de l' Energie*, volume 7 of the *Oeuvres de Teilhard de Chardin*, pp. 103-34, particularly in connection with his concept of the "differentiated Union." Also K. Rahner, "The Theology of Freedom," a lecture delivered at Georgetown University, November 30, 1964; and "The Dignity and Freedom of Man," in *Theological Investigations, II* (Helicon, 1963), pp. 235-64.

8. P. Smulders, *La Vision*, pp. 197 and 199; P. Overhage and K. Rahner, *Das Problem*, pp. 85-88; R. C. Zaehner, *Matter and Spirit*.

9. In *Teilhard de Chardin: Pilgrim of the Future*, ed. Neville Braybrooke (Seabury, 1964).

In this survey of theological thought, we have clearly tried to avoid anything in the way of a full explanation or definition of the immense and deep reality known traditionally as "original sin." We have rather tried to present some new insights into that deep reality, insights based on modern knowledge from psychology, biology, scripture and theology, which we hope will lead us to a more meaningful and relevant exposition of the traditional doctrine of original sin.

In this attempt to reform our picture of original sin and to restate the basic question we do not intend to go beyond the modest proposal suggested by Thomas Aquinas when he studied this same reality seven hundred years ago. In attempting to restate the question we have, however, tried to indicate how the classical exposition has been crippled by non-Christian assumptions and that these can now be replaced by a better set of assumptions rooted in modern psychology and biology. Secondly, we have tried to show how the reality of original sin has been rendered irrelevant and meaningless to modern man because of these invalid and inadequate assumptions from Greek philosophy and the pre-Darwinian world-vision. Finally, we have tried to indicate how a new exposition of original sin might be worked out.

The results of this attempt should be clear in the following sketch. Transferring the reality of original sin into our four-dimensional dynamic, evolving world vision, we can see that it is a cosmic reality, rooted in the finiteness of all nature. In this sense, we need a new term to express this reality. But we have also seen that the finiteness of our created nature with its incumbent vocation to complete and perfect our unfulfilled nature in love of God and neighbor is only one aspect of the reality of "original sin," even though its analogies touch all finite creation. The other aspect of this reality is the sinful situation-state into which every human being is born by the very fact of his being a member of the human race, an unwillingness to love and admit our dependence on others which each of us "inevitably but freely ratifies," culminating in the crucifixion of Christ.

In all this we have shifted the archetype of Adam and Eve from the past to the future, the preternatural gifts becoming more potencies in the line of our human vocation than gifts actually given in the Garden of Eden. We have tried to show the meaning and relevance of this archetype by demonstrating its personal existential reality. We have tried to recover the Christian meaning of our personal encounter with Christ, the Second Adam, which is achieved in the sacramental union in the progression of time. This encounter with the true archetype, the Second Adam, is completed only in the fullness of time and not through any impersonal ritual imitation of a Platonic type. The relevance of the Eden account for the future rather than as a golden age in the past would shed some light on the suggestion of R. C. Zaehner that early mankind was not psychologically or spiritually mature enough to take the "step into the future" offered by the Creator. This would seem to dovetail also with Smulders' suggestion that the preternatural gifts are potencies in the line of the human vocation and were never possessed by early man. We have likewise attempted to restore the eschatological meaning of the Eden account by emphasizing Christ, the Second Adam, rather than the first parents. Finally, in all this we have exposed certain aspects of the synthesis of the linear and cyclic views of time by incorporating the best of both views into a world vision symbolized by an ascending spiral converging on Christ the Omega.

Bibliography

Anshen, Ruth Nanda, ed., *Alfred North Whitehead: His Reflections on Man and Nature.* Harper & Row, 1961.

Barrett, Paul. "A Theology of Death." *New Blackfriars* (Cambridge, Eng.). 46:536 (1965), pp. 266-73.

Barthelemy-Madaule, Madeleine. *Bergson et Teilhard de Chardin.* Du Seuil (Paris), 1963.

Bergson, Henri. *Creative Evolution.* Modern Library, 1944.

Boné, Edouard. "Polygenisme et Polyphyletisme," *Archives de Philosophie.* 23 (1960), pp. 133ff.

Boros, Ladislaus. *The Mystery of Death.* Herder & Herder, 1965.

Braybrooke, Neville. ed., *Teilhard de Chardin: Pilgrim of the Future.* Seabury (N. Y.), 1964.

Bruns, J. Edgar. "God Up Above—or Up Ahead?" *Catholic World* (N. Y.). 191:1141 (1960), pp. 23-30.

Bulst, Werner. *Revelation.* Sheed & Ward, 1965.

Chauchard, Paul. *Man and Cosmos.* Herder & Herder, 1965.

Colbert, Edwin H. *Evolution of the Vertebrates.* Wiley & Sons, 1958.

Coon, Carleton S. *The Origin of Races.* Knopf, 1962.

—————. *The Story of Man.* Knopf, 1962.

Crespy, Georges. *La pensée théologique de Teilhard de Chardin.* Universitaires, 1961.

Cuenot, Claude. *Teilhard de Chardin. A Biographical Study.* Helicon, 1965.

Cullmann, Oscar. *Christ and Time. The Primitive Christian Conception of Time and History.* Westminster (Philadelphia), 1950.

Defraine, Jean. *Adam et son Lignage.* Desclee (Brouwer), 1959.

—————. *The Bible and the Origin of Man.* Desclee (N. Y.), 1962.

De Lubac, Henri. *La Pensée religieuse de Père Teilhard de Chardin.* Aubier (Paris), 1962.

289

Dobzhansky, Theodosius. *The Biological Basis of Human Freedom.* Columbia Univ., 1956.

—————. *Genetics and the Origin of Species.* 3rd ed. Columbia Univ., 1951.

—————. *Mankind Evolving.* Yale Univ., 1962.

Donceel, Joseph F. *Philosophical Psychology.* 2nd ed. Sheed & Ward, 1961.

Dorlodot, Canon. *Darwinism and Catholic Thought.* Benzinger, 1922.

Dubarle, Andre-Marie. *The Biblical Doctrine of Original Sin.* Herder & Herder, 1964.

Eiseley, Loren. *Darwin's Century. Evolution and the Men Who Discovered It.* Doubleday; Doubleday Anchor, 1958.

Eliade, Mircea. *Cosmos and History. The Myth of the Eternal Return.* Pantheon; Harper & Row Torchbook, 1954.

—————. *Images and Symbols. Studies in Religious Symbolism.* Sheed & Ward, 1961.

—————. *Myth and Reality.* Harper & Row, 1963.

Elkin, Henry. "On the origin of the self." *Psychoanalysis and the Psychoanalytical Review.* 45:4 (1958-59), pp. 57-76.

—————. "Psychotherapy and Religion." Connecticut Conference on Pastoral Counseling, The Partnership of Clergymen and Psychiatrists. United States Public Health Service, State of Connecticut, Dept. of Mental Health. Connecticut Assoc. for Mental Health, pp. 58-69.

Fothergill, Philip G. *Evolution and Christians.* Longmans (London), 1961.

—————. *Historical Aspects of Organic Evolution,* Hollis & Carter (London), 1952.

Francoeur, R. T. "Cacti, Mushrooms, and the Mystical Life." *Spiritual Life* (Milwaukee). 10:4 (1964), pp. 255-62.

—————. "The Cosmic Piety of Teilhard de Chardin," in: *Cosmic Piety.* ed. Christopher Derrick. P. J. Kenedy, 1965.

—————. "The Dimension of Evolution: Aquinas and Teilhard." *The Dayton Review* (Univ. of Dayton), Summer 1965.

—————. "Evolution and 'panpsychism' in Teilhard de Chardin," *American Benedictine Review.* 12 (1961), pp. 206-219.

—————. "The future of man." *The Lamp* (Garrison, N. Y.), 62:8 (1964), pp. 4-7, 30-31.

—————. "Intellectual freedom—a question of geography?" in: *Generation of the Third Eye*. ed. Daniel Callahan. Sheed & Ward, 1964.

—————. "The Phenomenon of Man," in: *Masterpieces of Catholic Literature*. ed. Frank Magill. Harper & Row, 1965.

—————, ed. *The World of Teilhard de Chardin*. Helicon, 1961.

Freundorfer, J. *Erbsunde und Erbtod beim Apostel Paulus*. Aschendorf (Munster), 1927.

Glass, Bentley, Owsei Temkin, & William Straus. *Forerunners of Darwin: 1745-1859*. Johns Hopkins Univ., 1959.

Greene, John C. *The Death of Adam*. Iowa State Univ.; Mentor New American Library, 1959.

Gregory, William K. *Our Face from Fish to Man*. Putnam's Sons; Capricorn, 1922 & 1965.

Howells, William. *Mankind in the Making*. Doubleday, 1959.

Hunt, Ignatius. *The Book of Genesis*. Paulist, 1960.

Huxley, Julian. *Evolution: the Modern Synthesis*. Wiley & Sons, 1964.

Irvine, William. *Apes, Angels, and Victorians*. McGraw Hill; Meridian, 1955.

Kobler, John. "The priest who haunts the Catholic world." *Saturday Evening Post*. 236 (Oct. 12, 1963), pp. 42-51.

Korn, Noel, Harry Reece Smith. *Human Evolution*. Holt, Rinehart & Winston, 1959.

Labourdette, M. M. *Le Péché Originel et les Origines de l'Homme*. Alsatia (Paris), 1953.

Lasker, Gabriel W. *The Evolution of Man*. Holt, Rinehart & Winston, 1961.

Lecomte du Nouy, Pierre. *Human Destiny*. Longmans Green; New American Library, 1947 & 1965.

Lepp, Ignace, *The Authentic Morality*. Macmillan, 1965.

—————. *Psychology of Loving*. Helicon; Mentor Omega New American Library, 1963 & 1965.

Lohfink, Norbert. "Genesis 2-3 as 'historical etiology'," *Theology Digest*, 13 (1965), pp. 11-17.

Lovejoy, Arthur O. *The Great Chain of Being. A Study of the History of an Idea*. Harper & Row Torchbook, 1960.

Lynch, William F. *Christ and Apollo. The Dimensions of the Literary Imagination*. Sheed & Ward; Mentor Omega New American Library, 1960.

Lyonnet, Stanislaus. "Le sens de *eph'ooi* en Rom. 5:12 et l'exegese des Peres grecs." *Biblica.* 36 (1955), pp. 437-56.

Mayr, Ernst. *Animal Species and Evolution.* Harvard Belknap, 1963.

Messenger, Ernest C. *Evolution and Theology.* Burnes Oates, 1931.

——————. *Theology and Evolution.* Sands (London), 1949.

——————. *Two in One Flesh.* Newman, 1956.

Moore, Ruth. *Man, Time, and Fossils. The Story of Evolution.* Knopf, 1961.

Murray, Raymond, W. *Man's Unknown Ancestors.* Bruce, 1943.

Nogar, Raymond. *The Wisdom of Evolution.* Doubleday, 1963.

North, Robert. "Teilhard and the many Adams," *Continuum.* 1:3 (1963), pp. 329-42.

O'Brien, John A. *Evolution and Religion.* Century, 1932.

——————. *The Origin of Man.* Paulist, 1947.

Onimus, Jean. *Pierre Teilhard de Chardin ou la Foi au Monde.* Plon (Paris), 1962.

Peattie, Donald Culrose. *Green Laurels.* Garden City, 1938.

Peirce, Charles S. *Collected Papers* (8 vol.), Harvard Univ.

——————. *Essays in the Philosophy of Science.* Bobbs, 1957.

Poulet, Georges. *Studies in Human Time.* Johns Hopkins Univ., 1956.

Rabut, Olivier. *A Dialogue with Teilhard de Chardin.* Sheed & Ward, 1961.

Rahner, Karl. *On the Theology of Death.* Herder & Herder, 1961.

——————. "Zum theologischen Begriff der Konkupisens," in: *Schriften zur Theologie, VI.* Benzinger (Einsiedeln), 1956.

Rahner, Karl, & Paul Overhage. *Das Problem der Hominization.* Herder (Freiburg), 1961.

Raven, Charles E. *Teilhard de Chardin, Scientist and Seer.* Harper & Row, 1964.

Riesman, David. *Faces in the Crowd.* Yale Univ., 1952.

——————. *Individualism Reconsidered.* Free Press, 1954.

——————. *The Lonely Crowd.* Yale Univ., 1950.

Romer, Alfred Sherwood. *The Vertebrate Story.* 4th ed., Wiley & Sons, 1959.

Russell, John L. "The principle of finality in the philosophy of Aristotle and Teilhard de Chardin, I & II." *Heythrop Journal* (Oxon, Eng.) 3:4 (1962), pp. 347-57; 4:1 (1963), pp. 32-41.

——————. "Teilhard de Chardin, *The Phenomenon of Man, I & II.*" *Heythrop Journal* (Oxon, Eng.) 1:4 (1960), pp. 271-84; 2:1 (1961), pp. 3-13.

Scheuer, Pierre. "Notes on Metaphysics," *Cross Currents.* 7 (1957), pp. 337-46.

Schoonenberg, Pierre. "Erfzonde en 'zonde der wereld'," *Ned. Kath. Stemmen.* 58 (1962), p. 77.

——————. *God's World in the Making.* Duquesne Univ., 1964.

——————. *Het Geloof van ons doopsel, I-IV.* Malmberg ('s Hertogenbosch) Notre Dame Univ., 1966. (Volume four of the Dutch will be replaced by a newer book, which will appear first in English, entitled: *Man in Sin.*)

——————. "Natuur en zondeval." *Tijdschrift voor Theologie.* 2 (1962), pp. 199-200.

Sertillanges, A.-D. *L'Univers et l'Ame.* Ouvrieres (Paris), 1965.

Sinnott, Edmund. *Biology of the Spirit.* Compass; Viking, 1955.

——————. *Cell and Psyche.* Harper Torchbook, 1961.

——————. *Matter, Mind, and Man.* Atheneum, 1962.

Smulders, Pierre. *La Vision de Teilhard de Chardin.* Desclee (Brouwer), 1964.

Tax, Sol. ed. *Evolution after Darwin.* Univ. of Chicago, 1960.

Teilhard de Chardin, Pierre. *Oeuvres.* Ed. du Seuil (Paris).

1. Le Phénomène humain, 1955.
2. L'apparition de l'homme, 1956.
3. La vision du passé, 1957.
4. Le Milieu divin, 1957.
5. L'avenir de l'homme, 1959.
6. Hymne de l'univers, 1961.
7. L'energie humaine, 1962.
8. L'activation de l'energie, 1963.
9. La place de l'homme dans la nature (Le Groupe zoologique humain).
10. Elevations et prières.
11. Teilhard de Chardin explique sa pensée. Textes choisis.
12. Science et Christ, 1965.
13. Le coeur de la matière, 1965?
14. Christianisme et évolution, 1965?

——————. *Cahier.* Ed. du Seuil (Paris).

1. Construire la Terre. 1958.
2. Reflexions sur le bonheur, 1960.
3. Pierre Teilhard de Chardin et la politique africaine, 1962.

————. *Ecrits du temps de la guerre 1916-1919.* Grasset, 1965.

————. *The Future of Man.* Harper & Row, 1964.

————. *Hymn of the Universe.* Harper & Row, 1965.

————. *La Genèse d'une pensée.* Grasset, 1961.

————. *Letters from a Traveller.* Harper & Row, 1965.

————. *Letters from Egypt, 1905-1908.* Herder & Herder, 1965.

————. *Lettres de Voyage de 1923 a 1955.* Grasset, 1957.

————. *Making of a Mind.* Harper & Row, 1965.

————. *The Divine Milieu.* Harper & Row, 1960.

————. *The Phenomenon of Man.* Harper & Row, 1959.

Towers, Bernard. "Man in modern science." *The Month* (London), 217:1157 (Jan. 1964), pp. 23-36.

Tresmontant, Claude. *Pierre Teilhard de Chardin, His Thought.* Helicon, 1959.

————. *A Study of Hebrew Thought.* Desclee (N. Y.), 1959.

Troisfontaines, Roger. *I do not die* . . . Desclee (N. Y.), 1963;

Van Melsen, Andrew G. *From Atomos to Atom.* Harper & Row Torchbook, 1960.

Vawter, Bruce. *God's Story of Creation.* Knights of Columbus, 1955.

Vollert, Cyril. "Evolution and the Bible," in: *Symposium on Evolution.* Duquesne Univ., 1959.

Wendt, Herbert. *In Search of Adam.* Houghton Mifflin; Collier, 1956.

White, Leslie A. *Evolution of Culture.* McGraw Hill, 1959.

————. *Science of Culture. A Study of Man and Civilization.* Grove; Evergreen, 1958.

Whitehead, Alfred North. *Adventures of Ideas.* Mentor New American Library, 1933.

————. *Modes of Thought.* Putnam's Sons & Capricorn, 1959.

Whitrow, G. J. *The Structure and Evolution of the Universe.* Harper & Row Torchbook, 1959.

Zaehner, R. C. *Matter and Spirit. Their Convergence in Eastern Religions, Marx, and Teilhard de Chardin.* Harper & Row, 1963.

Index